PERMACULTURE GARDENING FOR THE ABSOLUTE BEGINNER

FOLLOW NATURE'S MAP TO GROW YOUR OWN ORGANIC FOOD WITH CONFIDENCE AND TRANSFORM ANY BACKYARD INTO A THRIVING ECOSYSTEM

JOSIE BECKHAM

ALL WE NEED PUBLISHING

ISBN

978-1-962344-00-5 (Ebook)

978-1-962344-01-2 (Paperback)

978-1-962344-02-9 (Hardcover)

☙ BOOK AWARDS FOR THIS TITLE ❧

American Legacy Book Awards - *American Book Fest*

🏅 2024 Winner: Home & Garden

American Writing Awards

🏅 2023 Winner: Home & Garden

Best Book Awards - *American Book Fest (20th Annual Best Book Awards)*

🏅 2023 Winner: Home & Garden

Firebird Book Awards - *Speak Up Talk Radio*

🏅 🏅 2023 Winner (2 categories): Home & Garden, How-To

Next Generation Indie Book Awards

🏅 2024 Finalist: Science/Nature/Environment

Reader Ready Awards - *Author Shout*

🏅 2024 Winner: Top Pick

Reader Views Reviewers Choice Awards

🏅 2023 Winner (Bronze): Cooking, Crafts & Hobbies, How-To

Royal Dragonfly Awards - *Story Monsters Book Awards*

🏅 🏅 2023 Winner (2 categories): Home & Garden, How-To

PRAISE FOR JOSIE BECKHAM

☆☆☆☆☆

"Who would have guessed that a gardening book could be such an enjoyable read? *Permaculture Gardening for the Absolute Beginner* is not only inviting and informative but also genuinely inspiring ... the best permaculture/gardening how-to book I've ever read!"

~ C.E. Flores for <u>Reedsy Discovery</u>

"I really enjoyed reading this. Beckham has a lot of enthusiasm for permaculture gardening, and she makes this a fun topic!"

~ Paige Lovett for <u>Reader Views</u>

"I loved reading *Permaculture Gardening for the Absolute Beginner* ... Whether you are a novice like me or an advanced gardener, this book is an ideal resource."

~ Vernita Naylor for <u>Readers' Favorite</u>

"I am a landscape planner, designer, and permaculture consultant ... Well this is THE book for gardening. From now on, this will be the main book I recommend to my clients who are beginners, inspired by permaculture, and have no idea where to begin ... An *essential* companion book for those getting started."

~ Grant Depoy (Goodreads)

"This book is an absolute must for everyone. My kids know that this will stay in our family's library for generations to come."

~ Prickly Paradise Homestead (Amazon)

"This book is a living book. Reading it makes you feel like you are sitting by your garden with a friend ..."

~ Nathalie Claire (Goodreads)

"Beckham's book fulfills its promise to instill confidence in new gardeners. Her passion and ability to simplify complex concepts make it an essential companion for those venturing into permaculture."

~ *Ola (Goodreads)*

"Josie Beckham has a gift for explaining complex concepts in easy-to-understand ways ... There seems to be nothing Josie has not thought of, and I can heartily recommend this book."

~ *Janelle Komorowski (Goodreads)*

"This book on permaculture exceeded my expectations... Written in a language that we can all understand, it will be my reference book for gardening. It fills a gap and answers a need."

~ *Reader (Amazon Canada)*

"I shall continue to use this book and share with the young people I mentor. Good practices like these are soon going to be vital."

~ *Miss Rebecca K Spencer (Amazon UK)*

"Beckham has written a step-by-step guide to help beginner gardeners, filled with encouragement, humor, and anecdotal stories that make it highly entertaining and fun to learn!"

~ *Sarah Lawton (Goodreads)*

"This book went beyond my expectations. There are no questions left unanswered. This will be my go-to for all my permaculture needs ... The author is very knowledgeable of permaculture and it shows."

~ *B'Elanna (Amazon Canada)*

"*Permaculture Gardening for the Absolute Beginner* isn't just a gardening book; it's an invitation to join a delightful journey into the world of permaculture."

~ *Sergio (Amazon)*

"A masterpiece on permaculture! It's a complete guide, written in a simple and somewhat humorous manner. A must have for every farmer, of whatever scale, from windowsill gardener to commercial farmer and everyone in between!"

~ Patrick Simbeye (Goodreads)

"I love this book! It is written in such an easy-to-read style, almost like you are sitting and listening to the author talk to you. I am a gardener and I found it very informative. ... It is so refreshing to have a book be such a balance of useful information and entertaining at the same time. Very well done!"

~ Judy (Amazon Canada)

"This book was great. It is real art to write a book that is not only a pleasure to read but is also bursting with encouragement, information, how to and of course, the rationale while we should also be involved in permaculture. This book is successful on all counts."

~ Duncan (Amazon)

"I could hardly put this book down because I wanted to keep reading. I have taken an introductory Permaculture course, but did not really understand what permaculture meant. The language in this book is easy to read, ideas are fully explained, and easy to remember."

~ Horn79bell (Amazon)

"It's like having my own cheerleader encouraging me to get started with the smallest steps that are right for me. I love how all the aspects of permaculture come together to support even me - in an apartment. I feel empowered to take my tiny baby steps toward gardening this way."

~ EnnEll (Amazon)

"I found this book very refreshing and delightful like I was having a conversation with the author ... and after reading the book, I feel empowered and motivated to implement what I have learned from the book to my garden."

~ Joie (Goodreads)

"You won't believe the number of permaculture books collecting dust on my shelf, all of them seemingly too complex and dry. But then there's *Permaculture Gardening for the Absolute Beginner* by Josie Beckham, and it's like stumbling upon a hidden treasure chest in the world of gardening."

~ Tina Tolle (Goodreads)

"I felt like this was a friend sharing good advice with me ... The book covers about everything you could really want to know in this important and exciting way of seeing not just your garden, but even the rest of your life. I can pretty much guarantee that you will find the end of the book has come too soon."

~ Brian Saunders (Amazon UK)

"If you're new to permaculture READ THIS BOOK! If you own a library of permaculture books like me, you will still want to READ THIS BOOK! It's beautifully written and removes all intimidation about a seemingly complex subject. You will feel like your best friend is walking you down permaculture lane mentoring you in every aspect of the subject."

~ Kristi J (Goodreads)

"Having started my own intentional permaculture garden on 1/4 acre 15 years ago, when permaculture was a new idea to the general public, I truly could have used the guidance this book offers ... No matter where you are in your gardening journey please consider this incredible resource for your own shelf. You will turn to it time and again, I am sure."

~ Nancy Wells (Amazon)

"This book really answers all the questions a beginner like me is asking. Yet it contains SO much useful knowledge of permaculture that it will take me years of application to fully execute. Yes, this is the handbook I needed!"

~ Ivy Mackelin (Goodreads)

"This is the book I wish I had when I first felt a desire to plant a seed."

~ Audun Bartnes (Goodreads)

CONTENTS

Part IV

EXPANDING THE DESIGN

INTRODUCTION: TO PLANT A SEED

 Inside every seed is the potential for an incredible harvest.

— FARRAH GRAY

I'll never forget it.

It wasn't a special occasion, not a holiday or a celebration, but that ordinary family dinner is one I'll always remember.

My Great Aunt Shelby declared that my collard greens were the best she's ever tasted. Coming from a woman raised in the South, this is like the Oscar of compliments.

And she wasn't the only one who loved them. The bowl went *fast*. Even the kids, who usually turned up their noses at green food, went in for seconds.

I remember the warmth of that smile that spread across my face. I knew why the dish was such a hit. Not because I'd used some new recipe or secret ingredient. The difference was I'd grown those collards myself. Straight from the earth to the kitchen table, with nothing in between.

I'd say the moment filled my soul as much as it did their bellies.

And to think, it all started with *one simple seed*.

Well, friends, it's like they say. *"Never underestimate the power of planting a seed."*

So, what does it mean to plant a seed?

Literally, it means putting a tiny, dormant plant embryo in the ground, caring for it, and watching it grow.

Then, someday later, it means basking in the approving smiles of Great Aunt Shelby and the delight of your kiddos as they excitedly chow down upon your own home-grown organic veggies. Now that's a satisfying harvest!

However, planting a seed can also mean starting something new. Planting an idea and watching it blossom into something extraordinary.

Permaculture starts with an *idea*. It's the idea that humans and nature can work together in this remarkable, harmonious way, where we *all thrive together.*

Resilience. Resourcefulness. Interconnectedness. Multiplication. Abundance. Those are pretty fun words! And they're all included in the satisfying harvest of planting this seed.

Let's take another gander at our metaphorical seed packet here.

Permaculture explores the question: What if there were *timeless principles* we could tap into in order to cultivate life here on Earth to its fullest potential? It also answers with an excited, "Yes!" It's true! *And,* there is latent power all around us that we can harness, which has been at work since … well, *forever.*

Although "permaculture" may be a word of the last century, nature has been living it since the dawn of time. One needs only to step into the wild, lush forest with an open mind to be amazed by the remarkable circle of life at work.

See, natural ecosystems are awe-inspiring because they can *maintain and regenerate themselves,* and have done so for many years. In this book, we'll explore what this could mean for our lives and gardens.

For now, a simple example. Think about the lifecycle of an apple tree. The tree grows from a seed. It drops fruit that deposits more seeds. As the fruit rots, it fertilizes the soil. New apple trees sprout from that same soil. Multiplication, abundance, so on and so forth. This is a self-maintaining and regenerating system on a tiny scale.

Well, by mimicking nature — *watching* and *replicating* how its complex parts work together — we can create self-sustaining mini-ecosystems right in our own gardens and farms. In essence, we can "bring the forest back home."

And here's the fun part: we can do this *anywhere*.

Whether on a farm across the globe, or right in your own backyard: permaculture principles can powerfully influence projects of any scale and in any place.

The ideas of permaculture have certainly grown and spread around the world. More people are catching on. *There's a better way to grow food, and it's been around for a long time*. It's a back-to-our-roots kind of idea in the truest sense!

When I started my homestead, I had no idea what "permaculture" was. I just knew I liked animals, nature, and producing my own food. I was tired of relying on whatever produce the grocery store had in season. And I felt like there was a better way to utilize my space that was lower-maintenance, cheaper, and had less of an environmental impact.

When I discovered what permaculture was, something clicked. The more I learned about its ideas, the more I thought, *this just makes sense*. So the seed was planted, and it kept growing.

On the one hand, I realized something cool: in many ways, I had basically been practicing parts of permaculture all along! And on the other hand, I wish I'd found out about this sooner! I couldn't wait to learn more about these ideas and incorporate them more and more into my life & homestead, and *make everything better*.

Because, simply put, *permaculture works*. And it gives so many great solutions for living out the ideals and dreams that are important to me, and even vital for us as a human race!

Maybe you can relate with me. Check YES if any of these statements apply to you:

- You're blown away by the ever-increasing grocery store food costs, especially fresh meats, fruit, and vegetables.
- You're concerned about the chemicals they might be putting in the fruits and vegetables you buy at the grocery store. This includes the antibiotics, hormones, and supplements in commercially raised meats.
- You're conscious of your impact on this planet and want to make a positive change during your stay here.
- You like to think of creative ways to reuse empty containers, leftover building materials, broken furniture, and kitchen scraps.

- You're looking for a fun, natural hobby that you and your kids can participate in together, outdoors and away from electronic screens.
- You're tired of the basic row-by-row garden plan and wish there was a way to fit more abundance into your garden space.
- You want to make a positive change in your community.

Whether you checked off all these boxes or just one, you'll benefit from incorporating permaculture into your life.

So, maybe you've heard this buzzword "permaculture" and are excited to learn more about it. But it sure sounds like a lot to take in, especially if you're new to gardening. I felt the same way!

But pretty soon, you'll find that transforming your space into a permaculture paradise is easier than you thought! Of course, this is a journey of *many small steps*. The map is already there, etched into nature's code. This book is here to help you open that map, and take action, so you can start making your dream a reality, one step at a time.

We'll start by diving deeper into what permaculture is and the principles and goals behind it.

Then, you'll learn how to look at your space through permaculturist eyes and explore all the possibilities open to you, whether you have dozens of acres or just a few square feet.

And hey, if you can't tell the difference between a perennial and a porcupine, you're in luck! We will be going over all the gardening basics from a permaculture point of view.

Don't worry, you won't be going it alone. I'm here to guide you, and together, we'll be following blueprints that have stood the test of time. After all, the Earth's been spinning and food's been growing naturally for a long while now, right? The answers are out there. All we have to do is look with fresh eyes.

But before we get started, I want you to open your mind to these four simple principles:

#1: YOU'VE GOT THE RIGHT STUFF.

Throw those limiting misconceptions out, friend! Skip the recycling bin on this one. Permaculture and gardening ain't just for the professionals, farmers, rich folks, and people with vast expanses of acreage. It's for everyone! *Yes, this includes you.* Say it with me, with a big ol' cheesy grin … "I've got what it takes!" Feel goofy? Good. Embrace the goof.

Look, any time we try something new, thoughts and feelings of self-doubt are common for anyone to experience. In fact, the presence of doubt is a *great sign you are stretching beyond your comfort zone.* It means you're growing!

With this perspective shift, we can recognize the doubts for what they are when they do pop up. They are simply this — *thoughts and feelings* — and nothing more. They're *not the truth,* but defense mechanisms against the "unknown" that everyone else goes through, too. I've felt doubt plenty of times! Recognize all this as you feel it, and let it pass right on through. Thanks for trying to protect me, doubts. But I'm working with new information now.

You gain *confidence* through *knowledge* and *experience.* Sometimes just *knowing* how something works can demystify those daunting "unknowns." And *experience* gained through simple, consistent action builds competence. By reading this book and taking action from what you learn, you'll gain both *knowledge* and *experience!*

#2: DEVELOP A GROWTH MINDSET.

Alright, let's talk about that nasty F-word. Yep, you're going to *fail.* Ouch! I know, it stings. But, happily, it's true. And it's okay. *And, it's useful!* Failure = feedback! When dealing with the natural world — a world that is often outside of your control — failure happens, and again, it happens to everyone. You're not alone.

The key here is context. Consider the words of Janet Kilburn Phillips:

 There are no gardening mistakes, only experiments.

Let's really let that sink in. What if there are no "failures" here, only experiments and lessons? Experience is the best teacher, and each "mistake" provides valuable feedback. Consider your gardening journey to be one big learning experience! So, if spittlebugs decimate your first crop of strawberries, embrace it, learn from it, and move forward, Champ. Permaculture is all about trial and error. And *if you stay the course,* what doesn't kill your garden only makes it stronger.

#3: WORK WITH WHAT YOU'VE GOT.

Embrace your space! If you find yourself up against a mental block that sounds like, "Aw, I wish I had land so I could *really* do this," do yourself a big favor now and shift your perspective. Flip that thought to a positive: *"Look at all this space I have* right here on my 4' x 6' balcony!" See? Much better.

This journey is built on *seeing potential everywhere.* There's a space for everyone in permaculture, no matter how big or small.

#4: TAKE YOUR TIME AND ENJOY THE RIDE!

In permaculture, we practice small, slow solutions. Although there are things you can do to start producing today, a permaculture garden doesn't happen overnight. It takes years to establish, and it's constantly developing. And that's part of the fun! You can spend the rest of your life perfecting your permaculture plan.

For now, focus on baby steps. Something as small as planting a single seed will multiply in time.

Just like my collards did. And just like these great ideas have in my life, and I believe they will in yours too.

$\sim$

There are many ways you can use this book. You could pick a topic from the table of contents and use it for a reference as needed. Or you could read it from start to finish.

The ideas do build on each other, like the layers of a tasty cake. The first three chapters explore permaculture from the 30,000-foot-view. And while I believe the *mindsets* of permaculture lay an important foundation for its *practical application*, you may want to skip past theory and principles, and get right into the "how to" of your garden. I totally get it. If that's you, I'd suggest jumping in at Chapter 4, where we'll apply those core principles as we look at *your* space, and begin building your dream garden.

If you're looking to reference a certain method or idea, this book is divided into five main parts:

1. **SEEING THROUGH A NEW LENS:** This is the foundation I talked about above. We'll dive into the core concepts of permaculture, and really hear its heartbeat. We'll get motivated and look at what makes a permaculture garden so powerful and exciting. We'll learn to see with new eyes, and how to apply the principles of permaculture, not just to gardening in general, but to your specific space, design, and journey.

2. **METHODS AND MATERIALS:** This part will really pack your tool belt. We'll cover a large scope of gardening methods you can use to carry out your design. From containers and raised beds, to different ways to prepare the ground. We'll also cover a variety of materials you can use to build not only your garden structures but the soil as well. Whatever your budget, skill level, or space, you'll have what you need to build a garden!

3. **PLANTING THE GARDEN:** This part will empower you with all you need to do the main thing: plant stuff! We'll learn all about your soil, how to check it and give it what it needs to optimize it for plant growth. We'll cover the details of growing plants, from starting seeds to transplanting, seeing them all the way through their life cycle. I'll help you decide what to plant, when to plant it, and where. We'll explore some advanced planting techniques to help you create a balanced, full garden and get the most out of it.

4. **EXPANDING THE DESIGN:** This is where your design really becomes enriched, integrated, and complete. From incorporating animal life to making use of the resources that are all around you, we'll take steps to create a thriving mini-ecosystem. We'll harness natural resources, like rain, sun, and wind, to help your garden thrive. We'll learn the art of composting, and make powerful use of garden waste, food scraps, and even weeds, so everything serves a purpose.

5. **THINKING AHEAD:** This is where you pack your bags for the years ahead, so you are thoroughly equipped for this journey. We'll cover how to harvest your crops, as well as various methods of preserving food and extending the growing season for year-round abundance. We'll also brainstorm and troubleshoot, covering common garden issues from a permaculture perspective.

Maybe you're new to permaculture, or maybe you're already familiar with its concepts. Maybe you've already discovered your green thumb, or maybe you're wondering if you're even capable of growing a single bean. (Hint: You are! Do we need to do another goofy pep-talk?)

Wherever you're at, *I believe there's something in these pages for you.* As you read through the ideas inside, remember the power of the seed being planted. With dedication and nurturing, a seed brings incredible rewards.

Dr. Seuss may have been writing children's books, but he was really onto something when he wrote about the power of a single seed:

> Plant the seed in the middle of town, where everyone can see. Change the way things are. I know it may seem small and insignificant, but it's not about what it is, it's about what it can become.

— DR. SEUSS, *THE LORAX*

A seed becomes a plant, which leads to more seeds, which leads to more plants. And eventually ... it becomes a forest.

In the words of Ralph Waldo Emerson, *"Thought is the seed of action."*

As thoughts become actions, with consistency, it all builds up to an *abundant* and *satisfying harvest*. That's the circle of life, friend! Multiplication. Abundance. So on and so forth.

So. Are you ready? Let's plant the seed.

PART I

SEEING THROUGH A NEW LENS

THE MINDSET OF A PERMACULTURIST

Q uick! Answer this question:

What do a Pawnee tribesman, your great-grandmother, and the guy who picks up your recycling all have in common?

(It's a tough one, I know).

Answer: They're all people who have practiced permaculture, whether they knew it or not. In some way, each one has worked with the land to survive, thrive, and make the Earth, and their community, a better place.

WHAT EXACTLY IS PERMACULTURE?

So what is permaculture? It sounds like a fancy technical term that belongs to landscape architects and environmental scientists. But for the rest of us, **permaculture** simply means *humans and nature working together in harmony.*

It's the idea of creating a self-sustaining agricultural ecosystem that follows nature's blueprint and can benefit the entire community. This idea has truly been around since the beginning of humanity. Pocahontas even sings about it in her musical debut.

Since the first civilization began in Mesopotamia, people have found ways to work with nature in a symbiotic relationship. It's an "I'll scratch your back, you scratch mine" kind of thing: utilizing the land to your benefit and giving back by improving it in the process.

As Pocahontas so sagely expresses, it ain't about owning the land like some dead thing, but realizing the Earth is brimming with life, and working in a *partnership* with it. Which just so happens to be one of the ethics behind permaculture. Way to go, Po.

INTRODUCING THE GREAT BILL MOLLISON!

Although the ideas behind permaculture have been around forever, the word "permaculture" hasn't. It's a mashup of the terms "permanent" and "agriculture." It was coined by a man named Bill Mollison in the 1970's. A native to Tasmania, Bruce Charles "Bill" Mollison spent the early part of his life in the bush and at sea, hunting, fishing, doing odd jobs, and researching the natural world around him.

Mollison later received his degree in biology from the University of Tasmania. He stayed on to lecture and teach, founding the university's Environmental Psychology unit. It wasn't until after he put his teaching hat aside that he pursued his lifelong passion for permaculture.

The idea had actually come to him years before. While observing marsupials browsing among the trees in the Tasmanian rainforest, he was inspired by the amazingly sustainable inner workings of the natural ecosystem.

Remember how planting a seed can mean an idea that starts a new journey? Well, this was that "seed" moment for Bill. That seed began to germinate, and one day he thought to himself and scribbled in his journal, *"I believe that we could build systems that would function as well as this one does."* (Hemenway, 2009).

And that's precisely what he did.

Drawing upon his own observations and some tried-and-true industrial-agricultural methods, Mollison spent the next 30 years as a scientist, teacher, and campaigner for permaculture.

And my, how the seed has grown.

PERMACULTURE DEFINED (WHEW!)

Mollison defines permaculture as:

> ... a philosophy of working with, rather than against nature; of protracted and thoughtful observation rather than protracted and thoughtless labor; and of looking at plants and animals in all their functions, rather than treating any area as a single product system.

In his first book, *Introduction to Permaculture* (Mollison & Slay, 1991), Bill explains that permaculture aims

> ... to create systems that are ecologically sound and economically viable, which provide for their own needs, do not exploit or pollute, and are therefore sustainable in the long term. Permaculture uses the inherent qualities of plants and animals combined with the natural characteristics of landscapes and structures to produce a life-supporting system for city and country, using the smallest practical area.

Thanks, Bill! Well put! But, um ... what the heck does that mean?

To understand what Mr. Mollison was trying to tell us, it might be helpful to break his words down into small, digestible chunks that we can all understand.

To go about that, let's open our eyes and ears ... to *see the picture* of permaculture at work, and *hear the heartbeat* of its greater mission.

First, we'll follow in the footsteps of our fearless leader, Bill, and take a little stroll through the woods.

SEE THE PICTURE: A WALK IN THE WOODS

Think of the forest.

Nobody tills the land. Nobody sows seeds. Nobody waters the plants or pulls out the weeds. Nobody fertilizes the soil. Yet, the forest thrives and feeds and shelters its residents.

No waste comes out of the forest. That's because everything here is a resource. The leaves that drop from the trees decompose on the forest floor and feed the soil.

Plants flower, set seed, and die back. Winds or birds pick up the seeds and scatter them throughout the forest.

Nobody here sprays insecticides to kill pests. The birds do the job by pecking at and wolfing them down. Somehow, it's like every living thing works together and has its place, and there is this ... beautiful balance.

Look around (the forest, that is). Can you see it? All the lush, vibrant, and *abundant* vegetation? Can you feel the crunch of leaves decomposing beneath your feet? Hear all the wildlife chiming in like a grand symphony?

That's the sound of life, baby. An ecosystem at work, and fully taking care of itself. The great circle of life. (Also movie musical reference number 2).

The cycle is complete, yet no human "made" it that way. How can this be?

Well, call it what you want, but it *works*. In fact, it excels! This is nature at work and shining, like a fine-tuned, well-oiled machine.

Can you imagine having a micro-version of that *in your own garden?* What if a home garden could regenerate itself like this? That's the vision Bill saw.

Let's take a page out of nature's playbook. Or heck, just read the book!

Masanobu Fukuoka was a famous Japanese farmer celebrated for his natural farming, also called "do-nothing farming." He authored the highly influential book, *The One-Straw Revolution*, and is considered by many to be the Master Farmer of Japan. He was also a great inspiration to Bill Mollison. Masanobu said it like this:

 Observe nature thoroughly rather than labor thoughtlessly.

Indeed. Permaculture's ideas for designing gardens are filled with the philosophy of "work smarter" not *unnecessarily* harder. Minimum input for the maximum output. Nature's been doing this gig for a while now, and as they say, *"If it ain't broke, don't fix it!"*

Now that we're catching a vision of permaculture at work for food-growing purposes, let's listen to the heartbeat of why it's important in the big picture.

HEAR THE HEARTBEAT: PERMACULTURE'S 3 CORE VALUES

This is the "why" of permaculture — what kept Bill up at night. You can break down the mission of permaculture into three core values, which are:

1. **EARTH CARE:** Treating the Earth with a sense of responsibility and stewardship,
2. **PEOPLE CARE:** Responding to the needs of ourselves and those in our community, and
3. **SHARE THE SURPLUS:** Reinvesting our surplus into the above two so that it doesn't go to waste.

Check this out. If you've ever planted and grown a few seeds organically, harvested their yield, then given away some to your neighbor, you've practiced the three core values of permaculture. Look, you're a permaculturist, and didn't even know it!

EARTH CARE

Symbiosis is a major factor in permaculture. If you don't remember it from third-grade science class, it's a close relationship between two different kinds of organisms: a clownfish and an anemone, an oxpecker and a rhino, or man and nature.

More specifically, permaculture embodies a kind of **mutualism**. This is where two organisms work together to benefit one another. The oxpecker enjoys a free buffet of blood-sucking insects while the rhino gets personalized grooming services.

We as humans enjoy the fruits of the Earth. This includes literal fruits, vegetables, meat, and natural materials like firewood, lumber, and fibers. In return, we can give back, sowing into this Earth we've been given, by caring for its soil, optimizing our use of renewable resources, reducing waste, and leaving things better than we found them.

And hang on, before you tune out another voice shouting from a soapbox, this is also a pretty smart investment. Look at it this way. All the essentials that keep us alive — air, water, food, shelter — are all sourced from ... you guessed it. There's no Planet B, am I right?

And permaculture comes in with *good news!* We can *work together*. The Earth is ready and willing to give back abundantly to us, and clues have been left for us on how to maximize our stay here while also making a positive impact during it. And that's good for the Earth *and* for us. See, symbiosis! And if we learn our part in the dance with nature, there are a ton of benefits we *all* reap.

Permaculture is a carefully balanced choreography of *natural ecosystems* and *human-designed systems* aimed at *food production*. It embraces natural and sustainable agricultural methods, renewable energy and resources, and the biodiversity found in nature.

In short, live in harmony with nature, and everyone comes out on top. This means cleaner, tastier tomatoes for you, and healthier soil and life for the Earth. Teamwork makes the dream work.

PEOPLE CARE

"People care" is why many would-be permaculturists are fascinated with the system. The ultimate goal of many is to sustain yourself and your family for an entire year on fresh, organic produce you've harvested at home.

And for many people, the goal is also to eliminate dependence on the grocery store or food supply chain. With ever-climbing food prices and sometimes questionable commercial farming practices, many see a homegrown strawberry or salad as the Holy Grail.

A permaculturist lifestyle can also provide water, shelter, and overall sustainability. Incorporating these ideas into your home can better prepare you and your family in the case of a catastrophic event (when the you-know-what "hits the fan", as doomsday preppers like to call it). These are all fantastic goals.

But can you hear that heartbeat singin', *"zoom out a little"*? In fact, the idea of total "self-sufficiency" may well be a myth. After all, we all need each other to survive and thrive! We are not unlike that fine-tuned forest ecosystem, each with our unique part to play. Someone else made the computer I used to type up this book, after all.

In fact, remember how the word "permaculture" is a mashup of "permanent" and "agriculture"? Well, over time the word also developed the meaning of "permanent *culture*" and incorporated social aspects. Mutualism on a whole nutha level.

Yessir, permaculture extends beyond the walls of our own off-grid cabins and into the greater community around us. This can be your neighbors, friends, extended family, and community members. No man is an island. Even that crazy hermit guy who lives in a shack at the edge of town is part of this "human ecosystem". And hey, maybe he'd like some strawberries too.

Permaculturists believe that taking care of the Earth is just as important as taking care of the people who live on it. They believe in everyone having opportunities to feel secure, satisfied, and sustained. They work toward the goal of everyone's basic human needs being met. They're just plain good neighbors.

Just ask great-grandma. Back in the day, one neighbor might have grown corn, another might have raised pigs, and another might have made homemade soap. Rather than let the extra go to waste, each neighbor would share what they had so that everyone got a little of each.

No corn rotted away in the silo, and no fresh pork spoiled in the summer heat. That's a fine real-life example of the *people care* ethic, and also a great example of the next one.

SHARING THE SURPLUS

The core value of sharing surplus is all about taking only what we need and reinvesting the rest. In a world increasingly overrun with waste, permaculturists are all about moving excess resources back into the *earth* or the *community*. This could mean composting yard waste and food scraps, donating surplus crops to a food bank, or contributing to an accessible community garden.

The third ethic extends from the first two. The complete heart of these ethics is, as Bill Mollison puts it, *"care of the earth, care of people, and reinvestment in those ends."*

Now, while some permaculture purists would rather focus solely on giving away the excess (which is noble!), it's worth noting that for others with an entrepreneurial spirit (which is also awesome!), selling excess produce at a local farmer's market can really benefit the community as well.

It boosts the local economy, promotes community interconnectedness, provides fresh organic food to the community, spreads awareness to more people about permaculture, and helps fund the future growth of your garden, which will then help more people. So on and so forth! There's nothing saying you can't set up a fine stand at the market or even build a thriving business, all while cultivating generosity simultaneously. In fact, they can build on each other beautifully.

As you go digging through permaculture literature, you'll find that the community of permaculture is just as diverse as its gardens. Permaculture values diversity, and it is inclusive! And so, this third ethic has been the topic of a lot of discussions that extend far beyond the scope of this book. Some people call this ethic "fair share" (which rhymes nicely with the other two), and some have suggested that it be rebranded to "future care" ... and there are a lot of different beliefs and reasons behind all that.

Whichever way you lean in your unique beliefs, there's a basic heartbeat to embrace within this third ethic.

Permaculture is centered on the inherent abundance, generosity, and reciprocity written in the Earth's DNA, and this ethic is all about moving in that flow. It's less about some rule or law, and more about cultivating awareness, responsibility, gratitude, teamwork, legacy, long-term thinking, hope, and a heart of "giving back." At the risk of turning this chapter into a movie musical "Greatest Hits" album here, let's put it this way: *we're all in this together.*

So as we grow and as we consume food, permaculture invites us to consider the needs of both present and future generations. Without a doubt, there's plenty of cause for concern about our future, and our resources.

But where some voices seem to paint a hopelessly bleak outlook, or sound kinda heavy-handed or doomy-and-gloomy; I see permaculture looking once again into the wells of nature's abundance and drawing out great optimism. Maybe that's my unique perspective and I sound a little like Pollyanna Permaculture ... but it's what I see!

 No gardener would be a gardener if he did not live in hope.

— VITA SACKVILLE-WEST

And lemme tell ya, I caught the vision from permaculture's finest. 'Twas the people of permaculture who taught me the power packed within a single seed! Remember? If we keep in mind the principle of multiplication over time, we see how there are entire forests inside of that one tiny seed. One of the world's leading permaculturists put it this way:

> Permaculture gives us a toolkit for moving from a culture of fear and scarcity to one of love and abundance.

— TOBY HEMENWAY

Yes! Nature's message is not one of scarcity, but *abundance* that we can all tap into! And indeed, there are *many* ways to share the love.

On that note, this tenant of permaculture embraces the pass-it-on principle. One fun idea is to organize a community produce swap, where local gardeners can swap their surplus and enjoy variety. You can also share your spare seeds with a neighbor or strawberries with a hermit. You can distribute excess produce to the community, throw a berry-preserving party with your friends, or teach a child about permaculture. Knowledge is a great resource to distribute, and I'll bet you have a surplus building!

Helping others to achieve sustainability makes the world a better place. And it makes Bill Mollison smile.

SEEING THE WORLD THROUGH PERMIE GLASSES

Are you a permie? Not to be confused with babies born before their due dates, **permies** are people who are *totally into permaculture*. Whether you're a first-time infant permie (a premie permie?) or a professionally certified card-carrying permaculturist, everyone has a place in the permaculture world.

That's because permaculture doesn't have to be an all-or-nothing, sign-your-name-here kind of thing. Like the natural world, it's organic, flexible, and adaptable to your unique situation.

If you take only one thing away from this chapter, I hope it's this: *permaculture is not a set of rules. Instead, it's a way of thinking.* It's viewing the world through a different lens. It's part curiosity, part resolve, and a willingness to live harmoniously with the planet and your fellow creatures.

You may be thinking, "Get me to the part where I'm feeding my own home-grown tomatoes to my family and friends!" Rest assured, we will get there. But truly, the mindsets in permaculture are the foundation on which the rest of its design principles are built. And if you can learn to see more possibilities in your daily life, you can learn to see more possibilities in your garden.

As you see how you can reuse daily items, for instance, you start to see how you can reuse your fallen trees. Your eyes open to multiple uses everywhere. You start to see how you may not need all this extra external input you thought you needed. Perhaps there's a lot more potential right in front of you than you realized.

We learn about gardening from life. And we learn about life from gardening.

… That was fortune-cookie-worthy right there.

As you try on permie glasses, remember, you don't have to transition to some new lifestyle all at once. Baby steps are perfectly great, especially if you're a permie premie. Start with thinking about little ways you can practice awareness in your daily life.

- Instead of thinking, "Where will I get my food?" … put on your new permie glasses and ask, "What kind of food can I grow myself?" Growing food — no matter how little — is good for you, good for the planet, and 100% doable. Learn to see potential all around you (and within you)!
- Instead of thinking, "How much stuff can I buy?" … embrace the joy of simplifying! Try to reduce the new things you buy and focus on quality rather than toss-it-and-replace-it items. Minimalism isn't just on trend, it's also super relieving to the mind.
- Start asking, "What resources do I already have all around me?" Repurpose the waste that you can and recycle the waste that you can't. For example, reuse grocery bags or donate old clothes to a thrift store. And those food scraps? Punch a few holes in the top of a $7 plastic tub from Walmart and dump kitchen waste and shredded paper into it. Pretty soon, you'll have your own "black gold" to feed your plants! (More on this in Chapter 13).
- Instead of thinking, "I don't have the time to save the world!" (How true) … Think, "How can I get involved?" You don't have to start a nonprofit organization or even volunteer at the local soup kitchen to get involved with your community. Visiting a farmers market, shopping locally, or donating to a community initiative are all fun, fulfilling ways to contribute that don't take much time. Reach out to the community to share resources and ideas.

There are so many things you can start incorporating now — and have fun trying on — as you continue living your life. This isn't about some radical overnight overhaul. You don't have to cancel your Netflix subscription to get started growing your own tomatoes.

Will you find permaculture purists who say you should convert your home to solar and cut ties with your municipal waste facility? Sure, and more power to them (literally!). But not everyone can be that person. I certainly am not. Going in whole-hog can be overwhelming, especially when you love the creature comforts that modernity has blessed us with.

Not to mention, a complete lifestyle change is often unrealistic, due to limits in resources or time, dietary considerations, and other important factors.

Here comes permaculture once again to reassure us that it's all about "small and slow solutions," and working with what you have! Right here and now. So relax, breathe in the fresh air, and take the next step you can.

Then hey, who knows? Maybe someday, you'll be installing those solar panels on your roof as you look upon your backyard Eden, brimming with life. You'll think fondly back to these first steps, smile, and say to yourself, "My my, how far we've come."

For now, take the step you can … and take the next step that *excites* you, because this journey is definitely about having fun, too.

Wrap-Up

Okay Josie, I've got a basic feel for the permaculture vibe. Check. I get that being a permie means looking at things differently. Check. We took a cool field trip through the forest, and we heard Papa Mollison's heartbeat and all about the mission, double check. So …

What does this have to do with gardening?

I'm glad you asked. Follow me to the next chapter, where we'll explore the power of a permaculture garden.

2

THE POSITIVE POWER OF A PERMACULTURE GARDEN

 You can solve all the world's problems in a garden.

— GEOFF LAWTON

Holy Marigolds, Geoff! Talk about motivation!

And that, my permie pal, is what this chapter is all about. *Motivation*. Stocking up on it is like packing trail mix for the journey. It'll give you energy when you run out.

Geoff, by the way, is another hardcore perma-legend. He trained under Bill Mollison, and he's an all-around great guy. You gotta get to know him!

Okay, so you may know your way around a garden on some level. And you may even know some of the massive benefits that gardening can bring, perhaps even from first-hand experience.

But you may be asking yourself …

WHAT DISTINGUISHES A *PERMACULTURE* GARDEN?

All permaculture involves gardening, but not all gardening involves permaculture. Capiche?

No? That's okay. Allow me to explain.

Permaculture is *similar to*, but at the same time *unique among*, traditional landscaping and gardening methods, even the organic kind. It's also not mutually exclusive to homesteading.

You'll remember from the last chapter that permaculture is a way of seeing. Ultimately and more specifically in food-growing, permaculture is a set of **design principles**, which are a set of values that act as a compass for your project. (We'll go over 12 specific principles in Chapter 3 that make up the parts of *our compass*).

In this case, our *project* is a *garden*. And a *permaculture* garden has several things that make it special.

It involves more than just planting crops. For example, embracing natural resources, reducing waste, and creating sustainable self-regenerating ecosystems, all with the greater community in mind.

As we look at how permaculture stands out in a crowd, my approach here is to examine its powerful strategies and solutions, without totally dismissing other camps or ideas. In fact, we may often have much to be grateful for in regard to their contributions, have a lot to learn from them, and may even stand on their shoulders. And often, there is a good bit of common ground.

So let's engage in conversation, glean from the wisdom of others and see how permaculture can bring its unique influence to the table. You know, that whole, "don't throw the baby out with the bathwater" thing. (Or maybe don't throw out the bathwater at all! Reuse that grey water in some garden beds, right Bill?)

A great question to ask ourselves is, how can we start *incorporating permaculture principles* into our gardens, our landscapes, and our homesteads, even in small ways? While at the same time asking, how can these other worlds positively influence our permaculture journey?

Alright, let's take a look around the garden with our new permie glasses on.

Permaculture and Traditional Gardening:
Growing Food, Nature's Way

Permaculture brings its influence to the gardening world in a few ways:

- Maximizing the use of space. Think of it as a "no soil left bare, no square inch left unused" philosophy.
- Maximizing the use of freely and naturally occurring resources. A permaculture design asks, "What is nature already doing here, and how can I work with that as my canvas?" It seeks to harness the most out of the available sun, rain, wind, and soil. And through those permie glasses, even what we'd usually call "waste" can be seen as a resource (even weeds, believe it or not)!
- Embracing the location and its climate, by bringing in lots of native plants.
- Seeing the *garden* as *part of the whole*, creating an *ecosystem* that feeds the health of the soil and benefits not just the individual crops, but also the animals and insects that live alongside them.
- Practicing polyculture planting. That means planting more than one different crop in an area to increase biodiversity, as opposed to "monoculture" which means one crop repeated in rows.
- Using organic practices, and going *beyond them* (see other points). There's a lot of overlap between permaculture and organic farming and gardening. Both advocate an eco-friendly approach, with natural solutions rather than manmade ones. Such as utilizing insect predators and organic solutions to kill pests rather than chemicals.
- Typically, starting with perennial food crops at center stage. These are ones that come back year after year rather than dying off after one growing season. These include fruit and nut trees, berry bushes, and perennial herbs.

With a little forethought and observation, all of this is intended to mimic nature and create a garden that's more like the forest that takes care of itself.

Fun fact! Permaculture is often referred to as "lazy farming" or "lazy gardening." And on that note, Bill Mollison was well known for his aspirations to "maximize hammock time" by "working with nature, rather than against it."

Well dang Billy, count me in!

PERMACULTURE AND TRADITIONAL LANDSCAPING:
Form and Function Unite!

Ah, the landscaper and the permaculturist; it's a tale as old as time. Both ultimately wanted the same things: to live among beautifully blooming flowers, lush gardens, shady trees, and trickling fountains. But they just couldn't get past their differences. So, like Romeo and Juliet, they were fated to fail.

Or were they?

See, traditional landscaping and permaculture have some crossover. In a perfect world, they can live happily ever after. Let's mention a few ways permaculture brings its contribution to this conversation. Much could be repeated from the above section on gardening.

- Focusing on function over form. Rather than asking, "What would look aesthetically pleasing here?" Permaculture asks, "What will serve a practical purpose?" (e.g. food production, feeding the soil, inviting pollinators). Some other key questions asked when creating a permaculture design include: "Does this element serve more than one function?" Or "Does this make use of another resource or benefit something else in the design?"
- Working with naturally occurring resources, to create productive, low-maintenance, no-waste spaces that will, in turn, *reinvigorate* the soil. Rather than creating an artificial environment that requires a lot of upkeep, permaculture seeks to create spaces that sustain themselves as much as possible. Minimum input for maximum output.
- Plus, much of what was mentioned above, such as focusing on organic methods, seeing the garden as one part of the whole, and focusing on native plants, which don't take as much human input to sustain.

More and more, landscapers are focusing more on working with the environment rather than against it, by doing things like working with native plants and using a site's natural resources and topography to feed the plant life.

And let's just hold our permie horses, cus we can learn some stuff in this relationship too! Permaculture designers aim to create sustainable landscapes with less ecological impact, such as strategically placing companion plants or earthworks to catch runoff. But does that mean we can't put any artistic flair in our designs?

It doesn't have to be this way! There's nothing saying we can't have our nature and eat it too.

Now maybe that wild and free look is what you're into. If that's you, then work that *"au naturel"* beauty, girl! But search online for "edible landscaping" and you'll also find folks who are interested in combining conscious curb appeal with sustainable food growing.

There's a reason you can feel instantly peaceful when you look at a well-designed and manicured landscape or flower garden. The creative use of levels and layers, straight lines and curves, color diversity, and things like evergreens for year-round interest, are all parts of the expert artistic intentionality that comes with landscape design.

You can take notes from ornamental landscaping ideas and exchange some of the usual plants for edible ones like fruits & vegetables. Or think of herbs and flowers used for medicinal or culinary purposes, which also benefit nearby plants by attracting pollinators or repelling pests.

There are so many beautiful options, like amaranth, plum and peach trees, chives, lavender, or blackberry or raspberry growing up trellises. Some greens are quite stunning, too, like lettuce, kale, artichoke, and swiss chard.

And edible landscaping doesn't have to mean everything is edible, either. It can be a blend.

Perhaps a permaculture design can incorporate some aesthetic finesse from landscaping design principles. Working harmoniously with nature while also reaping a harvest of stunning beauty from a well-thought-out "edible" landscape design … hmm, sounds like the best of both worlds to me.

Maybe the story can have a happy ending, after all!

PERMACULTURE AND HOMESTEADING:
Livin' the Dream … Together!

Homesteaders are experts at getting back to our roots and working with the land. I am one, and proud of it! While both include providing food for your family, permaculture and homesteading aren't necessarily the same thing. You can be a homesteader without practicing permaculture and vice versa. But as a way of homesteading, permaculture can add even more purpose to your homestead lifestyle. I mean, just think how cool it could be to add bee boxes, rain barrels, and earth houses to your homestead!

The major influence of permaculture here is about diving deeper into the *why*. Rather than thinking about what to plant in your garden this spring, think deeper. Think about what plants work together, what they do to the soil, and what they can contribute to the sustainability of both your kitchen pantry *and the land*. For years to come, even after you're gone from it!

And unlike some off-the-grid homesteaders (not pointing fingers at the old guy who lives in the shack at the edge of town), permaculturists take the community as a whole into the equation, going outside the box of one's own genetic lineage. Permaculture infuses homesteading with a broader perspective and a longer legacy.

And that's an even more satisfying harvest!

THE BIG PICTURE

Indeed, there's something special about a permaculture-infused garden, landscape, or homestead. It's definitely not the *only* way to do these things successfully. But perhaps, it provides a more holistic, more organic and natural, more optimized and sustainable, and maybe ... even an all-around *better* way. So:

WHY SHOULD I START A PERMACULTURE GARDEN?

Are you lacking something in your life? Are you feeling lonely, depressed, tired, disconnected, frustrated, like your life has no purpose? Ask your doctor if PermaCulture™ is right for you.

Side effects may include sudden feelings of purpose and fulfillment, an unexplainable connectedness to the Earth and your community, an influx of fresh vegetables, and a suntan.

Okay, that might be stretching it. But it's not far from the truth! Because a garden can provide a bounty of benefits. And not just the literal bounty you'll get from it. Just ask the great poet Alfred Austin:

 The glory of gardening: hands in the dirt, head in the sun, heart with nature. To nurture a garden is to feed not just the body, but the soul.

I couldn't have put it better myself.

Permies join the cause for a range of reasons, whether it be out of a desire to fulfill personal needs or address broader concerns, or both.

We'll break down some of those areas of concern, and how permaculture looks to address them, in this handy table (because who doesn't love a good table?).

The Power of Permaculture

The Concern	How Permaculture Addresses It
Environmental	Give back to the Earth, enhancing it as we partner with it, and improve sustainability with a more productive, no-waste lifestyle. Reduce, reuse, recycle to the fullest.
Social	Permaculture lends itself to connectedness, community building, and interdependence in a world that's becoming increasingly isolated and consumeristic.
Economic	Having your own reliable abundance helps you to break away from dependence on the supply chain, shake loose the cords of consumerism, and save some money, too.
Health	Many are concerned with the GMOs, hormones, pesticides, and preservatives packed into store-bought foods. When you grow your own produce, you know exactly where it came from, how it was grown, and what's in it. As a plus, you'll finally know firsthand what a real homegrown strawberry tastes like!
Family	Permaculture is the ultimate "back to roots" movement. It's an excellent way to teach your children, grandchildren, nieces and nephews, or that weird kid who's always hanging around your backyard, about not taking for granted things like food, nature, or life itself. It teaches children the value of hard work, a love for the outdoors, an honor for nature, and that food comes from the ground, not the shelf. Plus, it's super fun and rewarding to harvest food you grew together!

Speaking of growing together, research has shown community gardens to have powerful community-wide social and therapeutic impacts. Improved school performance and socialization in children, increased place and community attachment, reduced community crime, and improved access to healthy and affordable food, are all on the list. (Hall & Knuth, 2019a).

But maybe you're thinking, "Whoa dude, I'm just searching for my own inner peace here." Well hey, that's okay too. For many people, permaculture is "living the dream!" It isn't a drug that will magically change your life (or is it?), but it can release those endorphins that bring you feelings of peace and happiness. It can improve your physical and mental health in many ways.

You know what they say: *"Gardening adds years to your life and life to your years."* Well, whoever "they" are, they might just be right! Let's take a look at a few of the many positive effects that can happen when you:

- Transform your backyard, patio, or balcony into your own little Garden of Eden. It's a "happy place" where you can go to experience the beauty of nature when you're feeling stressed, anxious, or just overwhelmed with fast-paced modern life. You get to slow down, away from noise and distractions, and simply be.
- Get back to your roots! Learning to grow like your ancestors did brings deep purpose, gratitude, and connectedness to the past, and future as well.
- Feel empowerment, hope, and inspiration, knowing you created something out of nothing. If you can do this, you can do anything! Plus, you get the peace of mind of knowing you can provide for yourself and your family.
- Feel the pride and satisfaction of sharing something you've grown with others. Picking and eating something you have grown yourself is "true wealth". And the joy of giving it away is priceless.
- Support your physical well-being by working outdoors, under the sun, with your hands and body. Not to mention, the improved nutrition from eating high-quality, natural foods.
- Support your mental well-being as well, and experience the healing effects of getting your "hands in the dirt, head in the sun, and heart with nature." Research has long supported the idea that gardening can be linked with incredible mental health benefits, even for first-time gardeners. The benefits observed are many and include: reduced anxiety, stress, and depression; increased creativity, productivity, and

attention; enhanced memory retention and self-esteem; improved happiness and life satisfaction; and even mitigation of effects from things like PTSD and dementia; plus much more. (Hall & Knuth, 2019b)

- Get to be a part of making the world better. Look, even if you're on this journey to grow a few vegetables just for fun, it is a rewarding feeling to be a part of something bigger. To be a producer, and not just a consumer. Doing your little part to heal our planet one backyard at a time is exhilarating! Cue more inspiring quotes ...

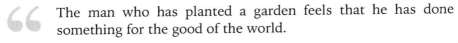

> The man who has planted a garden feels that he has done something for the good of the world.
>
> — CHARLES DUDLEY WARNER

> The greatest change we need to make is from consumption to production, even if on a small scale, in our own gardens. If only 10% of us do this, there is enough for everyone.
>
> — BILL MOLLISON

Ah Bill, there's that sparkle of permaculture hope again.

Now look, I don't know about you, but sometimes along the way I get to thinkin, "Well shoot, this sounds great and all, but *what can little ol me really do?*"

Remember how we talked at the start about baby steps? This would be a good time to reiterate the importance of those. I wrote this book partly to speak to folks who feel overwhelmed at the thought of going all-in. But they're looking to start somewhere. This is exactly what permaculture is about. Small, slow solutions.

And pretty soon, you'll also learn about how permaculture is about valuing the "margins" and "edges" in a space. And in our "people space", wouldn't this mean valuing all the people who are "on the fence" or just getting started?

A garden's a garden, no matter how small. Right, Dr. Seuss?

And oh, look! Here comes our buddy Teddy Roosevelt to motivate us, too.

Do what you can, with what you have, where you are.

— THEODORE ROOSEVELT

What's this? Margaret Mead, what are you doing here?

 Never underestimate the power of a small group of committed people to change the world. In fact, it is the only thing that ever has.

— MARGARET MEAD

Yes, this is an intervention. Well okay, more like another goofy pep-talk. We've all gathered here to encourage you, friend, to take that next step in your journey. It's a powerful step, that next one! And don't forget to smell the roses along the way. (It's good for your health, remember?)

Whatever your reasons are for taking this journey, *keep going!*

Cus there's a harvest waiting on the other side.

Lastly, as you progress along your permaculture path, you may learn so much more than simply what seed to plant and when. You might just learn something about yourself. Because the principles of permaculture don't just apply to the garden, they apply to life in general. Life reflects the garden, and the garden reflects life, remember?

By learning to be mindful, resourceful, and knowing that everything has its place, you can bring a sense of true contentment to your life. No drugs needed.

WHY IS PERMACULTURE FOR ANYONE?

Alright, maybe you're convinced. Maybe, you're even getting more excited.

But still, you might wonder: Okay but for real, though … to be a permie, do you have to move out to the middle of nowhere and walk barefoot through a pine forest until you've learned to talk with the trees and become one with the ladybugs? No! (I mean … that's cool if so!) But you can be a permaculture pro right from your own backyard or your apartment windowsill.

It doesn't have to be expensive to set up or sustain. It doesn't require X amount of acreage. All it takes is an open mind and a willingness to enhance your life through natural, sustainable living.

And a John Deere tractor.

Just kidding. The John Deere is totally optional.

Permaculture doesn't require you to buy any specific equipment or supplies. In fact, it's all about *encouraging* you to find creative ways to make do with what you have! And you don't have to sign on any dotted line, or join some membership or get a permaculture tattoo.

What permaculture is could be (and often is) described in many ways and can cover some broad areas. But basically, for our purposes here, it is a set of ideas, practices, and principles that allow people to become more self-reliant and sustainable.

And it is for absolutely ANYONE.

Remember how at the beginning of Chapter 1, we talked about your great-grandmother, the Native tribesman, and your friendly neighborhood recycling collector? Whether they knew it or not, they encompassed the heart of permaculture in their lifestyles.

The Native American tribesman was the OG permaculturist before permaculture was cool. He didn't have a tractor, a solar panel, or a seed catalog, but he worked with nature and his own bare hands to produce food from the land. He probably understood what the trees said, too.

Your great-grandma or great-great-grandma likely lived in a time when food and supplies weren't always readily plentiful. She learned how to make do with what she had, took care of things so that they lasted, and didn't waste a thing. She probably knew how to preserve food and, if she lived on a farm, how to sow and harvest with the resources available to her.

And then there's Bob, the recycling man. It's right there in his job description: recycling! Every day he picks up the waste that people throw out and brings it to a facility where it can be given a new life. He works with the community and, even if it's just for the paycheck, is working to make the world a better place.

Many kinds of people engage with permaculture in many ways.

Essentially, permaculture as it pertains to *gardening* is about aiming to grow your own food in a sustainable system. To grow your own food, you need light (sun), water (rain), soil, and food for the soil (compost). Naturally, if you have a larger garden, you can grow more. But even with a balcony and a tight budget, you can have light, water, soil, and good stuff to feed the soil. When you look at the essentials for any permaculture garden, none are related to lots of money or space!

Throughout the book, we'll look at ideas that allow you to implement permaculture practices regardless of your space. Window boxes and vertical gardening allow you to grow food in small spaces where no garden is available. You can collect water in buckets rather than barrels. A compost bin can be small enough to fit under the kitchen sink, and shared spaces are ideal for bigger projects like worm farms and livestock.

Wrap-Up

With all this empowerment and excitement packed in our backpack, you no doubt want to get started. Hang tight! One of the hardest things for any gardener, regardless of the principles they choose to follow, is the ability to be patient.

Plus, to garden like a true permie, you'll want to know the 12 Principles of Permaculture. As I said before, these principles are kind of like a compass that guides you in your project.

Since we're off on a great adventure, let's get ourselves a compass.

3

OUR COMPASS: THE 12 PERMACULTURE PRINCIPLES & YOU

 Permaculture is defined by consciously designed landscapes which mimic the patterns and relationships found in nature, while yielding an abundance of food, fiber, and energy for provision of local needs.

— DAVID HOLMGREN

Bill Mollison is credited as the father of permaculture. But his student and collaborator, David Holmgren, should at least be given the title of "cool uncle of permaculture." Working with Bill, he very effectively summed up the spirit of permaculture in 12 easy-to-understand principles.

"Principles" might come across as a daunting word, but these aren't rules and regulations; they aren't even commandments. The principles of permaculture are simply guidelines for you to think about as you take on your permaculture journey. And they can all be applied to your specific situation.

On that note, throughout this chapter and the entire book, I may make mention of ideas that go beyond the scale of your space. For instance, you'll see chickens mentioned several times below. Some permies add chickens or other livestock to enhance the whole ecosystem, but if your landlady doesn't allow chickens, no sweat! Or maybe you don't like chickens. Hey, you do you.

There are so many ways to incorporate these principles in your own way and scale.

Also remember, it doesn't have to be all-or-nothing. Pick a few ideas, start with a couple principles, try some things out. You know, like a permaculture buffet. I will include a variety of ideas at each turn in this journey, but this is all just a starting point and springboard for you to get creative.

Also know, I've dedicated chapters to dive deeper into specific aspects of a permaculture garden. Chapter 11, for instance, explores animal life in far more detail than the brief mentions below.

This chapter is all about the design principles of permaculture. Our compass. Ways of seeing things as we create our gardens.

So! Are you ready to get further inside the mind of a permie?

PRINCIPLE #1. OBSERVE AND INTERACT

As we've learned, permies take a page from nature's handbook. They observe the patterns and features existing in natural ecosystems. Then they find ways to recreate them. Sure, it's environmental plagiarism, but nature doesn't mind. In fact, she's quite flattered.

Ecosystems are different worldwide, so your mini-ecosystem will be unique to your location. Observe it to understand what is already there, then build on that to create a self-sufficient agricultural ecosystem of your own, whether it's on your ranch, in your backyard, or on your condo balcony. Work with nature rather than against it, and everyone's happy!

Oh, and get yourself a journal.

Some examples of observing and interacting are:

1. Watching your property throughout the day (and year) to see which parts get sun, which get shade, and at what times. This will be a big indicator of what plants will thrive where.
2. Studying the rainfall on your property. Are there certain areas that are always marshy? Does water tend to pour from a particular corner of your roof? Perhaps these would be good places for rainwater catchment.

3. Noticing what plants thrive or struggle in specific locations. For example, that potted oregano plant might hate it in your sunny kitchen window and feel more comfortable in your shady study.
4. Getting to know your soil! There's a whole lot more happening in there than just dirt. Different types of soil can grow different plants better, and you can amend your soil in different ways, based on its current condition and makeup. More on soil in Chapter 8.

The next chapter is all about applying this principle.

PRINCIPLE #2. CATCH AND STORE ENERGY

Not all resources are ready on demand whenever you want them. They ain't Netflix. So when the opportunity presents itself, capture and store what you can. You'll be reducing waste and making life easier for yourself. If you create a setup that collects resources when they're abundant, you can use them when you need them.

Permie glasses help you see potential resources everywhere, and help ensure no resource leaves your garden. Grass clippings could become compost. Tree prunings could become mulch. And those will help store the energy from the rain. Bam. Energy saved.

Energy doesn't have to be solar, wind, or water power; it can also be food as energy or your own physical exertion. Energy storage can be done anywhere, and it's a heck of a lot easier than catching time in a bottle. Here are some examples:

1. Use collection tanks to catch rainwater when it falls from your home's gutters, or simply place a five-gallon bucket out on your patio (covering it with a screen will keep the bugs out).
2. If you're designing a home, barn, or greenhouse, position it so that the sun heats it during the winter days. It will retain some warmth in the evening, lowering your electric bill. Study "passive solar design" to find out more about this.
3. Pickle extra summer veggies so you can enjoy them in the winter.
4. Harvest and save seeds!

Chapter 12 and Chapter 13 cover some more in-depth exploration of how to use the resources available to you.

As you consider your own human energy as a resource, you'll want to get the most out of it! This is where the next principle comes into play.

PRINCIPLE #3. OBTAIN A YIELD

This one requires little explanation: grow something! And once you've planted it, care for it so it thrives and produces. If you get just one blueberry off of that dwarf bush you planted on the patio, then you've succeeded! Now, see how you can make it even better next year.

In Chapter 14, we will talk more about harvesting your food and preserving it.

Of course, when we think about yields with gardening, we automatically think "food." But a yield isn't just edible rewards. A yield can be: happiness, health, peace of mind, and beauty.

Your permaculture garden could yield a relaxing place for your family to hang out, even if you didn't harvest the first tomato. Or it could be a beautiful pollinator flower garden that brings joy to your life, and to the plant and animal life around you.

1. If you live in an apartment, dorm, or condo, plant a few herbs in decorative pots on your window sill. These make delicious culinary seasonings.
2. If you have space for a traditional garden, start with a few hard-to-fail vegetable plants, like peppers, tomatoes, or zucchini.
3. Pull weeds from your flowerbeds or footpaths and give them to your chickens.
4. Give seedlings or cuttings to others to help them start their growing journey!

Bottom line: You want to make sure you're getting a worthwhile return on the valuable work you're doing, even if the return is knowledge and growth! This leads us to the next principle.

PRINCIPLE #4. APPLY SELF-REGULATION AND ACCEPT FEEDBACK

You're going to fail. Period. It's a rule of life, even in permaculture. But that's okay! Nature is forgiving. The way you interact with your garden might have positive effects … or negative ones. Listen to your garden and see what it's trying to tell you. Be open to modify, learn from your mistakes and move on.

 My green thumb came only as a result of the mistakes I made while learning to see things from the plant's point of view.

— H. FRED ALE

An excellent way to provide your own self-feedback is to keep that journal or notebook of your permaculture endeavors season by season. In it, record the specifics of the things you've planted, your changes or additions to your garden, and personal observations on the natural world. If you experience a future success or failure, you can go back and look at your notes to see what connections you can draw.

For example, I recently installed a rainwater harvesting system in my home. Gutters I'd installed around the roofline channel rainwater into large water tanks below. By closely monitoring how much water I was collecting throughout each season, I was able to adjust my system accordingly by adding more tanks or increasing the size of existing ones.

In Chapter 15, we will get into some troubleshooting to address common issues that may come up.

PRINCIPLE #5. USE AND VALUE RENEWABLE RESOURCES AND SERVICES

A permaculture garden aims to be self-sustaining. This means it can continue to thrive for years without bringing in many new resources or starting over from scratch. Think of ways you can use renewable resources like solar energy, wood, heat from the earth, and rainwater.

Here are some ideas:

1. Control weeds with newspaper or cardboard that biodegrades to enhance the soil rather than landscape plastic that just covers it up. Or maybe even *make use of* those weeds!
2. Burn trimmings from trees and bushes for warmth, cooking, or just to create a rockin' bonfire. Or *use those trimmings* for mulch or compost!
3. Harvest and save your seeds for a sustainable, regenerative garden.

4. Plant perennials first (plants that come back every year). Then plant your annuals (ones that die and have to be replanted each year).

Nature is abundant. The heart of this principle is to use that powerful fact to our advantage as best as we can, and decrease our dependence on non-renewable resources.

We'll talk about this all throughout the book. The next few chapters will dig into it some. And again, Chapter 12 and Chapter 13 — which are all about the resources all around you — provide some rich material for this principle to play out. There, we will also flesh out more of the next principle:

PRINCIPLE #6. PRODUCE NO WASTE

In the ideal permaculturist setup, nothing goes to waste. Not even actual waste. Setting out a compost bin for kitchen scraps or using livestock manure as fertilizer are all examples of zero-waste lifestyles. Heck, some people go the extra mile and invest in a composting toilet!

Don't worry; you don't have to do your business in the garden (unless you want to, just steer clear of the tomatoes). This is more about the things you throw away. Consider what can be used (or reused) to enhance your permaculture lifestyle instead of rotting away in a landfill.

Composting is a significant player in Principle #6. Rather than hitting the trash can, things like kitchen scraps, paper and cardboard, eggshells, coffee grounds, grass clippings, and yard waste can all go into the compost pile. Then, you can use the compost to fertilize your garden and build up the microbes in the soil. Win-win!

Some other things you can do are:

1. Only produce as much food as you will realistically consume, use, give to others or the earth, etc. Consider canning, freezing, sharing, or selling at your local farmer's market if you can't eat it.
2. Gather garden weeds rather than tossing them to the side. (I know, sounds crazy, but we'll talk later about what you can do with these in Chapter 13).
3. Take care of what you've got! Waste not, want not, right? Put away those garden tools when you're done, so they last longer.

4. Feed kitchen scraps to the chickens. In turn, they'll produce manure you can feed your garden. A perfect biological circle!

One man's trash is another man's treasure. And we just became treasure hunters!

PRINCIPLE #7. DESIGN FROM PATTERNS TO DETAILS

Don't miss the forest for the trees, brah! You've got to start with a broad view, then zoom in.

Check it out: the "patterns" are the "big picture." We're not talking about rows of raised beds in a neat pattern here. We mean things like observing your own daily patterns. What fruits and veggies do your family enjoy most? What path do you take when you walk from your car to your front door? What time of year are you too busy for much garden work?

And then also the patterns of nature, the four seasons, etc. When is the rainy season? The dry season?

Consider these patterns in your life, property, nature, and even the community surrounding you. These are the starting place, the foundation. Then, you can zero in on the details: all the little bits and pieces that make your permaculture plan unique.

So start from the broadest spot.

Along with Principle #1, this principle comes to life more in the next chapter.

Some examples of designing from patterns to details might be:

1. Plant the herbs and vegetables you use most near your kitchen door so they're easily accessible.
2. Place garden beds along the path you take to enter your house so you're more inclined to weed or harvest them when you come home from work.
3. Locate your chicken coop close to your garden so you can toss weeds and scraps to the very grateful fowl.
4. Understand the rainfall patterns in your area, as well as how rain flows on your land, before getting carried away with plant choices and then just randomly sticking seeds in some spot of soil.

PRINCIPLE #8. INTEGRATE RATHER THAN SEGREGATE

I have a dream that one day, the tomato and the basil will be planted side by side in the soil of brotherhood, and my chickens will live in a garden where they will not be judged for eating a few tomatoes because there will be enough for everyone!

Okay, well while Martin Luther King, Jr's speech was certainly more powerful, integration is key to the world of permaculture. And nature itself shouts an "amen" — we are better together, and more diversity means a better garden! (More on that in Principle #10).

In permaculture, integration can mean sharing your little slice of paradise with the local wildlife, livestock, neighbors, and community. You work with nature rather than segregating or kicking it out of your garden. And you integrate to build connections for a self-sustaining community.

Now, you may have strategic levels of this in your garden. You may need to fence off certain areas to keep them from being totally consumed by deer. We'll talk more about this later. But the point here is to think about *blending* certain things.

It can mean blending certain plants, or even certain *purposes* that we have traditionally kept apart. This creates *relationships* that are beneficial to those involved. Multiplication and abundance, so on and so forth.

Some ways to do this are by:

1. Cultivating companion plantings that benefit one another. Here's one example: Usually, we'd *segregate* trees into an orchard by themselves. Instead, *integrate* and plant nitrogen-fixing plants around fruit trees, which helps to increase soil fertility and thus produces better yields over time.
2. Planting a pollinator garden that benefits the local wildlife.
3. Swapping excess produce with other gardeners means community integration.
4. Also, this principle can mean *integrating functions* that are usually segregated, like composting along pathways, instead of in a bin off to the side. Or making sure elements have multiple functions or purposes. For example, a fence used for animals can also act as a trellis for plants to climb up, which can also serve as a windbreak. This is

called **stacking functions**, and it is a design principle that is core to permaculture.

You'll see bits of this Principle, and Principle #10, in Chapters 5-7 on planting methods, Chapter 10 on what to plant, and Chapter 11 on animals, as well as scattered throughout.

PRINCIPLE #9. USE SMALL AND SLOW SOLUTIONS

The permie lifestyle is exciting; we get it! But slow your roll! Permaculture is a journey, not a destination. There's no need to race to the finish line. Don't rush out and buy 50 varieties of heirloom squashes or blow your savings on a greenhouse right away. Instead, think frugal, sustainable, and attainable. And keep it simple.

Sometimes the hardest part of a project is starting it. In Chapter 9, we really explore the "beginnings" of a garden by talking in-depth about seed starting. Of course, the whole book is loaded with different ways you can take attainable next steps!

What is one little thing you can do right now, for free, to meet your permaculture goals?

Maybe you could:

1. Build a single 4' x 6' raised bed using salvaged or upcycled lumber.
2. Start a compost pile at the edge of your yard. Or in a container under the sink.
3. Place one small tank to collect rainwater.
4. Grow herbs and flowers in some upcycled pots.

You may find that you can gather materials at a lower cost (or free) if you're patient and keep your ear to the ground. When you take baby steps, you'll save energy and money, lower risks, and reduce waste along the way.

Don't you love it when two permie principles come together? Great, because:

PRINCIPLE #10. USE AND VALUE DIVERSITY

This one goes hand in hand with the integration one.

Simply put, **diversity** is a variety of living things coexisting in one place. Variety is the spice of life! It's an important concept in society, nature, and permaculture. Just like a diversity of people with different skills and traits enhances a community, diverse plant and animal species can benefit your permaculture garden.

Picture this: A vast field of corn. Yeah, I love me some corn, and yes, it's a productive commercial crop. But on its own, it may not be very beneficial to nature nor very sustainable, and some may even say it's boring!

Okay, okay, beauty is in the eye of the beholder. I guess cornrows can be pretty handsome.

But a garden of corn interspersed with pumpkins, pole beans, and marigolds is a permie dream come true. While all these plants couldn't be more different, they all work together in perfect harmony. They actually *help each other flourish*, a concept we'll talk about later. Plus, this garden is more resilient and less vulnerable than one with a single crop. And it also adds diversity to your diet, which your body will thank you for.

To take this further, grow some cover crops in the winter off-season to enrich the soil, like crimson clover, annual ryegrass, and radishes ... and some research says you'll yield even more corn the next year!

Wow. Now see, I'm not hating on corn. Au contraire mon frere, diversity helps the corn out!

This principle extends beyond the species you sow when planning your permaculture garden. Consider a diversity of:

- Growing techniques (containers, raised beds, in-ground, greenhouse)
- Pollinators and beneficial insects that you attract to your garden
- Colors and textures of plants
- Flavors (savory, sweet)
- Types of yields (food, recreation, beauty)

PRINCIPLE #11. USE EDGES AND VALUE THE MARGINAL

Think outside the box, friends. Because there's so much more outside the box than inside it. All those lovely edges, borders, and margins. All that unused space just waiting to be utilized!

What's more, the edges — the places where two different elements meet — can sometimes be more valuable and productive than the interior elements themselves.

To give an example, imagine a pond located at the edge of a forest. Due to its location at the meeting point between land and water, it has more biodiversity than either land or water alone would have. A lot of cool stuff can happen at the edge.

Look at the empty space around the edges and let your imagination run wild.

1. Utilize the vertical space on your balcony with hanging planters filled with strawberries, tomatoes, herbs, and flowers.
2. Plant trailing plants like nasturtiums around the edges of raised beds so they can flow down the sides.
3. Set up a compost station or worm farm in the no-man's-land behind your garage or garden shed.
4. Use your backyard fence to grow climbing plants like cucumbers, beans, and hops.

PRINCIPLE #12. CREATIVELY USE AND RESPOND TO CHANGE

 Despite the gardener's best intentions, Nature will improvise.

— MICHAEL GAROFALO

In my first year, I planted a few vegetable plants in containers, keeping them safe on my back porch while I worked on improving my soil. The following season I could directly sow seeds in the soil that I'd spent a whole year getting just right. I kept them weeded and watered. I thinned out the weaker ones so the plants had enough space to grow.

Between the wildlife, the weather, and my own chickens, I was lucky to salvage only a few tomatoes and zucchini. The best-laid plans ... well, you know what they say.

I learned, took notes, and made the garden better and better each year.

Permies roll with the punches. As we learned in Principle #4, make the best of failures and unexpected changes. After all, nature may be our friend, but she's great at throwing curve balls.

Think about how nature is constantly changing: the seasons change, weather is unpredictable. You may be struck with an unexpected blight or an influx of new pests in your garden.

So how do we respond? Planting plants that repel those pests? Rotating crops to mitigate disease in certain beds? Harvesting rainwater during a rainy season to use for a dry season? It's like a dance with nature, and we get more nimble on our feet the more we go.

As mentioned above, we'll explore some troubleshooting for your garden in Chapter 15, so you can think ahead, envision possible scenarios, and hopefully intervene in some effective ways. But your interventions will become *even more effective* as you get to know your garden more, just by watching what happens and responding creatively.

Once your permaculture site is set up, give it time to get established. And nourish it along the way. You'll need to make little tweaks as you learn what works and what doesn't. Observe everything that changes, write it down in your handy, dandy notebook, and respond accordingly.

A certain spot in your garden doesn't get enough sunlight so plants are dying there? No problem. Don't abandon that area altogether. Instead, get creative and plant shade-loving varieties there. As a bonus, now you have more diversity in your garden!

Not to mention, we are going to encounter all kinds of changes: economical, technological, etc. Change, as they say, is constant. The ones who truly thrive through it are the ones who learn to use this concept to their advantage and grow stronger. In the face of change, permies stay true to themselves, and dig deep, asking, "Alright, how can I use this to grow?"

So, expect the unexpected, stay true, be nimble, and sharpen that growth mentality. Because after all, it's all an experiment, right?

WRAP-UP

Just like Principle #9 says, take baby steps! It's easy to get overwhelmed when you try to do it all at once. One thing you could do in your garden is pick the few principles that most excite you as you read, and try really exercising them first.

And *have fun with it!* Cus, you know:

If you're having fun, you've got the design right.

— GEOFF LAWTON

Well said. Thanks again, Geoff!

So let's smile big and take heart: these principles aren't a rulebook. It's not so much about making sure *all* of them are happening *all* the time. They're like a powerful mindset toolkit to have as you plan your garden. A compass for an exciting adventure, made of many small steps.

Now that you've got your compass in the bag, it's understandable if the first thing you want to do is plant a seed and watch something sprout. But I know first-hand how this can do more damage than good. I promise we'll get there soon!

Principle #1 is number 1 for a reason! The first step is to observe and "get in tune" with your space. Only then will you be able to really design like a permie!

4

OBSERVE AND INTERACT WITH YOUR SPACE

 Bloom where you are planted.

— SAINT FRANCIS DE SALES

Are you ready for the fun part, my friends? It's time to dream! Seriously, I'm so excited for you. Because this is where you get to start your permaculture plan, and the possibilities are limitless from here. Permaculture is for anyone, and adaptable to your own unique situation.

But, before you start your permaculture design, before you plant the very first seed, you need to study and observe your space. This step is so important. It saves a lot of time and energy in the long run to simply get to know your space so you can work powerfully with what you've got.

Trying to fit a square peg in a round hole can lead to frustration and disappointment. Let's say you really wanted to plant some blueberries. Well, if you didn't know that blueberries love acidic soil, and you didn't know your soil was alkaline … you might be working against nature, rather than with it. And we know that ain't the permie way.

A little bit of know-how could lead you to plant some delicious kale and have more success, or grab a pot for your blueberry bush, where you can control the soil a little better.

In this chapter, we'll talk about what to look for in your environment — whether urban, suburban, or rural — and what you can learn from it. We'll cover the weather, climate zones, and permaculture zones. Then we'll talk about different ways to use all of these to maximize your space and yield.

You'll learn how to design with permie eyes and make it work in *your* space.

And remember, you won't be going it alone. The answers are written in nature's code, we're just learning to interpret. I'm here to help with that!

As you brainstorm, think of your space as the canvas. The design principles and the elements you bring in, and the plants you plant: these are the brushes and paints. When you *embrace the canvas you've got* and *work with nature* to create your permaculture garden, your masterpiece starts falling into place.

 It should look as if it has always been like that, as if Nature made it that way. That's good design.

— SEPP HOLZER

WHAT IS NATURE ALREADY DOING IN YOUR GARDEN

Hey Nature, get off my lawn! Oh wait, you were there first? Well, I guess we'll have to work together then. Thank goodness for permaculture!

Whether you like it or not, nature already existed in your space long before you got there. And it was doing a perfectly fine job without you. Now that you're a permie, it's time to take a good look at all that nature, doing its thing out there, and figure out how you can make it work for you.

To begin, it's crucial to observe everything that happens in a space or garden. You'll be aware of what nature is doing all by itself. This is the easy part of the process. The lazy part, even. All you have to do, literally, is sit there. Grab a chair and sit down outside. Or sit right on the grass; that's what a real permie would do (just saying).

Or if it's raining, you can sit on your chair and look out the window. Either way, take a good look at your space at different times of the day and throughout the different seasons. Here are some things to be on the lookout for and to jot down in your handy little notebook (trust me, you'll be glad you did later).

A lot of the examples we give are with North American gardens in mind. The principles, though, are universal, and with the wonderful internet, anyone can search for the specific information they need!

1. HOURS OF SUNLIGHT

Observe the number of hours of sunlight different areas get. Plants have different light requirements, such as 8+ hours of full sun or 4+ hours of partial shade. If you've already picked your ideal garden spot, the sunlight it gets will be a major determiner of what you can plant there.

Also, ask a local or Google what the average length of day is in your area during different parts of the year. The Earth is always on the move. Not only does it spin, but it tilts. And when it's on full tilt, one hemisphere ends up closest to the Sun and has the longest and brightest days. Then in half a year, it switches. The Earth's gotta make sure her suntan is nice and even.

The longest day of the year is called *summer solstice*, and happens around June 20-21 for the Northern Hemisphere, and December 21-22 for the Southern Hemisphere. These days swap for *winter solstice*, which ends up being the shortest day of the year.

2. DIRECTION OF SUNLIGHT

The direction the sunlight is coming from affects how many hours of light that spot will get each day, and how warm it will potentially be. As you most likely know, the sun rises in the east. Although, the exact point where the sun rises over the horizon, and its trajectory during the day will vary, as the axis of the earth tilts north and south during the year. As mentioned above, this leads to winter and summer in the hemispheres, and different arcs of the sun as the seasons change. Get out your boy scout compass for extra verification as you check out the sun paths and look at potential planting locations.

South-facing spots, like a south-facing window, balcony, yard, or slope, receive the most light, are the hottest, and warm up fastest in the spring. Meanwhile, north-facing spots receive the least light and are the coolest. Sun-loving plants will appreciate a southern exposure.

Check out https://sun-direction.com/ for a cool interactive map that shows you sun direction and day lengths in your exact location throughout different times of the year.

3. MOISTURE

Observe how rainwater falls and possibly collects in certain areas. Some plants like wet feet, while others prefer dry conditions. An area might be too moist for planting, but it might be an excellent spot for a rainfall catchment system.

Notice how much rain generally falls during each season in your area. If you're not sure (or don't have time to wait a whole year), you can always consult the National Weather Service at www.weather.gov (for US gardeners), or do an online search for rainfall in your area. This way, you'll know if you need to supplement your garden's water source during certain months.

4. TOPOGRAPHY

Does your land have a slope? Is it perfectly flat? Do you live on the edge of a cliff? The **grade** is how much the land slopes. It will affect what gets put where in your permaculture garden.

A steep slope can be difficult to mow, but it's an ideal spot for a wildflower meadow, tall grasses, or berry shrubs that will slow water runoff and prevent soil erosion.

Knowing the grade is important to your permaculture layout. Don't make the mistake I did as a first-time homesteader, and place your chicken coop at the bottom of the slope. The poor birds were standing in water up to their knees every time it rained. Instead, you might position your chicken coop at the top of a slope where rainwater will carry manure-rich runoff into your garden.

If you're looking for a fun way to get in touch with your topography, you could try this little exercise. Go to high points in your yard, and then just pretend you're a raindrop making its way to the ocean, and start slowly going downhill. Make note: where are the dips and curves? These are helpful things to know. This is not for accuracy, it's more about developing a general idea and familiarity with your space's unique features. Your friends might think you're kinda weird when they see you singing "I'm a little raindrop" and toddling in zig-zags around your yard. But when your water bill is down and your garden yields high, it'll all be worth it.

Of course, the real way to tell what rain does in your yard is to, well … watch it when it rains. Like we said before, just grab a chair and sit on the back porch, or watch from the other side of a window. Get a notebook and your favorite cup of coffee and just observe.

In Chapter 12, we'll talk about utilizing natural resources like rain, and also dive into an important permaculture topic: **earthworks**. This involves manually re-shaping the soil (topography) to make water go where you want it to go. Berms, swales, terraces: all terms we'll cover more later. This book won't dive heavily into the mechanics, but we will go over some basics so you can have another set of tools in your permie belt.

Calculating the actual slope of your yard can be helpful. One reason would be to see if your grade is too steep for certain structures. Berms and swales, for instance, don't work well on very steep grades. Calculating your slope usually involves special stakes (at least 2), with string between them, a string level, a tape measure, and some math. You can search online for tutorials on how to calculate your yard's slope.

Note to all you urban dwellers: the edge of a balcony, terrace, window, or rooftop qualifies as a really, really steep slope. A 90-degree slope, to be exact. That vertical space has possibilities!

5. WIND

Is your spot exposed to high wind, low wind, no wind? Wind strength can change from season to season, or may only come from one direction on your property. Often the area at the top of a slope is the windiest, while valleys or depressions are the least. You don't have to be that old sailor who sucks on his thumb and then sticks it in the air to test the winds. A simple Google search of "prevailing winds in [your town]" can help you determine wind conditions in your area.

While some air movement is good for a garden, constant winds can pull moisture from foliage, while strong winds can shred leaves, break branches, and even uproot plants, making it harder to keep them healthy. If you have a windy spot, plant heartier plants that are low-growing or adapted to the wind, like rosemary, lavender, and root vegetables.

In many situations, you can create a permanent or temporary windbreak to protect your garden. You can use manmade structures like fences, or natural solutions like trees, a hedgerow of perennials, or even sunflowers. Or a manmade trellis, with climbing plants! (Notice the combined uses?)

6. Extreme Weather Patterns

It's also great to get to know your local weather patterns further by asking: is your area prone to any kind of extreme weather? For instance, if hail is on the forecast, you'll want to think ahead. Before the storm rolls in, you'll want to bring container plants under cover. You could also benefit from having a structure set up for plants you want to protect. These can include: row covers, stakes and hardware cloth, hail netting, or burlap rolls.

This is all a great use of Principle #7: Design from Patterns to Details.

7. Wildlife

Permaculture is all about welcoming nature in, embracing biodiversity, and learning how you can work together. Aside from native plants, there are so many members of the animal family that live in every ecosystem: insects, spiders, birds, frogs, snakes, and small mammals. While not every animal is necessarily welcome in the permaculture garden — like moles, aphids, and slugs — many can be beneficial, like pollinating bees and butterflies or pest-eating ladybugs and toads.

What wildlife do you observe in your space? Are there potential problem children who may need to be dealt with (in a humane and loving way, of course) as you begin your garden, like fruit-stealing squirrels and ants? Are there beneficial species you'd like to welcome in, like frogs, bats, or bluebirds?

Your mission as a permie is to create a safe space for nature while still producing a yield from your garden. Maybe this will mean planting enough to share with the local wildlife or having specific areas fenced off from marauding deer and rabbits. It could mean leaving some areas wide open while using bird netting around the berry bushes. This can let in pollinators, but keep out other creatures who might *really* want to "observe and interact" with your garden, like birds, possums, pets, and you know, toddlers (bless their hearts).

Some netting is really fine mesh, and doesn't let much in at all. There are "fruit protection bags" and insect exclusion nets, depending on your particular needs and how close you are to harvest.

If there's not much movement on your plot, you can try inviting in helpful species by creating a pollinator garden or a wood pile where helpful bugs and amphibians can hang out. More on this in Chapter 11.

MICROCLIMATES

Becoming aware of all that's happening in your space is great for many reasons. One reason is that different plants have different needs, and would therefore thrive in different parts of your property or even apartment.

See, your space is full of **microclimates**, which is a term that refers to "the climate of a very small or restricted area, especially when this differs from the climate of the surrounding area." The shady area on the side of your house, or your sunny windowsill, or the place where water collects a lot, or that little patch of sand you brought into the backyard so you could feel like you were vacationing at the beach ... those are all *microclimates*.

Taking advantage of microclimates is great when embracing a diversity of plants. There can even be different microclimates within one feature, like on a mound-shaped garden bed, for instance. On top of the mound, it's sunny, dry, and windy. On the northern, lower side, it's more shady and wet. This opens up more opportunities for plants with differing needs.

You can even create microclimates strategically! Plant tall sun-loving plants next to low-growing shade-loving plants. The taller one then becomes like a **nurse crop**, which is a plant that helps facilitate the growth of another plant by doing things like sheltering it from the elements. Keeping in mind where shadows fall according to the sun's direction, planting the low-growing lettuce — which does well in shade — north of the sun-loving tomato.

Speaking of climates, it is also very important to know:

YOUR HARDINESS ZONE

Just like you can't change nature, you can't change where you live (assuming you're not currently house hunting). So, you need to learn about the climate in your hometown before you start your permaculture design.

The world is divided into six major climate zones: tropical, dry, temperate, continental, and polar. There is a sixth special zone called the highlands, which has different weather than what's around it because of mountains. Each of these zones have certain characteristics (temperature, humidity, weather/sun patterns) that make them conducive to different kinds of plant life.

In the US, when we think of what to plant where, we follow the USDA Plant Hardiness Zones. **Hardiness zones**, also called growing zones, are the areas in the United States (or any country) that are differentiated by their climate. They're important because certain plants will only grow in certain climates. For example, you can't grow oranges in Alaska (at least not without proper planning, and maybe the decision to grow your citrus as a potted houseplant).

Have you ever looked at the back of a seed packet and seen a little US map with different colored stripes? That's a **zone map**. It divides the country into regions based on their average low winter temperatures. North Dakota has different weather than Florida, so they're in different hardiness zones. Zones are listed by the numbers 1 to 13, and some maps include "half" zones divided into *a* or *b* subdivisions for more specific temperature ranges. Zone 1a has the average lowest temperatures of -60 to -55°F (-51 to -48°C) (brrr!). Then, each zone increases by 5°F (about 2.8°C). North Dakota is in the 2-3 range, while sunny Miami is a 10.

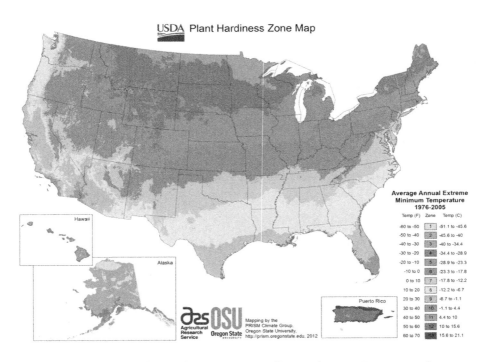

Figure 4.1. USDA Plant Hardiness Zone Map: Full Zones. (*Source: U.S. Department of Agriculture*).

A hardiness zone map is kind of like a garden planning cheat sheet. It tells you two things:

1. If a perennial plant can realistically be cultivated in your area.
2. When you should plant annual seeds in your area.

Many annual crops — like tomatoes, zucchini, and pumpkins — can be grown anywhere since they die off by the time winter arrives. But most perennials will only tolerate a certain degree of winter chill. And since perennials are the stars of a permaculture garden, this is some important info to have.

If you're new to the terms *annual* and *perennial*, have no fear. We cover them in detail in Chapter 10.

Bear in mind that the USDA hardiness zones only take into consideration the average minimum temperatures, so observation is still key. The average hottest summer temperature, precipitation, and frost dates are all important factors in your plant's survival, too.

Hardiness zones are great guidelines for what to plant and when but with some experience, you will be able to choose plants that are just outside your zone. For example, here in Virginia, I cover my lettuce beds with a cold frame in the winter to extend their growing season, and bring my potted citrus plants indoors.

If you live in the US, you can enter your zip code in the USDA plant hardiness zone website to find your zone: https://planthardiness.ars.usda.gov/.

Gardenia.net also has hardiness zone maps for some areas outside the US. Just go to www.gardenia.net/guides/climate-zones, or search within the site for "Hardiness Zones of Europe", for example. Otherwise, an online search for a hardiness zone map for a certain area should lead you in the right direction.

You can also talk to someone at your local garden center, ask a neighbor, or consult that old guy in the shack (he's most likely into permaculture, in case you didn't know). They'll be able to suggest plants that do well in your area.

Gardenia.net has an extensive list of plants that will grow in each hardiness zone. Just figure out your zone and enter it in. This will help narrow down your planting choices and optimize your chance of success from the start.

More resources on finding plants according to your hardiness zone can be found in the *Supplemental Resources* section in the back of the book.

HOW TO DESIGN GARDENS BY PERMACULTURE ZONES

Just like the country has different hardiness zones, your personal plot will have specific permaculture zones. It's like your own little world. Going back to Principle #7 (you know, the one about designing from patterns to details), your garden should be designed based on your individual needs and patterns.

This is where permaculture differs from traditional gardening. It's not "get in where you fit in." Instead, everything is planned with intention. **Permaculture zones** are areas of a property that are dedicated to specific elements. They depend on how often you need to visit the area. For example, things like gardens, orchards, and livestock pens are placed in their designated zones based on how much you'll need to visit them each day, week, or month.

Permaculture zones are listed from 0 to 5 and are as follows:

- **ZONE 0:** Your home. This should be ground zero of your plan; everything else branches out from here.
- **ZONE 1:** The kitchen garden. These are foods you cook with on a regular basis and will typically visit multiple times a day. It's also a good place for pets that you tend to multiple times a day, an outdoor gathering area, a kids' play area, or small outbuildings that you visit on a regular basis. Also, pretty flowers.
- **ZONE 2:** Low-maintenance area. This includes crops that need less attention or are only harvested once in a season — like potatoes and corn — and animals that need to be visited only once a day. It could also be an extension of your kitchen garden, a place for composting or worm farms, or fruit and berry bushes. The main shed or storage could be here. For many, the garden ends at Zone 2.
- **ZONE 3:** Wide open space. A large space for pastures, ponds, staple crops, orchards, and endeavors that require more room. Beehives, larger food forests, larger animals. Although it has regular use, it's not necessary to visit daily unless you have animals that need tending.
- **ZONE 4:** Wider opener space. This space is similar to Zone 3 but slightly wilder and less tended. It may include trees for wood, pastures, or recreational areas.
- **ZONE 5:** Natural habitat. This is an untouched area that doesn't require any attention but rather is enjoyed in its natural state. You can also think of your community outside your property boundaries as an urban Zone 5.

It's easy to think of the permaculture zones like a bullseye.

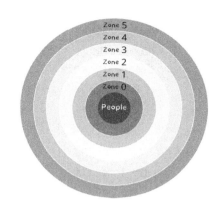

Your home right at the center and each zone spreading out in concentric rings. But all properties have different shapes and features, so feel free to take liberties with your design and make your boundaries more fluid.

Knowing your permaculture zones will help you to maximize the use of the land and minimize wasted time and energy (Principle #6). Three cheers for efficiency!

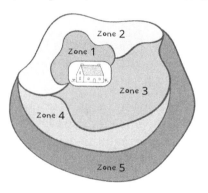

Think about what outdoor chores you'll need to do each day. You won't want to walk from one end of the property to the other to collect eggs and pick the dinner's vegetables.

While you wander around your property to observe and report, think of the potential each area has. Think about the places you and your family visit on a regular day. What spaces do you go through to get from your car to your front door? To get from your back door to your garden shed? Is there a place in your yard where you've never even stepped?

In your notebook (which I know you have by now), make sketches of potential zones. Your house and any existing structures are stationary, but the rest is flexible. Play around with it, but be realistic. Do you have time to manage everything you've listed? And the resources to maintain it?

And here's Principle #9! Small and slow solutions. You can plan in *phases*. Focus on building Zone 1 in your first year, and move out from there.

Just a note, there are plenty of urban permies. I heard of one who mapped out her apartment in zones, ranging from the south-facing windows right near the kitchen, to the walls and even dark corners!

Whatever your setup, be creative and do what works for you.

CREATING YOUR OWN LITTLE SLICE OF PARADISE

> No single sort of garden suits everyone. Shut your eyes and dream of the garden you'd most love then open your eyes and start planting. Loved gardens flourish, boring ones are hard work.
>
> — JACKIE FRENCH

PAINT THE PICTURE

Alright. Remember when you got this book? Well, there's a reason you clicked "order." Probably several! So, take a moment to think about those, and observe and interact with *your own dreams.*

What are your reasons for growing a garden? Is it the health benefits for you and your family? Is it wanting to make a positive impact on the world around you? Is it trying something new and fun?

Now, take those reasons and dreams and let them come to life in your mind. Forget whether or not you think it's possible. For this moment, just let your mind wander and dream of the garden you'd really love, and the harvest that would come from it.

What does the vision look like? Really paint a detailed picture.

Are the kids out picking juicy veggies, with fresh soil on their hands? Are guests gathered around a fire with soft music playing and string lights hanging on the porch?

Is the dream a big table full of food at a big family dinner, filled with home-grown vegetables and fruit? How about seeing the smile on your neighbors' faces when they open the door to a bowl of fresh blackberries you grew and picked for them?

Is it coming home and seeing the lively greens, bright yellows, deep reds, and rich purples splashing all over your space? Is it sitting in a quiet corner of a lush garden early in the morning, with no other sound than the birds singing and the wind gently blowing through the rustling leaves of tall trees?

Take those vivid pictures and let those intentions get rooted in your heart. You can write down what you saw or even print out pictures that inspire you and reflect your vision. You won't get to the "big picture" overnight. But your vision will provide great direction and motivation as you design and create your dreams, step by step.

CREATING A WELCOMING PLACE OF BEAUTY

 A beautiful plant is like having a friend around the house.

— BETH DITTO

Your permaculture garden may bless the Earth, but it's also a place to bless *you*. It isn't just there to produce a yield of food; it's also about creating a harmonious natural space where you feel joy and peace. You can create a welcoming place where you can invite others in and feel proud to share your permie journey. After all, beauty, peace, and joy are all yields!

Just as your garden is always growing, you are growing as a person. How can you make your permaculture space a reflection of your style and personality? A place where you can feel happy to be you at the end of a long work day. Remember, this isn't about nailing it the first time. It's about experimenting and going where the wind carries you.

SOAKING UP POSITIVE VIBES

You've already considered the important logistics of your permaculture garden: how to maximize sunlight and water, how to work with the elements, and what gardening methods and materials to use. You've got an idea or two of what plants you'd like to grow. You've even envisioned what your gardening dreams look like.

Now look at your space and ask how you want it to *feel*.

Fun, relaxing, peaceful, beautiful, lively ... how would you describe it? What adjustments or additions could you make to create a space that feels like that?

- Do you want to add a bench where you can sit and enjoy flowers?
- Should you raise the potted plants to eye level so you can see them better?
- Can you add a fire pit where you can roast marshmallows with the kids or burn trimmings for warmth?

Elements you may consider adding to emphasize the personality and purpose of the space are:

- A fire pit
- An outdoor cooking and dining area
- A potting bench or crafting area
- A conversation seating arrangement for entertaining
- A play area for kids with playground equipment, a tree house, or a soccer goal
- A stand for sharing your fresh produce with the community

WHO'S INVITED TO THE PARTY?

Your garden is ultimately an extension of your home. Consider who you will be spending time with in the garden:

1. *Yourself.* Maybe this is your inner sanctum. Your personal happy place. It's okay to create a space for one with a single bench or patio recliner (or hammock!) where you can meditate, read, or rest.
2. *Your family.* Children can learn lessons and have fun spending time outdoors. Make your permaculture garden a place where your entire family can find joy by creating secret hiding places, playground equipment like swings or monkey bars, a play house, or a firepit for family singalongs.
3. *Your friends and neighbors.* Your home can become the ultimate Friday night hangout when you've got a fun and funky fresh permaculture garden on your rooftop or in your backyard. Create group seating areas with patio furniture, pallet benches, or logs. A cooking area or firepit is excellent for outdoor entertaining. Unique personal elements can be great conversation starters and showcase your crowd-pleasing style.
4. *Your community.* If you're making your garden a welcome spot for everyone in the community, think about accessibility. Create clear pathways to the specific elements in the garden, like the greenhouses, raised beds, or a free-for-all produce stand. Remember that even though you're being a wonderful human by inviting strangers onto your property, it could be an insurance liability, so things should be safe, sturdy, and clutter-free. And don't leave anything too personal out that could potentially disappear. (Just lookin' out for you, buddy. Do it! But do a little research, too).

ADDING PERSONAL TOUCHES

Permaculture systems can be both functional and pleasing to the eye. After all, if your garden looks good, you're more likely to want to spend time there. Here are some tips for adding beauty to your design:

1. Add flowers and ornamental plants, with a focus on native plants that complement the natural setting.
2. Mix up your colors and textures with plants of different sizes, shapes, and types to give your garden an interesting visual appeal. (See, Principle #10 can be practical *and* beautiful!)
3. Use mulch for pathways and on garden beds. This will suppress weeds, give your garden a more attractive look and give you less work. Sweet!
4. Create a focal point with a unique planting arrangement, a water feature, or an interesting piece of outdoor artwork.
5. Use natural elements like stone, logs, and woven branches to make your garden more functional and attractive.
6. Add lighting to make your garden accessible and beautiful at night. This could be with path lights, hanging lanterns, strung fairy lights, or spotlights. And to be a next-level permie, make them all solar-powered.
7. Think about the seasons. Incorporate plants that will grow, bloom, and go dormant at different times of the year so that your garden is ever-changing.

GETTING TO KNOW THE NEIGHBORS

As you get to know your space, it's good to get to know the area around you, too. Community is a big part of permaculture, even if you prefer to keep your cool lil' hermit garden to yourself.

For one, it's good to think of your neighbors when you plan your permaculture design because, let's face it, they're going to be looking at it, too (even if they never traverse the inner sanctum). It's good to be considerate of how your garden will look during each season, if it will flow over into their properties, what sounds or smells it will create, and what kind of animal (or human) visitors it will attract. For example, if you want to incorporate bees into a suburban setting, it might be thoughtful to make sure your neighbors aren't allergic first.

Your neighbors and community are also a natural resource that is free and ever-flowing. They can be a rich source of local resources and information.

For example, local nurseries will be well aware of what native plants thrive in the area as well as information on the hardiness zones. They're clued into the local soil and climate, and they will be able to advise you on specific plant requirements. And don't forget that your neighbors and community groups may be well experienced in growing their own food and the local nature. The only way to find out is by asking!

A simple, *"What grows well here?"* to a local avid gardener is a great way to get awesome intel as well as connect with someone on something they no doubt really enjoy sharing. Trust me, gardeners *love* talking about their gardens, and what's working for them. Win-win!

Wrap-Up

Before you put this chapter to rest, I want you to do one thing. You know that notebook that I'm sure you've been keeping to record all of your observations? Now flip to a blank sheet of paper and draw up a plan for your permaculture garden.

This isn't a test. It won't be graded. And it's not in the least bit permanent. It's just the beginning of a dream that you'll turn into a reality. Remember that permaculture isn't about having clean pathways and neat rows of crops. It's about using as much of the space as possible in a way that works for you.

Remember some of the principles you've learned. Zones. Patterns to details. You can start by circling out general areas. Recreational area here, windbreak row there, annual kitchen garden over here. Then fill in details.

Rarely will you get the perfect design the first time around. So parchment paper might be a good friend to have. You can lay sheets of parchment paper over your original plan and make changes as you learn more. And boy, are you going to! Because over the next three chapters, we'll talk about different methods and materials you can use to put together your garden paradise.

PART II

METHODS AND MATERIALS

CONTAINED METHODS: CONTAINERS, RAISED BEDS, & MORE

> The garden reconciles human art and wild nature, hard work and deep pleasure, spiritual practice and the material world. It is a magical place because it is not divided.
>
> — THOMAS MOORE

> The garden suggests there might be a place where we can meet nature halfway.
>
> — MICHAEL POLLAN

By definition, the thing that separates a garden from a wild space is an element of *order* or *human design*. We permies like to bend the rules a little. We typically like to keep it natchy.

But in even the wildest, most natural permaculture garden, you'll find little glimpses of the human hand at work. We use nature as a guidepost and add our own creative twists based on our needs, desires, tastes, and 'dem plain old creature comforts.

Your garden can contain natural and manmade materials, native plants and non-native species, a balance of wildness and order.

For example, most common edible plants — tomatoes, watermelons, squash — aren't indigenous to North American regions. But they're vital food crops, so we incorporate them into our gardens.

While I discuss the different ways to plant a garden, think about how you'll make your permaculture space a happy marriage of wild nature and purposeful structure. The balance will be different for each person. You'll discover which planting methods are best for your space and what scavenged or purchased materials you can use to put it all together.

PLANTING METHODS: A CRASH COURSE

To the gardening newbie, growing plants is pretty straightforward: you take a seed and stick it in the dirt. But there's more than one way to plant a seed. Some, like hydroponic gardening, don't even involve dirt!

While permies focus on maintaining soil health and creating self-sustaining systems, they're open to many planting methods. And thanks to these various methods, you can do permaculture gardening virtually anywhere. I'll go over the basics of each; then, you can decide which best fits into your unique permaculture design.

Over these next three chapters, we'll explore a variety of different methods you can use as you build your garden.

Chapter 5:

- *Contained Methods:* Gardens planted in artificial structures, ranging in size from a small pot to a whole raised bed.

Chapter 6:

- *Filling Methods:* What to use to fill up your containers, beyond just soil, especially when there's a lot of volume to fill.
- *Layering Methods:* Different techniques to layer materials and build soil for planting, whether in containers or on the ground.
- *Building Materials:* An overview of all the different materials you can use to build garden beds, containers, and structures. And many of them are cheap or even free!

Chapter 7:

- *In-Ground Methods:* Different ways to plant straight in the ground and work with your native soil.
- *Larger Concepts:* Larger gardening concepts and strategies you'll want to consider at all levels of design.

Since this is a crash course, we won't be able to cover all gardening methods or the ins and outs of each one listed. But going through these is a great way to help make decisions based on your unique situation.

Also, throughout these chapters and the whole book, you may see a concept mentioned that you are unfamiliar with or have more questions about. Usually, I'll try to cover it in greater detail in a future chapter or at least briefly define things as I go. For instance, there's a whole chapter on soil coming up.

If I've missed something, never be afraid to ask questions! Internet searches, online forums/groups on gardening and permaculture, as well as local gardeners, are all fantastic resources.

At the end of the book, I've listed some *supplemental resources* for further study.

Well, as they say, let's dig in!

GARDENING IN CONTAINED SPACES

Contained methods are great for a variety of reasons. They're generally more adaptable to different spaces, and they can open the door to you growing more plants from outside of your geographic zone. Smaller containers have the benefit of mobility. You can control the environment and soil contents more, and therefore pamper your plants. Plus they're a great way to explore your creative and resourceful sides with different pots and DIY projects.

Containers are like a premie permie's best friend. Maintenance is easy and commitment is small. You can try different things in different containers, and set up your own little permie science lab! Different methods, different plants & combinations. And if your in-ground soil out in the backyard needs some help, you can be growing in containers while you amend and prepare your backyard soil for the following year.

However, they can sometimes mean more startup costs (but we'll go over some tips and tricks to lower this). They can mean more nurturing and watering since they drain out. You miss out on all the benefits of all the supporting actors that are alive in the regular ground (more on that in Chapter 8). Plus, while great for getting small wins, smaller contained methods do limit your harvest.

To explore this category, we'll start small and get bigger. The work required gets a little more with each method.

Are you ready to start building your micro-Eden?

CONTAINER GARDENING

Plants are grown inside containers rather than in the ground with container gardening. Containers can be any size, from a teapot to a concrete half-pipe, so this method is truly adaptable to any space.

Who It's For: Container gardening is great for small spaces. You don't even need an outdoor area to enjoy a container garden. If there's sunlight and a container full of soil, you can create a micro edible landscape.

Container gardens are great for people who live in apartments, condos, or dorms, whether you have an outdoor area like a balcony, patio, rooftop, or just a sunny windowsill. You can also add them to their traditional gardens. Also, if you rent and aren't able to plant in the backyard, or don't want to lose your garden when you move, you can take your garden with you in containers.

Why It's Great: Besides being accessible to anyone, container gardening is excellent because you, the gardener, control the planting parameters. Add your own compost to give your plants healthy soil, and move them as needed to ensure enough sunlight. And weeds are practically nonexistent. You can bring containers indoors or move them to a sheltered spot during the cold months. Container gardening also maximizes limited space. You can arrange pots at different heights by stacking them, placing them on shelves, or hanging them.

What You Can Grow: You can grow just about anything in pots, including vegetables, herbs, flowers, fruit trees, and bushes. If you're growing edible plants in pots, look for compact or dwarf varieties.

You'll want to get a container that's large enough for the plant's root system to thrive. In general, healthy plants want room to grow, and the plant on top of the soil mimics its root growth. In other words, if you expect a lot of plant above the soil line, you can expect it to need a lot of roots below. It's a great idea to find out your particular plant's root depth. You'll want to research its *mature* root depth, meaning how much space it will need at its biggest. Time flies by, and they don't stay kids forever! *(Sniffle sniffle, wipe a tear).*

As a rule of thumb, transplants from a nursery will pretty much always need bigger pots to grow into.

What It Involves: Container gardening requires — you guessed it — containers. These can be professional store-bought terra cotta pots, but they don't have to be. A container garden can be almost anything: recycled food jars and cans, milk jugs, coffee mugs, buckets, baskets, or heck, an old bathtub. Some more ideas on free and cheap containers are listed in the next chapter.

A great way to "use the edges" in your space is to get or make yourself some window boxes, which are long, rectangular boxes that go under the bottom edge of your window. They're stunning and can be functional with culinary or medicinal herbs, pollinator flowers (some are even edible!), or even some vegetables and fruit, like leafy greens or strawberries. Or some combination!

You'll also of course need sunlight, water, soil, and plants. Container gardening is much like traditional gardening, just on a smaller scale.

Potential Drawbacks: Since they live in a restricted environment, container plants need special care regarding water and nutrients. They can't suck water from the ground, so you'll want to study your plant's specific water needs and water more frequently to avoid them drying out. Since most potting mixes lack sufficient nutrients for growing plants, you'll need to supplement your soil with compost or organic liquid fertilizers.

You're also limited on how much food you can harvest with container gardens. When container gardening on a balcony or rooftop, just be aware of the site's load-bearing capacity. You wouldn't want your container garden to crash onto your downstairs neighbor's patio table.

How to Permie-fy it: Alright, so, maybe you're wondering … isn't this just plain ol' container gardening? Well, permaculture is a way of seeing, remember? There are a lot of its mindsets and principles which we've discussed that you can bring to a garden of any size. Maybe some come to mind already!

Here's something you can try … I first got this idea from the awesome blog *Kitchen Stewardship* by Katie Kimball, on a guest post by Nicky Schauder (2020) … As you'll learn, permaculture gardens often involve many layers, filled with diverse plants that support each other. Vines climbing up trees. Crawling plants used as ground cover.

So let's focus on 3 layers that we can build right in our containers. This is called the **"Thriller, Filler, Spiller" Technique**. This terminology is usually used in flower arranging, but you can bring it to your edible container garden. Let's go through the different layers.

- *The Thriller:* This is the main event, right at center stage. Think: What's the vegetable or plant I'm most focused on, or which is going to produce the most yield? Or you can think in terms of, what is the showiest or needs the most space? This could be a tomato, pepper, tomatillo, ground cherry, a tall grain (corn, quinoa), berry bushes (blackberry, blueberry), pole beans up a trellis or other climbers, bush squash or beans, or even a small tree (citrus, dwarf varieties, etc). Or you can even have an herb like borage be your thriller.
- *The Filler:* This plant is placed around the thriller, midway between it and the edge. Fillers make the container look full, almost like a fluffy ground cover, which helps the soil and main plant in various ways. Great ones for this are thyme, mint, oregano, beautiful greens (purple kale, lettuce), basil, chamomile, beets, and leafy green herbs. You could try some clover as well, which enriches the soil.
- *The Spiller:* These are trailing plants placed on the outer edge, and they spill over the sides of the container like a waterfall. These plants can attract pollinators and beneficial bugs, and deter pests. Nasturtiums, begonias, geraniums, strawberries, pole beans without the trellis, cucumbers, rosemary, and sweet potatoes are great examples. As well as some of the "fillers", just trained to spill over the side, like creeping thyme. This part puts that "use the edges" Principle #11 to practice!

Make sure to check for any competing requirements like water/sun/soil type, and root/space needs so you don't get too crowded. Some plants go really well together, some don't. For instance, in general, you wouldn't want to plant a sun lover with a shade lover in the same pot. I mean, where would you put the pot?

More details about plant pairing can be found in the "companion planting" sections of this book, found in Chapter 7, as well as Chapter 10.

This idea has the potential to put a lot of permaculture principles to work, and it can be used in any of the other planting methods below. Before long, you'll have a whole miniature permaculture guild in your own pot! (More on "guilds" also in Chapter 7 and Chapter 10!)

VERTICAL GARDENING

In a vertical garden, plants are grown upward along vertical supports rather than horizontally in rows. Since they maximize space, they can be any size and grown anywhere.

Who It's For: Like container gardening, you can do vertical gardening just about anywhere. Since it takes advantage of that empty space that's just hovering in front of your eyes, you can utilize it in even the smallest places. No floor space? No problem! With some creativity, a vertical garden can be grown entirely on a wall, fence, trellis, or other support. Vertical gardens and living walls are popular in urban settings.

Why It's Great: Vertical gardening takes empty space and makes it productive. Vertical gardens are excellent for people who don't have a lot of square footage or those who want to maximize their garden space with plants that reach for the sky. Vertical gardens are adaptable. They can be grown indoors or outdoors, large or small, inexpensive or elaborate. You can combine a vertical garden with other gardening methods.

What You Can Grow: Generally, any plant you can grow in containers can be grown in a vertical garden. This includes herbs, strawberries, lettuce, and greens but excludes most trees and bushes. Vining vegetables like beans, peas, and cucumbers are also excellent for vertical gardens. Many enjoy creating attractive vertical gardens, or "living walls," with succulents, ferns, mosses, and flowering plants.

What It Involves: With vertical gardening, plants are grown much like a container garden; only they are designed to grow in a vertical direction that maximizes limited ground space. For vertical gardening, you need containers, plants, and soil. You can fashion your containers to a vertical surface like a wall, or work with a vertical garden that has multiple levels built from the ground up like shelving, or a "plant tower".

This is a great place to get creative. You can use vertical items you already have around your home, like trellises, fences, bamboo stakes, old ladders, or shelving units. Pallets and old over-the-door shoe organizers are awesome and popular options for DIY vertical gardens.

Or you can take the easy route, go on Amazon, and buy a low-cost, pocket-sized felt wall planter. These are great for apartments and other small spaces.

You'll want to think about how the garden will drain. It doesn't have to be complicated, just involves a little thinking. As you know, water goes downward. If you have multiple levels right on top of each other, plant the most water hungry-plants at the bottom. Your levels may be more diagonal, like with a diagonal ladder structure. Either way, consider where the water eventually ends up: into drip trays or saucers, or right onto the soil, etc.

Potential Drawbacks: Since vertical gardens are often grown in containers, you will face the same drawbacks you do with container gardening, including the need to water and maintain your plants more often. Vertical gardening also takes a bit more setup and DIY skills than growing a traditional garden. You're essentially "building" the garden from the ground up.

RAISED BEDS

A raised bed is like a garden in a box. It's raised above the ground, so no digging is required, and you can better control the planting environment. A raised bed can be any size or shape, so it's adaptable to any space.

It can sit *right on top of the ground* or can be *built up on legs,* at an elevated height.

Who It's For: Raised beds are an excellent option for anyone with a few square feet of outdoor space. Even if you only have an apartment balcony, rooftop, or patio, you can set up a mini raised bed. Raised beds may be homemade or store-bought, so they're great for people who aren't great with DIY. They're also ideal for people who have physical trouble stooping, kneeling, and getting down on the ground. We've got you covered!

Also, depending on height, a raised bed can give great wheelchair access. An elevated raised bed can be a great option for pet owners or parents, too, since the height prevents pets or children from reaching inside and digging up this year's yield (bless their sweet lil curious hearts).

Why It's Great: Raised beds maximize ground space without requiring you to dig in the ground, so they won't disturb the soil. They're easy to set up anywhere the ground is level and are especially beneficial for spaces where the ground isn't workable, like pavement, gravel, hard-packed clay, or rocky soil.

The beauty of raised beds is that you can control the soil quality. Amend your raised bed with high-quality compost, and you're good to grow for years to come. Compared to traditional in-ground gardens, raised beds offer better drainage, better pest control, less potential for weeds, and are less prone to soil compaction.

We'll go over how to check your soil in Chapter 8. If you find you have very poorly draining soil, very rocky soil (more rocks than soil), or even contaminated soil (in which case you'll want a barrier between the ground and your raised bed soil), a raised bed is a great way to start fresh.

What You Can Grow: There is no limit to what you can grow in a raised bed, even fruit trees and shrubs! Your favorite garden vegetables, fruits, herbs, and perennial plants can be grown in raised beds. You're only restricted to the size of your bed. Raised beds are a smart solution for plants that like to spread, like mint, comfrey, and yarrow, keeping them in their confines where they can't take over the entire garden.

What It Involves: A raised bed may be a simple mound of earth you built up from the ground. But often, we think of raised beds as those with supported sides or fully enclosed containers. We'll mostly talk about the latter type in this section.

Once again, a raised bed can be built right on the soil surface, or some "hip-height" raised beds are on legs, eliminating the need to stoop.

- If it sits right on the ground, it has the benefit of connecting with the soil life below it and being more stable, since the ground is its bottom support.
- If it is raised up higher on legs, it has the benefit of being more accessible and you can control the contents more. Plus, you can really maximize the use of space, with a shelf (or 2 or 3) underneath the bed to neatly tuck away gardening tools and supplies. You can also fasten hooks on the side to hang tools.

You can construct raised beds from wood, stone, concrete, plastic, metal, and more. This is an excellent opportunity to take advantage of what you already have in your yard or can salvage for free, like logs, bricks, old metal sheeting, or concrete blocks. Some people use old animal troughs.

You want to steer clear of treated wood, due to the chemicals used for treatment and how they can affect the soil and plants. Some say newer treated wood isn't as bad because it's being made differently now. But if you can avoid it, this is the healthiest option. Keep in mind that non-treated wood will slowly wear down over time, but there are eco-friendly organic methods of sealing mentioned below.

If your raised bed is elevated, you might consider lining the bottom of the bed with some kind of weed fabric to keep soil in but let water go through. Some even line the inside of their walls (with any height of raised bed), especially if the building material has some cracks or pores. Soil-level raised beds often have a layer of newspaper or cardboard put down first. This will suppress the initial weeds, but eventually decompose and let earthworms through.

Aside from the bed, all you need is soil and plants. The rest is the same as traditional in-ground gardening. It's just a few feet above it.

Potential Drawbacks: Although raised beds can last for years, they have some startup costs. You'll need to purchase or salvage the materials to build the bed and buy the soil to fill it if you haven't already made your own compost. For this reason, many beginning permies start with one raised bed and expand as their budgets allow. Like a container garden, a raised bed will require more water than an in-ground garden. And since the soil tends to heat up faster in the summer and cool quicker in the fall, perennials need to be heartier.

How to Get Started: There is no shortage of free DIY plans online, if you just search "Free DIY raised garden plans." Add your material of choice to the search terms to get more specific. Pinterest is another great resource to search for and generate ideas.

If you want the work done for you and you've got the cash, then you can buy pre-made raised beds, or raised bed kits with instructions!

Most of the time raised beds are basically rectangular, though permies have definitely experimented with different shapes for creativity and efficiency's sake. For now, we'll focus on a rectangular raised bed.

How big should a rectangular bed be? Of course, it depends on your space and the types of plants you want to plant! But there are general rules of thumb.

Width

Ideally between 18 inches - 4 feet. Anything less than 18 inches, and you won't be able to really zone in on raised bed advantages. At least 2 feet gives you breathing room for rows of plants. If you can access both sides, 4 feet is okay, maybe up to 5 feet. Anything wider, and you can't reach the middle plants without stepping in the bed.

The best way to get the width that is best for *you specifically* is to measure your personal reach. Get a tape measure and two pencils. Kneel down on the ground, putting one pencil where your knees are. Then stretch in front of you (like you'd be reaching for a big juicy squash). Not as far as you can, but as far as you can *comfortably*. Put your other pencil there, and measure the distance. This is your reach. You can do this same exercise on a table or countertop to measure reach for a hip-height raised bed. *You want your raised bed width to be no more than twice this reach measurement.*

Length

Ideally between 4-10 feet. A common length is 8. Really there's no limit, so you can try longer if you want, especially if you are using a sturdier material than wood like stone or brick. With wood, anything longer than 10 or 12 ft, and you start needing extra support to keep from bowing, etc. There's a lot of material inside, so remember to research what kind of reinforcements you'll need along the sides of the bed, depending on its size. Kind of like the studs of a house.

Depth

Basically, tall enough to where your plant's full root system can spread out. 1 ft usually accommodates root crops and medium plants. 18 inches is good for most kitchen garden plants, and is really common for raised beds. Some plants require 2 ft or deeper (tomatoes and sweet potatoes like deep root systems). Between 1-2 ft is the usual raised bed depth.

Again, you can make them as tall as you want, just keep in mind that taller means you'll need to fill more. This means a couple things. First, wooden beds will need extra buttressing to keep the walls from bowing. Second, if you are buying potting soil, that can get pricey fast! Not to worry though, we'll go over some creative ways to fill containers of all kinds in the next chapter.

Paths

You'll want to think about paths between. You can simply let grass grow, but that might also mean considering it being wide enough for a mower to get through there. You can have gravel or stepping stones. Or you can even use Permie Principle #8 and integrate functions, by tossing clippings and leaves along the path, allowing them to compost as you walk over them, and get yourself a compost yield after some time!

Ideally, the width between beds are around 18-24 inches for comfortable access. To give room for wheelchairs, or wheelbarrows and carts, you'll want 4 ft.

Other Notes: Building a raised bed can be such a satisfying experience. Get some good plans, and go for it!

Here are a few other things you might want to consider:

Sealing

If you use wood to build a raised bed, you might find yourself wanting to go the extra mile and seal it, so it lasts longer. Just make sure you use a non-toxic, natural wood preservative. Linseed oil, tung oil, beeswax, Eco Wood Treatment, or Lifetime Wood Treatment are good options.

Fence-line Beds

You can also place raised beds along the fence, which is a great use of space! Just remember that even if they're along a fence, raised beds still should have 4 sides. Fence planks can be pressure treated, which isn't good for your bed's soil, and if they are untreated planks, they can rot with moist garden soil against them.

Orientation

You may want to consider the orientation of your raised beds, according to the sun, rain, and wind patterns in your space. For instance, in a bed of low-growing crops, some gardeners like to run the long side of their beds north to south, so direct sunlight hits both sides of the bed throughout the day.

Remember that elementary class photoshoot, where they put all the tall kids in back so you could see the shorter kids? Think of the sun like the camera, and use that same concept when you set your beds up for the best sunlight.

You can run your beds east to west, with taller crops (tomatoes, pole beans) in the back (AKA the north side), and lower-growing plants on the south side, to make sure everyone is seen and sunny! Okay everyone, say cheese!

Shape

Lastly, as said before, many have tried other shapes for designing their raised beds. In fact, one of the most popular permaculture designs is the "keyhole" raised bed. This is usually a circular bed, with one "keyhole" notch cut out, so you can walk to the center and access the bed from there, with the garden all around you.

Some take this concept and design their raised beds like three rectangles in a "U" shape, like a U-shaped desk.

These allow for great access and maximize space by minimizing the amount used for pathways.

One variation of the "keyhole bed" (sometimes called the African keyhole bed) actually places a cylindrical column in the center of the bed, made out of stakes and chicken wire or some other sturdy, porous material. This is the "composting cage" and you can throw your composting ingredients right in it. As the materials decompose, nutrients will leach out into the soil surrounding it. This idea can also be used in a rectangular, or U-shaped bed.

Permie-fy It: A lot of what we covered in the "containers" section can be applied here. Get some diversity in your garden beds!

One great rule of thumb for garden beds is to have at least 1 type of vegetable or fruit, 1 herb, and 1 flower present in each bed.

Another great concept to use, if you have multiple garden beds growing annual crops, is *crop rotation*. This is where you have multiple different raised bed layouts (4 is a good number for this), and you rotate them around the different beds each year like musical chairs. This is great for the soil, and the whole garden. More on this in Chapter 10.

Also, as mentioned above, a composting column is a great way to bring functions together, make an easy composting setup, and feed the soil in your bed!

From diversity to reused materials to utilized edges and multiple functions … there are many permaculture ideas you can bring to the raised garden bed. I imagine with those nifty permie glasses you're getting used to seeing through, the gears are already turning!

SQUARE FOOT GARDENING

Square foot gardening starts with a raised bed. It's divided into 1' sections with a grid, and a different mini crop is planted in each. These are *surface-level grid lines* creating a *visual* division on top, not actual walls. This method allows you to maximize your raised bed to get a quick yield and a big harvest without needing lots of space.

Who It's For: Square foot gardening is great for beginners and people who don't have a lot of space. This method needs to be done outdoors, preferably in a raised bed. You can do it with a single 4' x 4' bed, or any number of any size, really. It's excellent for people with small or large yards or apartment dwellers with a few square feet of space on their balcony, rooftop, or patio.

Why It's Great: Square foot gardening is an easy and dependable way to grow more food in less space. It's calculated and mathematical, so a lot of the thinking is done for you. Ah, how very nice ... In this way, it's a great way for a beginner to get started with things like raised bed gardening and companion planting!

It's low maintenance because you're working in a raised bed that requires less weeding. It doesn't require digging into the earth and doesn't waste water because there are no empty spaces between crops.

A square foot garden is easy to plan because it's a simple grid, which is perfect for companion planting. Since you're planting closer together, it makes excellent use of space and allows you to rotate crops easily each year. You can enjoy more fresh fruit and veggies in less space and in less time!

What You Can Grow: Like container gardening, almost anything can be grown in a square foot garden bed. It's all of your favorite summer and fall veggies. But there is one caveat: perennials don't do great in a square foot garden because they often require more space to grow. They like to set up permanent homes rather than being rotated to a new spot on the grid each year.

What It Involves: A square foot garden involves all the same stuff as a raised bed, with the addition of a planting grid. Instead of planting in rows, divide your raised bed into 1-square-foot sections (making a grid out of string or bamboo stakes helps keep everyone in their own zones), and plant a different variety in each section. Carry on with your seasonal gardening as usual!

Potential Drawbacks: Like raised bed gardening, square foot gardening does have its initial startup costs: constructing the bed, adding the soil, and purchasing the plants. But once you've got it, you've got it! The other drawback is that square foot gardening isn't ideal for crops that take up much space, including trailing plants like pumpkins and melons or sweet corn. Instead, you might use the square foot bed for small crops like carrots, lettuce, and herbs and plant the others differently.

How to Get Started: Well, you'll want to get your raised bed. This method involves dividing the bed into a grid of 1 ft lines, so it's best to have the width and length be whole numbers. The typical size is 4x4, which gives you 16 squares to work with. But some people like to use 4x8 (32 squares), or other sizes.

Search online for "square foot garden plans" to come up with some great design ideas for what to plant and where.

Different plants will have different amounts of space they take up on the grid. You can find "square foot gardening plant spacing charts" online, detailing this. Here are some examples:

- 3" spacing / 16 plants per square: carrots, radishes
- 4" spacing / 9 plants per square: arugula, bush beans, leaf lettuce, spinach, turnips
- 6" spacing / 4 plants per square: beets, garlic, parsnips, onions, thyme, swiss chard
- 12" spacing / 1 plant per square: asparagus, broccoli, cabbage, celery, eggplant, peppers, sweet potatoes
- 12-24" spacing / 1-2 squares per plant: squash
- 1 plant per 4 squares: melons, tomatoes, squash
- 1 plant per 9 squares: bush squash, zucchini

Then, you want to make a grid. Get your measuring tape and put some kind of line every 1 ft, both horizontally and vertically. You can tie string or tomato twine from one side to the other, on a nail put in each side. Or, you can simply lay down bamboo stakes or something straight.

Once you've planted the plants, you can honestly take the grid off, since it's really for designing and maintaining spacing for planting. And the grid lines can get in your way otherwise.

FINAL NOTES ON CONTAINERS

Now you know some of the best ways to contain your garden! Go you!

You'll want to pay attention to drainage with contained gardens. Water should be able to drain out so your plants don't get root rot. If you have a container or raised bed that is elevated (basically any container with a bottom), make sure you have drainage holes in the bottom. Add a layer of landscape fabric, coffee filter or fine mesh of some kind to the bottom before filling, to keep soil from draining out after watering or rain.

The water that does drain out the bottom can make a mess. If your containers are outside, that may not present much of a problem. In other cases, there are drip trays, plant saucers, or even double-potting methods that can help solve this problem. As with most things, there are cool "DIY" solutions to save money and reuse old stuff.

If your container doesn't have any drainage holes, you can drill some. It might help to do a little research on drilling into the material your pot is made from, if you're drilling holes in a pot you really like. While wood and plastic are pretty easy to drill into, ceramic is a little more delicate.

For ceramic, use a specific bit, like a diamond/masonry drill bit, slap some artist tape on the marks before drilling, and drill slow and steady, without too much pressure. Pour some water over the hole intermittently as you drill to help cool it off. That'll save you some cracks! You're welcome, pal.

If you really don't want to drill into your favorite pot, you could consider double-potting, where your plant is in a plastic container with adequate drainage, which is then placed in the decorative pot. Some people even put gravel at the bottom of the decorative pot, and the inner container on top of that. Just dump out any standing water regularly.

How many holes, how big, and how far apart? Here's a general guide:

- Containers *under* 12" in diameter: ¼" holes, 2-4" apart.
- Containers *between* 12"-18" in diameter: ½" holes, 4-6" apart.
- Containers *over* 18": ½" holes, every 6" in regular intervals.

WRAP-UP

Okay, the fun continues, and your plans expand! Do contained gardening methods appeal to you?

Take another walk around your space with your notebook. See any spots where containers might fill in your plans. Hanging, sitting, climbing up the wall, or perched outside your kitchen window.

If you're into the idea of raised beds, come up with some basic measurements for raised beds using the guidelines above. Are they elevated? On the ground? Using your observations from the last chapter, think of some spots in your yard that would make for a good garden area, with adequate sun, etc.

All these ideas can change and shift, but start drawing out ideas. The more you just put pencil to paper, erase and try again, the easier and more familiar it will become to try things out and take action.

So let's say you have some containers picked out. You're sure some plants go in there. And you're sure some soil goes in there. But it sure looks like a lot of space to fill …

Or maybe you're all jazzed about raised bed gardening, but wondering what building materials to use to make your first one.

In the next chapter, we'll answer the question, "What can I fill my container with?" You might think it's just plain ol' dirt. But as you'll soon see, there are important choices to make and considerations to keep in mind. Plus, there are some nifty permaculture methods we'll be adding to our arsenal.

Also, we'll explore building materials, and put on our permie treasure-hunting hats to find low-cost (and even free!) options for garden containers and structures.

Let's go find some materials!

FILLING, LAYERING & MATERIALS TO BUILD THE SOIL & STRUCTURES

 Our tendency is to be interested in something that is growing in the garden, not in the bare soil itself. But if you want to have a good harvest, the most important thing is to make the soil rich and cultivate it well.

— SHUNRYU SUZUKI

So. You've got your container ready!

You found this really cute pot that someone was selling for cheap at a garage sale. A pair of two, to be exact. They'd go great right outside your door. You're pretty sure you'll be getting compliments from the fam when they visit.

You start examining them at home and notice, they're super tall. You start to think, "Whoa, there's a lot of space in there. That's gotta be like ... 1, 2, 3 ... maybe 4 or 5 bags of soil for each one? How did that happen???"

Or maybe you're looking proudly at your first raised bed. And it looked manageable at first glance. But then you start doing the math ... 4x8 feet, and 2 feet deep ... let me see, that's ... 64 cubic feet. A bag of potting soil is usually 1-2 cubic feet, and can cost 5 or 6 bucks ... *Holy mackerel!*

Yep. Soil can cost some cash to bring in. At the time of writing, 1 bag can range from around $4-10 for a cubic foot, with the good stuff being on the higher end.

"Well can't I just go dig up some dirt from the backyard?"

Hang on, not necessarily. Not all dirt is the same! (More on that in Chapter 8). Besides, one of the benefits of contained gardening is you really get to control the soil quality.

So what do you do? Don't worry, you're not alone in this dilemma. Below are some ideas to conserve space, while still having rich soil. Hopefully, we can save some money while also saving the landfill from some perfectly good reusable resources. Double cha-ching!

In this chapter, we will talk all about materials! We'll cover a variety of ways to fill up pots and garden beds. Then, we will go over building materials you can use to build raised beds and different structures for your garden.

CONTAINER FILLERS

The following are some great ways to give some of that "waste" a second life and get extra stars on your permie sticker chart.

Let's look at two basic categories of fillers: **organic materials** and **non-organic**. Or in other words, **biodegradable** and **non-biodegradable**.

The first category (biodegradable) breaks down in the soil over time, and includes items like leaves, mulch, pine cones, branches, and newspaper.

The second category (non-biodegradable) does not break down in the soil, and can be anything from water bottles, soda cans, and packing peanuts, to rocks, bricks, and broken pieces of tile.

There are a few basic rules to follow here, especially if you consider filling your pot with anything that is non-biodegradable, like plastics, etc.

- Make sure you have good drainage. No matter what you fill your containers with, you want to make sure it doesn't pack too tight, and that water can pass through and out!
- When using *non-biodegradable* or *harder* fillers, only fill the bottom up to ¼ or ⅓ (maybe ½). You want soil and/or compost at the top, at least deep enough for the root system of the plant.

- Place some mesh, a screen, weed barrier, or pantyhose between the filler layer and the soil to keep it from mixing (mostly important with non-biodegradable fillers).
- Close containers like bottles so they don't trap water and get moldy.
- Make sure not to fill with any toxic or unhealthy stuff.
- You'll want the top layers to be softer organic matter, and definitely, the very top layer to be good soil and/or compost.
- Fill your containers up to 2" below the top rim, or closer. In smaller pots, you might only leave ½". Remember that planting a transplant will displace some soil, so don't fill it all the way to the top before putting a sizable transplant in.

LIGHTWEIGHT FILLERS

Lightweight filler in the bottom part of your pot is fitting for two scenarios: either the pot is heavy already (clay pots or other heavy ones), or you want to keep it lighter because weight would be an issue. Maybe you want to be able to move it or hang it, or it's on a surface you don't want a big load sitting on.

Some biodegradable fillers would include:

- Small branches and sticks, leaves, pinecones
- Sphagnum moss or coconut fiber (coco coir)
- Newspaper, recycled cardboard, crumpled-up paper bags

Some non-biodegradable lightweight fillers would include:

- Old junk: old cut-up pool noodles, soda cans (upside down or crushed), plastic Easter eggs, old bags from potting soil, bubble wrap.
- Recycled foam materials: styrofoam blocks or packing peanuts (just not the kind that dissolve)
- Recycled plastics: water bottles, milk jugs, take-out containers, protein powder containers. Or even open cup-shaped containers turned upside down, like solo cups or old nursery pots.

Also, there are lightweight commercial "garden container fillers" you can find online. But hey, why pay for it when it's all around you?

HEAVY FILLERS

Do you have a planter you want to be heavier? Maybe you want it to stay put, or be hard for toddlers to knock over. I'm sure those cute front door pots from the garage sale would make a nasty spill!

If that's you, then try putting some of these fillers in the bottom:

Biodegradable:

- Logs and big branches

Non-biodegradable:

- Sand
- Gravel, pebbles, and rocks (be aware, contrary to popular belief, these do not "improve drainage")
- Old tiles, broken pottery
- Cinder Blocks, bricks, and pieces of them

BIODEGRADABLE FILLERS VS. NON-BIODEGRADABLE VS. SOIL

There are many different opinions on what to put at the bottom of a large planter. Some will say only use soil, because a plant can never have enough good soil. If you want to spend the money, it's pretty hard to go wrong with pure soil! Read below to know what kinds to look for.

Some other folks see no problem with fillers and love reusing things.

Some say biodegradable material is great for the soil because it composts over time. Others say don't do it, because it will break down over time, the soil level will sink, and so it's no longer a filler, so you'll have to put more soil in.

People have had good results with any of these ideas, and the point is to try things and see what's best for you!

Here's one thing you can draw from these thoughts, *especially if you are considering filling the bottom with organic material:*

If you are planting *annuals*, organic filler like pinecones should be fine since the breaking down won't happen until after the growing season. Next season, just add more organic matter as you plant new plants.

If you are planting *perennials*, just be aware that the material will break down, so you'll need to put in additional soil, or more filler every couple of years.

False Bottoms

When we say false bottoms, we aren't talking about plastic surgery here!

I mean a piece of sturdy material that sits in the middle of the pot to "raise" the bottom, so when you start filling with soil, there's less to fill.

It's usually the shape of the pot and works best when the width is tapered as it goes down.

For instance, in a tapered circular pot, a false bottom would be a little plastic disc that is not as wide as the opening, but wider than the bottom. As you place it in, it stops near the middle.

You can buy these in a variety of sizes online, or figure out DIY solutions: like an old pizza pan you don't use anymore, or one of those circular microwaveable trays from an old freezer meal.

Self-Wicking Containers

A plant that waters itself? Count me in!

While I won't cover it step-by-step, this is definitely worth looking into.

This method involves turning the bottom part of a container into a water reservoir. A plant in this system will "self-irrigate" by "wicking" up the water from the reservoir to the roots. This happens through something called **capillary action**. Have you ever put the end of a paper towel in the water, and seen the water slowly climb up the rest of the towel? Yeah, that's what that is. Science!

Anyway, this is a super cool type of container. It's lower maintenance in the long run and has the benefit of giving consistent moisture to your plants.

A simple DIY solution involves only a couple of 5-gallon buckets and a PVC pipe. People have also repurposed old plastic containers like washed-out milk jugs or detergent containers to create their water reservoirs, for you recycled junk junkies.

For some extra fun on a weekend project, search for tutorials online!

These types of containers (also known as "grow boxes" or "self-watering planters") are available for purchase online, as well.

WHAT KIND OF SOIL DO I CHOOSE?

Whether you're looking to fill in that top layer of your container, or you've decided to be a soil purist and fill the whole container with soil, you might be considering bringing in new soil that's sold commercially.

As always, some purists would say skip the commercial stuff, since you don't always know where it's been, and because the good stuff (that's more regulated) can be really expensive.

And, as always, I want to give you some info so you can make the choice that's right for you.

Understanding what's happening in your soil is one of the most important parts of your permie journey. In Chapter 8 we will explore this wonderful underground world, and learn ways to test your native soil. Before you go sourcing dirt from your yard that may be nutrient-starved and in need of some TLC, consider purchasing some good soil for your containers.

If you walk through the aisles of bagged soil at the local big box or garden supply store, or if you peruse your local landscape/soil supplier, you'll find that there are many options to choose from. Potting Soil, Planting Soil, Garden Soil, Topsoil, and what in the actual heck is "Orchid Mix"?

What does it all meeeean??

Never fear, I've got your back. Here's a basic overview of what you might see, starting with the three main items we will be focusing on.

GARDEN SOIL, POTTING SOIL, AND COMPOST

Garden soil / planting mix

This is a pre-mixed blend of natural top-grade topsoil (I explain top-grade topsoil below), organic matter, nutrients, and minerals. It often has things mixed in like aged manure, well-rotted wood chips, compost, and worm castings. It's designed to be mixed in with your existing soil to improve it in areas like compaction or nutrients. Or it can be simply added on top, and used for new garden beds.

Garden soil is great for planting gardens. However, it is meant to be used *in the ground* and it is not intended for containers. This is because it retains water for longer, it is heavier, and it can really pack down in a container, which can lead to the soil becoming compacted and waterlogged. The air space around the roots is choked, and growth is poor or stunted. Yikes!

So, if you wondered why your potted star jasmine vine started to slowly wither, and you went to touch its soil to find it felt like poured concrete (can you see me blushing here?) … this might explain why.

All-purpose potting soil

This soil is formulated for containers or pots. It gives space for roots to spread out, has good water retention, and drains well. It usually has some additives like peat moss or coco coir, pine bark, and mined perlite and vermiculite. And sometimes has compost for added nutrients. Each potting soil is different, and you'll want to check the back label for specifics.

This is great for *containers*. It's sometimes a little pricier than garden soil. It's best replaced or amended annually. Quick tip: if the bag at the store has an especially "funky" smell, go with another bag.

Compost

This is that "black gold" I keep alluding to. Compost is rich with biological life, and giving this to your plants is like sending them to the spa. Later, we will learn how to make it ourselves.

Basically, this is decomposed organic animal and plant materials, and it's a fantastic way to invigorate the soil with new life. It's meant to be added to the soil of your choice. Compost is not actually soil *per se*, it's a **soil amendment**, or something you add to soil to improve it. Compost *typically* lacks the structure that soil has, which is needed to support strong plant root systems.

Manure-based composts are better in-ground, and other composts can be used in containers in smaller amounts.

One great way is to put a smaller layer of compost on the top after filling the rest of the area with soil. Or some people put compost as the second-to-last layer, with the soil on top. Or some folks will do compost, then soil, then mulch. Below, we'll explore layering methods more!

OTHER KINDS OF SOIL AND AMENDMENTS

Here are other things you'll see as you stroll down the aisles of your local gardening supplier, just to give you a lay of the land:

Seed starting mix / soilless potting "mix"

Believe it or not, there are mixes you can buy that actually don't contain soil! They're made up of natural additive materials instead, like peat moss, coco coir, pine bark, and mined perlite and vermiculite. A combination of these products together makes for a fine, light, and fluffy mix that retains moisture well. Also, these mixes don't contain organic material that might contain pathogens, and they've been sterilized with heat, to make a nice, clean bed for baby plants. We touch on this more in Chapter 9 when we talk about seed starting. This mix is for a very specific purpose, so you wouldn't want to use this as your main container soil.

Indoor potting soil

Sometimes you'll see potting soil specifically formulated for houseplants. The difference is usually that compost and bark are left out, which are components that can draw in fungus gnats. If you plan on keeping your plants indoors, this is a good option to explore.

Specialty potting soil mixes

Cacti and citrus potting soil, orchid potting soil, African violet mix, etc. These are all unique blends formulated for plants that don't handle standard all-purpose potting soil as well.

Topsoil

Many use "garden soil" and "topsoil" to mean the same thing, but these are actually different. Topsoil is dirt taken from the top 12" of the ground. It's dirt, plain and simple.

There are different "grades" of topsoil, depending on the specific ground it was taken from, and how nutrient-rich it was, etc. Read the contents of the bag to know the grade. You can use lower grade for filling holes, but you can mix the higher grade stuff in with your native soil if you want. But typically, neither grade is used exclusively for planting.

Some topsoil is "enriched" which means there is compost or manure of some kind mixed in with the topsoil.

Lawn soil / lawn top-dressing

Just like you'd imagine, this is meant for lawns/turf grass.

Mulch

This is usually something like wood chips or straw, and it's a great thing to cover your soil with. It helps keep moisture in and weeds out and regulates temperature.

Greensand, lava sand, worm castings, etc

There are a host of soil amendments that are mined from volcanic sites, the ocean floor, and the all-powerful poopoo of worms, that can improve your soil in some remarkable ways.

Other various amendments

From materials that make your soil more alkaline or acidic, to materials that improve drainage or aerate your soil, you'll see a whole lot of things in bags at the local garden store.

"Contains mycorrhizal fungi"

Mycorrhizal fungi or **mycorrhizae** are beneficial organisms that enhance the quality and growth of plants by increasing nutrient absorption, pathogen resistance, and water transport. If your soil contains them, this is great news. You can also add mycorrhizae to soil as an amendment.

A Note On "Organic" Soil

"Organic" is one of those words that gets thrown around a lot. One way of thinking about its meaning here is substituting the word "organic" for the word "living". Technically, it means that it came from an animal or plant and is free of synthetic chemicals or pesticides, which is great!

However, seeing as how this term is not regulated in the world of bagged soil, "organic" on a bag of soil doesn't always necessarily mean "totally friendly to the environment" or sustainably sourced, if that's what you're looking for.

If that level of "organic" matters to you, you'll want to look for the OMRI label, which stands for Organic Materials Review Institute, a non-profit organization that certifies that agricultural inputs (in this case, soil) are suitable for organic food production.

What Kind of Soil To Use

Now, with all that said, what do you use?

- *For starting seeds:* Use a seed-starting mix, usually soilless. You can buy this or make your own. More on that in Chapter 9.
- *For containers:* Stick with potting soil. You can add some compost on top, especially if your containers will be outside.
- *For raised beds:* You can go with garden soil if your raised bed is big enough, and especially if it's on the ground. Some do a mix of potting and garden soil, like 50/50. Some soil suppliers even sell a "raised bed soil mix," which is probably some kind of mix of garden and potting soil ingredients. If you're filling a lot of raised beds, you can check local landscape suppliers for bulk prices and have some delivered or carry loads in the back of your truck. You can save a lot on costs by buying in bulk.

Once you select the plants you want to plant, you'll want to check their specific soil requirements, like how acidic or alkaline they want their soil to be. Most are great in a neutral middle-ground, and that's where most soil is. If you have something outside of this norm, like acidic-loving blueberries, you either want the soil you get to be pre-formulated for the specific needs of your plants, or you'll need to get a soil amendment for the soil you get.

Also, check if your plants have any specific drainage or other requirements for their soil.

STERILIZING SOIL & COMPOST

Tender things need sterile environments. Just ask the hospitals!

I know the idea of cleaning your dirt might sound a bit wacky, but sometimes with seedlings or young plants, it's good to sterilize your soil before use. This is not so much for containers filled with *new, bagged potting soil* (which has typically already been sterilized) and *mature plants*. It's more important to consider when:

- You are *reusing* old potting soil.
- You are working with seedlings, or transplanting juvenile plants.
- You are wanting to sterilize soil you know is infected with pathogens (like in a raised bed where disease has spread), or where you want weed seeds eradicated.
- You want to take extra precautions when using compost from your heap in containers.
- You want to take extra precautions with indoor container plants.

Various pathogens, fungus, viruses, bacteria, weed seeds, and insect eggs can be in the soil, and tender or young plants can be particularly susceptible to their effects. Sterilization of soil *now* can also mean fewer problems *later* (when the problem has spread or sprouted).

However, mature plants might not need sterilized soil, since they're tough enough to fend for themselves. And sterilization can kill both the bad *and* the good stuff (e.g. insects). And if you heat soil up too much, you can increase chances of phytotoxicity. So there are potential pros and cons to this process. Drawbacks can be minimized if you follow steps carefully.

It's important to note that when you see "sterile" soil mentioned — in this book or otherwise — this usually means *mostly sterile*, or heated up to deal with *most* pathogens and seeds. As the folks at Phytosphere Research say in their article on soil sterilization:

Heat treatment is often referred to as sterilization, but temperatures routinely used to heat soil will not result in completely sterile soil / potting media. The goal is to heat the potting mix to a point that kills the plant pathogens of concern.

— BERNHARDT & SWIECKI (2021)

When heating at home, you can go up to 212°F (100°C), but staying at the 180°F (82°C) level is a safe bet. That's the temperature that eradicates most diseases, fungi, viruses, mold, and soil-borne insects, and renders most weed seeds non-viable. At the same time, it avoids potentially heating things up too much.

Since I know how much you love tables ... here's one showing what organisms are killed in the soil when it's heated to different temperatures.

Target Heating Temperatures

Moist Soil, 30 min @	Organisms Killed
120°F (49°C)	watermolds (oomycetes)
145°F (63°C)	most plant pathogenic fungi, bacteria, and viruses, worms, slugs, centipedes
160°F (71°C)	plant pathogenic bacteria, soil insects
180°F (82°C)	weed seeds
212°F (100°C)	heat resistant plant viruses and weed seeds

Table 6.1. The Effects of Heating Soil. (Source: Baker, 1957)

There are a few times I mention in the book where sterilization could be helpful. We'll go over the basics below, to reference in those times.

Sterilization is usually inexpensive, and pretty easy to do.

Here are some of the most common sterilization methods:

- solarization,
- steaming,
- microwave method,
- and oven method.

Solarization

This process involves covering moist soil in layers of plastic and leaving it in the sun during the hot season. 4-6 weeks in the sun (8-10 weeks for cooler climates), in a plastic bag, or covered by a plastic sheet. Transparent plastic may yield better results than black.

Many would say this is the best, most natural way to do it, with the least risk of damaging the soil. This is also good if you're working with a raised bed, and don't want to move a bunch of soil into an oven.

Steaming

This involves taking containers with soil, covered with aluminum foil, and placing them on a rack inside a pot with boiling water. Or, inside of a pressure cooker.

Microwave method

Basically, this involves zapping the soil until it heats up to 180°F (82°C), then leaving it to cool. You'll need some ventilation and microwave-safe containers or bags.

Oven method

We'll cover this one a little more in-depth. Here are the basics:

1. Preheat the oven to 200°F (93°C).
2. Fill a large, oven-safe container with soil, about 3-4 inches deep (no more than 4). Don't compact the soil, leave it loose.
3. Wet the soil to make it moist, not soggy. This will create steam to help sterilization.
4. Cover container with aluminum foil.

5. Put your soil-pie in the oven. The simplest method is just to take it out after 30 min, and let it cool. If you want a more accurate process, follow steps 6 and 7.

6. The best sterilization happens when the *soil temperature* reaches 180°F (82°C). You can use a meat or oven thermometer to check every 10 minutes or so. When the soil reaches 150°F (66°C), shut off the oven. The soil temp should then continue to rise to about 180°F (82°C). Let it hang out there for 30 min, then take it out to cool.

7. If the soil temp rises over 200°F (93°C), crack open the oven door to let some heat out. Too much heat can damage the soil.

8. Once your baking is done, drizzle some chocolate sauce and serve for dessert! Kidding. Put it in some pots and carry on with the great garden experiment.

Note well: baking soil doesn't exactly smell like baking fresh apple pie! It's best to do this on a nice day when you can have windows open.

BEYOND FILLING SPACE

You've learned some great ways to fill up deep containers.

But wait, there's more!

Maybe you're wanting to up your permaculture game and incorporate multiple principles all at once as you fill up spaces like a nature ninja.

Well, I'm excited to share the next section with you, because it's got some really neat methods for filling up containers and building the soil. With these, you can skip the commercially packaged soil if you want, and even make use of your native soil. Not only that, but these techniques also work great if you're planting right in the ground without containers.

It's about to get really permaculturey up in here, y'all. So, get your gloves on, kids, because it's time to talk about:

LAYERING METHODS

 If we surrendered to earth's intelligence we could rise up rooted, like trees.

— RAINER MARIA RILKE

Remember that inspirational walk through the woods we took together back in Chapter 1? You know, where Bill Mollison had his rainforest epiphany, and pondered upon ways we could replicate the secrets of nature in our own gardens?

Well, this is one of those ways.

The soil in the forest is rich in microbial life and nutrients, and this is for a lot of reasons. One reason is, it is created by layers and layers of living, nutrient-packed stuff that has fallen to the forest floor and decomposed. Leaves and twigs, plus other plant matter like fallen fruit, and animal material like manure.

And healthy soil means healthy plants. And healthy plants mean healthy people.

Below are a couple of ways of replicating that forest floor magic, and they can even work in containers.

Because these methods lead to the soil level breaking down over time, they're best for annuals and short-term perennials at first. When used in the ground, they flatten out over time and form fantastic beds for long-term perennials.

LASAGNA LAYERING

Ah, lasagna! A favorite around the dinner table and in the permie garden.

Known as "lasagna" in North America and "lasagne" in Europe and many other places. We tend to spell things differently. Stubborn Americans. Ah well. Lasagne, lasagna ... let's call the whole thing off!

This method is known by several names, actually. It's called lasagna "layering" or "composting" or "mulching", or "sheet mulching". It involves layering one type of material and then another, back and forth, like, you guessed it! Yummy yummy lasagna.

This is an easy form of composting, and you can keep adding to it as you get materials. It can be done on any scale, from inside a pot to all over your back-yard. It improves soil, and it's a great way to grow your garden with minimal input of time, equipment and extra material.

It's mimicking nature, with a bit of our human creative twist. Bellissima!

Maybe you're beginning to see why this is a permaculture fav!

In the next chapter, we'll talk about how to use this as an *in-ground method*, which leaves the soil and all the life in it undisturbed, while piling bunches of extra organic life on top. This leads to great drainage and aeration. And it works on all kinds of soil, even heavy clay.

For now, we'll talk about the different ways people employ this as a layering method.

Different people have different spins on the "layers" used. But the basics are the same:

- *Weed-suppression base.* If planting on top of the soil — whether in a raised bed or simply in-ground — the first layer will be a light-blocking material like newspaper or cardboard. This is to suppress the weeds and grass underneath with biodegradable material. It also attracts beneficial earthworms.
- *Lasagna layers.* After that, the layers alternate between "green" layers and "brown" layers, always ending with a brown layer on top. We'll go over composting more thoroughly in Chapter 13, where we'll talk about greens and browns. But we'll cover the basics here.
- *Soil topping.* Many will put a layer of soil and/or compost on top, as we'll see below.
- *Wells for plants.* When it comes to planting plants in this, you dig out "wells" to put the plant in (a hole big enough for its roots), and stick the plant in the well, with soil and/or compost surrounding it. If planting a seed directly, just surround it with a bit of soil.

Here are the steps to follow, with some different variations interspersed throughout:

If you're using this as a container-filling method, skip to the next section on "layering." If planting in-ground or in a raised bed that's built right on the soil, start here:

Prepping the ground:

1. Mow down grass and weeds to the lowest possible level in your growing area. You may want to remove any especially persistent weeds.

2. (Optional) Some people aerate the garden area with a pitchfork or ground-breaking tool.
3. (Optional) Some add layers *before* the cardboard layer for different reasons, and water them in. Examples are: Greensand or other mineral amendments to feed the soil. (*Or if building a bed on top of grass*): manure and lime to break down the grass. (*Or if building a bed on top of a hard surface*): twigs to keep water from pooling and create good drainage.
4. Suppress the weeds! (This step takes the longest). Lay down overlapping newspaper (6-10 sheets thick) or cardboard. Overlap a few inches to make sure weeds don't find their way up.
5. Water down the cardboard or newspaper. (TIP: You may want to water *as* you put down newspaper, or even *before*, and/or bring some rocks for paper weights until you add on top, to prevent the chasing of runaway sheets on a windy day. Trust me.)
6. Build the lasagna layers! (See below).

Lasagna layering:

- Now, you'll start layering greens and browns, back and forth. If you're on the ground, start with greens. If you're in a container with a bottom, start with some straw or browns wetted and packed down. And always end layering with browns on top.
- Each layer should be 1" thick and can be up to 4", with the brown layers being slightly thicker than the green layers (2:3 or 1:2 greens:browns, but doesn't need to be exact).
- Wet down each layer with water after you put it in.
- Build it up until you reach the final height. 6-12" is an ideal start, and some go up to 3 feet.

What are "greens" and "browns"? Go to Chapter 13 for more specifics. Here's a crash course:

- **Green materials** are *nitrogen-rich*, and here are some ideas: kitchen scraps (fruit and vegetable waste), grass clippings, well-rotted manures, green leafy materials, coffee grounds, loose tea, compost, alfalfa pellets, cottonseed meal, etc.
- **Brown materials** are *carbon-rich*, and here are some ideas: dead leaves and grass, shredded paper, straw (pea straw is a fav), shredded & chipped wood, sawdust, egg cartons (minus the label), cornstalks, etc.

It's really as easy as that. Build up to your desired height, and you've got a power-packed bed ready to be gardened. Dig out wells for your plants, fill them with soil and/or compost, put in the plants, and surround them with some more soil and/or compost.

Now, just like there are different lasagna recipes in the kitchen, there are in the garden too. Let's look at variations, tips, and tricks:

Harder on the bottom

Some suggest putting the materials that take longer to break down on the bottom layers, like twigs and food scraps. Stuff like more finished compost and straw is gentler on those new roots, so can be on your top layers.

Two-layer vs. three-layer

Some will add a thin "fertilizer" layer (even as small as 25mm) in the rotation. This doesn't mean traditional "fertilizer" like you might think, but instead, a nitrogen-rich amendment like worm castings or manure. With this, the layering could go greens → browns → fertilizer → greens → browns, etc.

Top layer variations

Some will bring in high-quality soil just for the top layer (around 6" deep, or the depth of the root ball for transplants). Some will top off with nice compost and then the soil. Or soil, then compost. Or some will add compost, then soil, then compost again, then a mulch layer of either wood chips or straw, to suppress weeds. And some will sprinkle parmesan cheese on top.

Well not really that last part. But as you can see, there are many ways to make lasagna!

Experimenting with layer recipes

Different kinds of things have been tried in the mix. Here are a few examples:

- *Lucerne hay:* Some will put a layer of lucerne hay about 3-4" thick right after the newspaper layer, which is high-nitrogen hay.
- *Up-sod-down:* Some will actually dig up their sod, replace it with some kind of filler like twigs, put down the newspaper, *then* turn the sod

upside-down as the first layer. Add manure and lime to break down the sod, and cover with another layer of newspaper.

- *Cover crop top:* If you're building your layers ahead of time — such as in the fall — you can sow a cover crop on the top, like clover, which will fix nitrogen and enrich the soil even more. You'll just chop it or mow it down before its seeds develop, and let it decompose in the bed.

In conclusion …

I suggest following the basics, don't get stuck thinking you need to have it "right," use what you've got, and then just have fun! You can always start with basic newspaper, lasagna, soil, mulch, and then experiment different twists in future versions.

In the long run, lasagna layering decreases work and can do great things for your soil and therefore your plants. There are still unique challenges. There still is upfront work. But permaculture is all about the maximum output for minimum input, and this technique aims to zero in on that.

Another thing about lasagna layering (sheet mulching) is that it takes some time for the layers to become rich "finished" compost. Those layers take from 6 months to a year to decompose. If you think ahead, it's a great idea to start lasagna beds in the fall, so the lasagna will be "cooked" and ready for spring planting.

If you want to plant right away, I've got you covered with a workaround! Just do what I mentioned above: dig holes/wells to accommodate planting your plants, and surround the plant or seed with soil and/or compost.

Over time, the organic layers will break down, and the soil level will drop. No problem, just keep adding the main alternating layers. A great thing to do is add layers each time you plant something new.

Ciao Italia! It's time to skip over to Germany now for some …

HÜGELKULTUR

Welcome to possibly the most fun word to say in permaculture. Hügelkultur! Pronounced HOO-gul-kul-tur, and rhymes with "Google culture." Tell your friends you've started a couple of hügelmounds or hügelpots, and it's bound to spark curiosity and a fun conversation.

It's a word from German origin, and translates to "mound" or "hill culture". Herman Andrä coined the term in 1962, and the idea really spread through Sepp Holzer, the famous Austrian permaculturist.

It's really helpful where the soil is struggling with aeration and drainage. It improves soil quality, is low-maintenance, and helps with water retention. And in the long run, it makes your gardens more resilient.

It also helps with soil temperature. This is a great application of "catching and storing energy" (Principle #2). Imagine a bonfire, and all the energy released by the firewood. Now, think of that same stored energy being released into your garden bed, over the course of many years. Pretty cool, huh?

It's very similar to the lasagna layering from above, with one key difference: at the core/base layer, there are a bunch of logs and branches. The core of wood is like a slow-release storehouse of nutrient power. A big bed could provide a constant flow for 20 years!

So if you're wondering what to do with piles of wood, this is a great idea!

The basic hügel is wood and soil, plain and simple. Traditionally about 30% wood core and 70% soil.

However, just like with the lasagna method, there are many variations.

Having seen a lot of them, I'll break down the layers into 3 basic sections:

The Base Layer — Wood Layer

This consists of logs, branches and twigs. Below, we'll talk about what kind of wood to look for.

Within this layer, it goes from the *hardest and biggest* wood at the *bottom*, to the *smallest and softest* at the *top*.

So … Big/new logs & hardwood → medium/older logs & softwood → rotten wood → branches and twigs → leaves.

The Middle/Inner Layer — Hot Layer

Some people call this the "mulching" layer, but that can get confusing, since mulch also refers to that top layer of straw or wood chips. So we'll call this the *hot layer*. It's called hot, since the materials heat up as they're composting!

You could easily call this the lasagna layer. Why? Yep, that's right, this is the same thing as above. You alternate between greens and browns.

Some people skip this and just do wood and soil for an easy hügel-project. (Side note. Adding "hügel" in front of words is a lot of fun, just saying.)

The Top Layer — Soil Layer

This consists of soil. Often, soil you want to amend.

Within this layer, you can get more complex, just like with lasagna layering. You can put compost, then soil. Or you can put compost, soil, then straw or mulch.

Other Considerations

Also like lasagna layering, you can experiment with different layers along the way. Here are some things people have done when using this technique:

- Manure layers.
- More wood on top of the hot layer, and before the soil layer.
- A cardboard layer between the hot layer and the soil layer.
- Hay/straw between the wood layer and the hot layer.
- Straw mulch on top.

As you can see, it's like a hügel hamburger. The basics are the meat and the bread. Then, a bunch of things you can do in between.

Basically, start with wood and build your layers. Water layers well as you go.

Also, you may be wondering where the "mound" part comes in. We'll discuss that more in the next chapter, but basically, you can build in-ground hügels with different depths.

- *Above ground:* where you just start layering right from the soil level.
- *In-ground:* where you dig a hole big enough for all the wood.
- *Something in the middle:* where you have the wood partly in the ground, and some continuing up into a mound.

And, you can fill a raised bed, or even make a "hügel pot" with these concepts!

This is great for when you want to use a pot more long-term, and have that flow of nutrients for years to come. Here's one method:

- Start with larger sticks/logs at the bottom of the container, and get smaller going up. Some people mix in fresh grass clippings or nitrogen-rich material to balance with the carbon of the wood. Around ⅓ or less is good for the wood layer.
- Some will add a cardboard layer before continuing, separating the wood layer from the rest.
- Add alternating layers of greens/browns. Some people will even sprinkle in soil from the yard that needs amending, since it will be surrounded by all this soon-to-be compost.
- Add any soil/compost to the top layer, and then top it with mulch/straw if you'd like.
- Plant the plants!

There are some questions that may come up when you're using this method, like what kind of wood do you use? Or *not* use? Here are some basic considerations:

- Hardwoods are great for the base, softwoods are great as you go up the layer. Some of the best woods include birch, alder, maple, oak, willow, cottonwood, poplar, acacia, and apple.
- Also, the deader the better! You want wood that is fully dead.
- A good combo of freshly dead and rotten woods is great. The fresh ones will last longer, and the rotten ones will support your plants with nutrients quicker.
- Some trees have chemicals in them that can inhibit plant growth, so you'll want to stay away from these. These include sycamore, red oak, butternut, and black walnut.
- Also, some trees like black cherry, black locust, and cedar are rot-resistant and are best used for building.
- Research your area to see if pests like termites or carpenter ants are a big problem, and look out for wood that might be affected.

One consideration of this method is the concept of *nitrogen pulling*. The process of that raw, woody base breaking down in the ground can use up nitrogen for the first year or two. You can counteract this by:

- adding more nitrogen like compost and manure around the wood and as you go up
- surrounding your plants with compost as you plant
- cover-cropping with nitrogen fixers in the off-season
- growing plants at first that aren't super nitrogen-hungry

Using this technique is a great addition to your permaculture garden, and it pays dividends for years to come. Danke, Hügel!

But what are some other things you can do with that pile of wood (or other stuff) you have lying around? Now, we'll talk about:

ROUNDING UP BUILDING MATERIALS

So, you're walking around your property, checking out the bugs floating around, noticing what direction the sun is coming from, and you come upon a pile of leftover lumber from the deck you had built last year. What would a permie do?

1. Think, "Oh, I am so writing a bad Yelp review on that sloppy contractor."
2. Wonder if the garbage truck has room for 16' boards.
3. Excitedly start planning how you'll use this treasure trove of wood to construct a raised bed.

While all these thoughts might flit through your head, someone in the permie mindset is always thinking about how to recycle and reuse building materials. As a permie, you'll see trash as treasure.

The zero-waste principle (you know, #6) encourages us to use what we already have rather than buy new materials. Once again, you're saving valuable materials from rotting away in the landfill, and you're saving money. And who doesn't love saving money?

As you start your permaculture garden, you'll need materials to create features like raised beds, rainwater collection systems, compost bins, benches, and more. Not everyone has the budget to buy professional pre-made garden supplies; a permaculturist wouldn't want you to anyway. So, let's look at some of the materials you might already have lying around your yard, that you can salvage, or buy for cheap.

Wood

You can use wood to build raised beds, greenhouses, benches, storage areas, workstations, and more. When it comes to lumber, cedar and redwood are the best choices for long-lasting structures like raised beds because they are naturally moisture, rot, and pest resistant.

Other hardwood lumbers that are dense and durable are maple, beech, black walnut, locust, and oak. Softwood lumbers like Douglas fir, pine, and spruce will do in a pinch (and they're cheaper) but won't last as long in an outdoor setting. Think 5-7 years compared to 10+. The "heartwood" from a tree will last longer than the "sapwood" from the same tree.

Red cedar is often a favorite when building garden beds. Or redwood. It's naturally resistant to bacteria and fungi, decay-resistant, and it has oils that keep the wood preserved even in humid conditions. It has a pleasant smell to us, but the pests don't like it! Plus it looks pretty!

As mentioned before, when building garden beds, you'll want to avoid treated lumber, because the chemicals used in the wood have been shown to leach into the soil of the bed and the plants.

Of course, if you're not trying to put money in the pocket of Big Lumber, you can always look around your yard (or neighborhood) to see what's available. You can use old logs for so much more than firewood! While they won't last as long as treated lumber, you can use logs, tree branches, and bamboo canes to build raised beds, planters, trellises, and outdoor furniture. You might also find old railroad ties, landscape ties, pallets, or reclaimed barn wood.

So next time you trim your fruit trees or cut down that giant oak hanging dangerously over your bedroom roof, save that wood and repurpose it. Aside from building materials, piles of logs, branches, and trimmings make lovely refuge areas for local insects and wildlife. And as we learned, they are the backbone of hügelkultur planting methods!

What if you're concerned about wood that was infected or destroyed by pests or diseases? Well, there are some differing opinions here. Some would say burying it usually means the disease will be eaten up by a bunch of critters and microbes. Plus a birch-specific disease typically won't affect tomatoes, etc. Yeah, maybe chipping up a diseased pear tree limb to use as a top mulch layer for a new pear tree might not be a smart idea.

Others say that some disease spreads in the soil (like oak wilt) and can cause issues for nearby trees. This is why some areas have laws about only using firewood that's been harvested locally, and not transporting firewood from over 50 miles away. This is to prevent new pests and diseases from being introduced to the area.

If you're really concerned about diseases or pests in the wood, a great option is to burn the wood as soon as you know about the problem, and that'll take care of it. You can then use it for wood ash or biochar.

Local knowledge really helps here, so these are great questions to bring to your local garden store or avid gardeners, or you know, our friend Jimmy the strawberry-loving hermit in his shack on the edge of town.

METAL

Metal is becoming an increasingly popular material for outdoor applications because it's virtually indestructible. You don't have to worry about moisture, rot, or insect damage with metal. Although it's a manufactured material, it will have little to no impact on your garden soil and is safe for growing food crops in. You can buy reasonably cheap corrugated metal at your local hardware store or salvage it from an old building project.

You can use sheets of corrugated galvanized steel to build raised beds around a wooden frame, put a roof over your chicken coop or other structures, create rainwater drainage chutes, and more. Prefabricated metal containers- like an old animal feed or water trough- and gutters are also good options for raised bed planters. Just drill some drainage holes in the bottom.

BRICKS, CINDER BLOCKS, & STONE

Although bricks and cinder blocks don't sprout naturally out of the earth, they are made from natural resources like clay and shale, so they're one of the most eco-friendly construction materials you can find. Two of the most significant benefits of working with bricks and cinder blocks are that they're highly durable and adaptable.

You can build raised beds, planters, retaining walls, pathways, potting benches, fire pits, and more with the bricks, cinder blocks, and pavers you have left over from previous building projects. Maybe someone nearby just ripped out their old chimney and they're wondering, "What do I do with all this brick?" Here you come to save the day! Score.

If you have to buy them, you can find some that don't cost much, and they last, like, forever.

Natural stones are another durable and cost-effective option. You may have some lying around your property or your neighbor's yard (he'll probably thank you for hauling them away). Building with stones may require more creativity since they aren't uniform in size or shape, but you can create some beautiful structures to add aesthetic appeal to your permaculture garden.

While they are incredibly sturdy, the one drawback of building with bricks or stones is that they are very heavy. They are not the best option for non-permanent structures, especially if mortared together.

ODDS N' ENDS

While wood, metal, and brick are readily available at the big Orange and Blue stores, don't limit yourself to the classics. As you look at the world with a new eye — a permie eye — see the opportunity in all discarded materials. Old tires and wash basins make excellent planters. Upturned wine bottles can become garden edging. An old shoe organizer can be reborn as a vertical herb planter. You can even repurpose old furniture as unique garden decor.

While your permaculture garden is designed to mimic nature, it will have elements of your personal flair. It can look chaotic and wild, or there can be some finessing in all the little details. But as you plant, remember the potential in all things.

More and more on your permie journey, you might find yourself getting hooked on this unmistakable feeling of fun and satisfaction that comes from repurposing something you thought was all used up.

And then of course, there's always:

FREE & CHEAP CONTAINERS

Ah, two of the greatest sounding words! Free and cheap! You'd be surprised at how many folks are ready to get rid of old nursery pots, planters, and containers. And here's that ol' permie double whammy once again: keeping stuff out of the landfill while finding low-cost solutions for your own garden. Bam.

Free ideas:

- Ask your local big box store or garden store if they have leftover nursery pots.
- Search the free section of Craigslist and Facebook marketplace.
- Look around the neighborhood: yard waste day, bulk day, curbs, bushes, etc.
- New builds where there is landscaping.

Cheap ideas:

- Yard and estate sales
- Thrift stores
- Plant nurseries, in their leftovers and discarded piles
- Clearance sales in August - October
- Craigslist, marketplace, etc.

Disinfecting used containers and pots

It's great to get a used container on the cheap, but you'll want to clean it up for a couple of reasons.

First, old pots can have bug eggs & disease spores that are hard to see.

Also, salt deposits can build up, which can harm your plants later on.

Besides, cleaning them up is easy, good for plant health, and it makes 'em look nicer, too!

You may ask: Do you reuse the soil that was in the pot? Look at you, thinking like a permie. Reusing is a great practice, for sure. On the other hand, disease spreading is a concern. So if you're unsure about the health of the previous inhabitants, you can either toss the soil on an outer zone of your property or try sterilizing it with heat (out in the sun, or in an oven, as mentioned above). Be sure to replenish the soil's nutrients with some compost.

Now here's how to clean up those pots:

1. Remove any dead plants and empty out the soil.
2. Remove all the loose particles with a brush or rag.
3. Wash with some soapy water (try dish detergent) and rinse clean.

4. Soak in a solution of 10 parts water to 1 part bleach, 10 min - 1 hr. If you want, you can use vinegar instead. Just soak for a few hours more.
5. Scour off any old deposits with a scouring pad, steel wool or stiff brush.
6. Rinse off with water and let it dry in the sun.

There! Good as new. (But cheaper than new).

WRAP-UP

Alright! WOW. We covered a lot.

You may find that as you grow in knowledge, you're also growing more confident: in your local gardening store, and in your garden.

Maybe ideas are generating. All those mindsets and concepts we developed in the first chapters are becoming more and more practical.

You're looking at your fruit basket filled with bananas. You're seeing not only the tasty snack inside, but now you smile at that golden peel on the outside, which you know could someday turn into rich soil for your tomatoes and cucumbers ... or maybe even a banana tree!

As you drive around your neighborhood, you see piles of leaves on the edges of people's yards and think to yourself, "I wonder if they'll let me scoop up some of that treasure." (Hint: they're probably more than willing to let go of it, and happy you'll be saving them a step!)

You're at your local coffee shop, and you notice all the spent coffee grounds behind the counter. You wonder if you could bag some up for your lasagna layering. (Did you know that the largest coffee shop chain has a program called "Grounds for Your Garden" and you can get pre-packaged used coffee grounds for free? Just ask the barista, and if they've got some, they'll usually pass you as many bags as you want!)

You're seeing potential everywhere. In your kitchen, around your property, at local shops, driving through your neighborhood, and past new builds. Write these ideas down, and make note of the methods and materials in this chapter that really jumped out at you.

And then — if you feel so inclined — try making a call, knocking on a door, or talking to a barista, to see if someone would part with extra or used materials that you could use for your garden. The worst someone can say is no, and most people are grateful to get rid of junk, or excess or used supplies they haven't known what to do with.

It's a service to them and to the garden. Which sounds a lot like those core ethics coming to life, too.

Well up to this point, we've covered a lot of contained methods.

But what if you want to think outside the box? You know in your heart you were made to be wild and free, and you're ready to plant the big garden. Or at least start!

In the next chapter, we'll touch on some ways to do just that, and plant right into the ground, which is ultimately where plants love to be. We will also cover some larger planting concepts for the permaculture garden, so you can be thoroughly equipped.

IN-GROUND GARDENING METHODS & BEYOND

 My garden is my most beautiful masterpiece.

— CLAUDE MONET

I can see it in your eyes. That spark. That hunger. They say, "Go big or go home." But you? Ha! You laugh and tell 'em, "I'm going big *right at home, fellas.*"

When we closed our eyes to see the dream back in Chapter 4, you imagined the whole rainforest in your backyard, didn't you? The birds perching on your shoulders, singing sweet melodies in your ear. The frogs bounding joyfully across the winding path, as you walk barefoot across your squishy forest-floor yard. You pluck ripe, juicy fruit from the vine. And there's a lot to pick. Waterfalls of rich green and rainbows of color spill all over your yard, in layers of abundant, lush foliage. Your food forest feeds the whole town. And then, renowned permaculturists assemble from all over the world to award you with the coveted Bill Mollisonesian Nature Ninja Black Belt with proud tears rolling down their cheeks. "Well done, child," they say, "Well done."

… Or, ya know, maybe you at least want to work with your backyard soil a little.

However the dream looks to you, it can be done. Okay, maybe the black belt ceremony is a stretch. But the sky's the limit with your garden! With time and patience, careful observation, some flexibility, and basically using those principles we talked about, you can work together with nature to create something truly beautiful and abundant.

Larger projects are often done in stages. You can prepare the ground for a larger garden while you try out different methods in containers. You can cultivate the part of your yard closest to the house (Zone 1) while you build and prepare Zone 2.

In the next chapter, we'll finally learn all about the soil in your yard. Understanding your soil and what it needs is a vital step in turning your backyard into a permaculture paradise. It deserves a whole chapter (and even a whole book) because of how important it is!

 Essentially, all life depends upon the soil ... There can be no life without soil and no soil without life.

— DR. CHARLES E KELLOGG

For now, we'll explore a few in-ground gardening methods and larger permaculture planting concepts. If you find something that appeals to you here, let it springboard you into some more research, and adapt it to your own space!

IN-GROUND PLANTING METHODS

Transforming your backyard into a thriving garden is living the dream. Instead of just sticking seeds in the dirt, permies look for ways to work with the ground strategically in order to create a better growing environment, which leads to a better harvest. Below are a few of those ways.

NO-TILL GARDENING

No-till gardening is a favorite of hard-core permies because it doesn't involve altering the earth. Instead, you add to it in a way that improves soil health by layering cardboard and compost right on top of your garden plot.

Most of the time, the term "no-till" is used interchangeably with "no-dig" gardening. While there are differences between *tilling* and *digging*, we will use "no-dig" and "no-till" basically the same way here.

Who It's For: No-till gardening is great for permaculture purists who don't want to disturb the soil microbiome. Aside from that, it's a sweet method for people who just plain don't like to dig or till. This method does require some land, so it's only practical for people with yards. But even a small yard will do.

Why It's Great: No-till gardening offers "the greatest effect with the least change," a core concept of permaculture and one of Bill Mollison's favorite things! Since you're just tossing good compost on top of the existing earth, it's an excellent method for improving poor soil without disturbing nature at work. It builds a healthier soil ecosystem and creates the perfect environment for plants to thrive. It also reduces weeds and pests.

What You Can Grow: Anything can be grown in a no-till garden. Anything! The rich soil makes the ideal home for vegetables, fruits, herbs, and perennials to thrive. Your no-till garden can be as large as you want, so the possibilities are endless.

What It Involves: No-till gardening is often called lasagna gardening (mmmm lasagna …) because it utilizes the lasagna layering method from the last chapter. It's called no-till or no-dig because it doesn't involve any digging. Instead, layer cardboard, brown compost, green compost, soil, and mulch over your garden spot. Just like making a delicious lasagna.

Potential Drawbacks: No-till gardening is a somewhat slow process. But most low-impact methods are. Like a fine wine, the soil will get better with age. It can also get costly if you don't have loads of your own compost to use, so you will be limited in size when you start. You'll need a steady mulch supply to keep the soil healthy and weeds at bay.

How to Get Started: Measure out your garden plot, and then use the layering method of your choice to get started. It's called "no dig" but you still go down into your top layers a bit to plant things!

If you're planting seedlings, carve out little wells in the top layer of soil or organic matter for the plant's root ball, and put the seedling in. Surround it with top layer material, and mulch on top.

If you're working with seeds, read the seed packet for specific instructions on how and where to sow them. Seeds sometimes have different requirements for sowing, like some want to be covered with soil and some don't. A general rule of thumb is to plant a seed at a depth of 1-2 times its diameter. We'll talk a lot more about starting seeds in Chapter 9.

If you want a fun research project, look up different methods of no-till gardening. Here are a few variations. They're similar, with differences here and there.

- *The "Back to Eden" Method:* Focuses on using *wood chips* for a thick layer of mulch on top (contributes carbon to the soil, lasts longer).
- *The "Ruth Stout" or "No-Work" Method:* Focuses on using *rotted hay* for a thick layer of mulch on top (which breaks down quicker than wood chips). (Note: contrary to what its name suggests, it probably does involve *some* work).
- *No-Dig / Lasagna Gardening:* Basically what we've already covered in the "lasagna" sections. Similar to the above two, but uses compost, organic matter, and loose soil on top.

Lasagna? Back to Eden? No work? Geez, with names like that, who can resist???

You can even become a backyard scientist, and try mulching with hay in one bed, and wood chips in another. Observe the differences over the years. Or do some combo, picking your favorite elements of each and mixing them together like a big permaculture casserole.

At the end of the day, as you build your soil quality, you can do the old tried-and-true method of planting a seed right in the dirt! With some basic mulching on top, and the basics of permaculture gardening in mind, you're pretty set.

DOUBLE-DIG GARDENING

To dig or not to dig, that is the question.

So, this method is sort of on the *other* end of the spectrum. This method involves removing a layer of topsoil temporarily, loosening the subsoil beneath it, mixing in organic matter, and replacing the topsoil.

"Wait. First you tell me we won't be digging at all. Now you tell me we're *double digging?*"

I know. Well, sometimes you need a hammer, and sometimes you need a screwdriver. Let's talk about some pros and cons of *this tool.*

It does involve digging, it temporarily disrupts the soil life, it's labor-intensive, and therefore some no-dig purists are opposed to it. And yes, many of those purists have indeed seen even the most compacted, driest soils be revived with years of no-dig layering methods employed to transform the soil.

However, other permies think that double-digging can be a method that, if done well, can be really beneficial in certain situations. *Especially* in the first year of establishing *especially rough* soil and preparing it for a garden. These proponents of double-digging have also had wonderful results. Like surgery, it's invasive, but it can be helpful in the right situations.

In that vein, some gardeners' approach to this is to double-dig thoroughly and correctly once to establish the beds, then use no-dig and layering methods from there on out. Mulch the beds, keep roots in the ground, and don't step in the beds. In fact, many would say that *double-dig* is the ideal way to *lay the foundation for a no-dig garden.*

If the method ain't for you, no prob. Just skip and move to the next one!

Whether you choose to use double-dig or not, remember that permaculture is about careful observation, interaction, and adaptation. The wisest permaculture gardeners are able to evaluate methods for their merits and setbacks, consider their unique situation, study the best natural/organic practices, and pull the best strategies together to fit their garden's needs. And then, try new things next year.

That's you, my wise friend.

Who It's For: Do you find rocks all over your soil, or does the dirt in your backyard feel like a brick? This may be for you. This is a great method for those with especially *rocky, compacted,* or *poor soil.* Also for folks whose soil is very *clay-heavy* (tough) or *sandy* (little to no life). It can help loosen compacted clay, remove rocks, and get life and nutrients to your soil.

Double-dig is often used for intensive spaces in the garden like a Zone 1 kitchen garden, where you might need to enrich or loosen soil quicker. Or in areas that have not previously been cultivated, or where new development has moved out any good topsoil, this method *resets the space,* forming a clean slate.

There may even be a *specific patch of land* on your property that needs this kind of help. There can be a variety of soil types even within one geographical area.

If your soil is fairly "loose" and you can move your soil around decently already, and it doesn't seem to be filled with many rocks, you may not need this method.

Why It's Great: This provides a quick way to improve soil fertility by adding organic matter and nutrients. It also gets rock out of the way. It's like a "fresh start" for your garden plot. Many have employed this during their first year working with compacted soil plots. Those same people report their gardens are bursting with life from the first year onward, with no need for double-digging after the first year.

Loosening the soil can allow plant roots to grow down rather than out, and for oxygen to reach all parts of soil.

This method also allows you to amend and enrich the subsoil, beneath the topsoil. This is really important, because organic matter added to the top may not be digested by the soil below because of lack of air.

This is a "groundbreaking" way to create fertile, well-drained soil in a pinch, and to prepare your garden for years to come!

What You Can Grow: You can grow anything in this method, since it's simply a way to prepare a garden bed. This method is especially useful for planting root crops (those that grow underground like carrots and potatoes), which don't like to grow in soil that is dense and compacted or filled with rocks.

As a bonus, if you're really thinking ahead to build your soil for future years of gardening bliss, you could plant plants in the first year that really serve to build the soil. Some ideas include:

- Some plants "fix" nitrogen in the soil and bring nutrients into the soil (like legumes).
- Some annual cover crops can be chopped down and add great organic matter (oats, wheat, crimson clover, winter rye).
- And some act like "living aerators" with thick roots that break up the soil (radish, turnips, buckwheat) … for these to work in this way, don't harvest the root. Let them go deep and die in the soil, where they'll break down.

Cover cropping is a strategy of its own that you can use alongside any of these: no-dig, double-dig, etc. We'll touch on this a little more in Chapter 8, our highly anticipated soil chapter.

If you decide to do some kind of cover cropping, just be sure to do your research, dig in the late summer so you can grow cover crops in the off-season (winter), and chop down the cover crops before they seed.

What It Involves: This involves a shovel or spade, a digging fork/broad fork, and some soil amendment like compost. And some good old-fashioned manual labor.

You can also bring a rake for the finishing part, and a wheelbarrow or tarp for the first mound of soil you dig.

Ultimately, the cure for rough ground is going to be building it up with organic matter. Double-dig is simply a method to get it "down in there."

It is a very methodical way of digging, in which the *topsoil* is removed temporarily in increments of 1 ft wide trenches; the *subsoil* is aerated, loosened, and enriched with organic matter; and then the topsoil is replaced, across the whole garden bed.

Here are the basic steps:

1. Plan out your garden bed, and mark it somehow (e.g. with string).
2. Get your shovel and start digging! Dig a trench 1 foot wide, across the entire length of your garden bed, So, in a 4x8' bed, your first trench should measure 1'x8'. How deep? Go the depth of your shovel (should be 9-10"). Put all that topsoil aside. Tip: use a wheelbarrow or tarp to make transportation on the last step much easier.
3. Use the fork to aerate/loosen the subsoil beneath. This is the "double" part of the dig. However, you don't actually want to dig it up, stir it, upend or spread it. Instead, you stick the fork as deep as you can, and then rock it back and forth like a lever. This aerates the soil.
4. Add compost over the bottom of the trench — about a 2" thick layer. You can also add well-rotted manure, food scraps, or soil amendments your yard might need like phosphorus or some kind of nitrogen-rich organic material. Gently work it in with the fork, poking it down.
5. You'll repeat steps 2-4 for the *next 1 ft-wide trench*, the length of the garden bed. Now, as you dig out the soil for a new trench, you fill the previous trench with the topsoil you just dug. Dig the *next hole*, and move that topsoil into the hole you just made. (i.e. Fill the first trench with the soil from the second one, fill the second trench with the soil from the third one, etc.) Just lay it on, no need to do any mixing.

6. Keep repeating until you get to the end of your bed. What do you fill the last trench with? This is where you'll put the original topsoil from the first trench you dug.
7. Sprinkle the top of your new bed with compost (about 1-2"), gently mix it in and smooth the top with a rake, and mulch on top.

Voilà! A little bit of sweat and time later (or maybe more than a little sweat), you've got yourself a double-dug bed.

Remove big rocks as you go. Make a pile to use for some project or put them somewhere else in your yard. You can leave behind little pebbles, though.

Be aware, the soil level will settle over time. You can just keep adding layers in future years. If you do this in autumn, the soil will naturally settle by spring.

If your ground is especially hard clay, you can water down the garden bed area to soften it the night before you plan on double-digging. If it's still pretty hard the next day, try wetting it down for a few nights in a row. Also note, doing this in the fall would make for a cooler day of work, and that water would evaporate less.

Be careful not to step on the bed during the process or after. This will lead to compaction, the very problem we're trying to solve.

Potential Drawbacks: The biggest drawback people mention is that this temporarily disturbs the soil life. However, if there isn't a whole lot of life going on in the first place (in rocky, hard, and nutrient-depleted soils) the pros may outweigh the cons here.

Also, yes, some are understandably wary of annually tilling the soil and how that can damage the complex underground ecosystem and the soil food web. However, it's possible to use the double-dig method only in the first year, and if you do a great job the first time, you won't need to use this method again. Some double-dig for the first two years if they have really compacted soil, getting deeper in the second year.

But once you set it up, life begins to build again with a better chance: from earthworms, to fungi networks, and all the millions of other fun things happening down under.

It should also be noted that this method is not the same as turning and rototilling. Instead, with double-dig, you remove the topsoil and aerate the subsoil with a fork.

In the right situations, double-dig can lay a great foundation for no-till methods to take over for years to come. You just keep building good, rich soil on top, layer after layer, year after year.

Some would say the labor involved is a drawback. True, there's some serious elbow grease involved in this one, so watch out for any health concerns or recruit some neighbors! It's tough work to break hard ground, but hey, hard work under the sun can be satisfying! (And it can be really good for you, remember?)

Plus, the overall labor may not be much "more" than that in lasagna layering, just a different kind.

HÜGELMOUND

Hey, there's our friend Hügel! I bet you wondered if he'd make an appearance in this chapter.

Well, before pots and raised beds, the "Hügelmound" is the Original Hügel, since — as you'll recall — the word actually does mean "mound" or "hill". Most of the time, hügels are put above grade because they are essentially a big compost pile that will settle over time.

Since we covered most of the ideas of hügelkultur in the last chapter, I won't say much here. You know how great this technique can be for your garden.

However, keeping in mind all you learned, there are just a few basic questions to ask, if you want to do this in the ground. Here are the two big questions:

- How deep of a hole do I dig for the wood?
- How high do I want the mound to be?

To help you answer, let's discuss *in-ground hügels* and *above-ground hügels*. I'll briefly cover the basics of each, as well as their pros and cons.

In-ground hügels

These are made by digging a pit (the dimensions of your garden bed), filling it with the wood core, covering it with soil and growing medium of choice, and growing your plants. You can even build walls around the bed to make this a raised bed, or put one in a greenhouse.

It's like having a secret layer of awesome hügelpower going on right beneath the surface. Plus, you can still make it into a mound by continuing to build up (see "something in between" below).

When started under the surface, they can tend to be usable quicker than the above-ground option, and you can hide the power of this technique underground.

However, digging can be really difficult in some areas, it's labor intensive, and as we've learned, digging has its drawbacks!

Above-ground hügels

This is where you basically start piling the wood layer on the ground, then the rest of the layers on top.

The mound shape is great for creating microclimates. This means some parts are shady, and others sunnier. Drier at the top, wetter at the bottom. You can plant a variety of plants with different needs accordingly.

Also, the mound shape is almost like having a raised bed, since it's lifted off the ground.

However, these usually aren't ready for planting as quickly and may need to settle for up to a year before using. You can help this along by getting good soil for the top.

Something in between

And, as mentioned in the last chapter, you can do some version with the wood partly in the ground and partly mounded up. Adapt it how you want to your own space!

You can hügel in a pot, you can hügel on a plot …

As with any technique involving biodegradable material, remember that this will sink over time. If holes pop up from the sinking, no worries. Just drop some compost in there.

Because these sink, some have said they're best for annuals, since the soil level will be different each year. However, many have done great with perennials in hügels. Some do annuals in the first year, then perennials. This is one of those "research and try things" topics.

Truthfully, now that you know the basics, you can make a hügel as big or small as you want. You can dig a trench, stick a few logs in it, and pile the dirt back on top for some extra moisture, nutrients, and warmth for the plants that grow on top. Maybe this wouldn't be considered a "true" hügel by *some*. But ahhh who cares about those guys! This is your garden, buddy. You hügel however you wanna hügel.

IN-GROUND METHODS: FINAL THOUGHTS

As you design your garden beds, you'll want to keep pathways in mind. Will you be pushing a wheelbarrow through certain paths? Do you need a place for wheelbarrow turnarounds? How much space will you need for walking between beds?

Just like with raised beds, you want to be able to reach the middle of your garden beds without stepping in them or compacting the soil.

Not all garden beds have to be rectangular, either. Remember too, sometimes different shapes can not only provide some aesthetic finesse to your garden, but they might also be more efficient.

And permaculture is all about thinking of multiple uses for things. Remember that pathways can be a place to mulch with materials that will produce nice compost after some time, a place to upcycle old supplies like extra rock for stepping stones, or a growing place for sturdy ground covers (or even mushrooms!) that can benefit the soil life and nearby beds.

LARGER PLANTING CONCEPTS

The following concepts are larger concepts used in permaculture gardens. Any of the above methods can be used in partnership with them.

COMPANION & GUILD PLANTING

Both companion planting and guild planting showcase Principles #8 and #10. You know, the ones where we integrate rather than segregate, and embrace diversity? These concepts involve a planting plan in which you carefully choose which plants to grow together to create a thriving mini-ecosystem. You can use them with any of the other gardening methods.

We will dive deeper into these concepts in Chapter 10, but briefly:

Companion planting in gardening is the practice of planting at least two different species of plants nearby one another strategically for some kind of benefit(s). Usually, the benefit is mutual to both plants. Companions could be planted for natural pest control, soil improvement, attracting pollinators, or boosting growth and even flavor!

Companion planting is closely related to terms like polyculture, intercropping, and interplanting. All of these terms are based on the idea that the best way to grow plants is to mimic nature by having different plants grow next to each other.

Guild planting takes these concepts to another level. It goes beyond thinking of 2 plants going well together, to the creation of a family of 3 or more plants. Usually, guild planting focuses on assembling a helpful team, or "guild", around at least one central, key plant. Often this plant is a perennial but can be annual as well. Using companion planting principles, a team of companions is planted, and together they form a mini-ecosystem.

Who It's For: You can implement companion and guild planting in any space if there's enough room for a few different plant varieties. Companion plants can even be grown in containers, so you can use this method if you live in an apartment with a deck or balcony.

Why It's Great: Companion and guild planting enable you to grow more foods with minimal effort since the plants work together to do the job for you. It also maximizes space since crops are interspersed with one another rather than segregated into rows. With these methods, plants work together to repel pests, produce natural fertilizers, improve soil health, and enhance flavor.

Guild planting creates a self-sustaining garden that requires less maintenance. And you can pick out a "spot" in your yard to plant a guild if you're over-whelmed with options on how to handle the whole property.

What You Can Grow: You can grow anything with companion and guild planting methods; your only limit is your space. Some classic garden besties that love being planted together are tomatoes, basil, parsley, corn, squash, beans, and cucumbers, oregano, and dill. We'll talk more about this in Chapter 10, and you can find a list for reference in Appendix A: Companion Planting.

What It Involves: Companion and guild planting involve all of the elements of any of the other methods that you choose, including soil, plants, and a place to put them. When it's time to start planting, place the teams you've planned together.

When planting a *guild,* the plan usually involves choosing an "anchor" plant which is the star of the show you focus the guild around (kind of like the "thriller" plant in the container method we talked about a couple of chapters ago). This is usually a perennial of some kind that will stay there longer, like a fruit tree or bush. Then, it involves casting "supporting role" plants that fill certain other needs and functions in the guild and planting them strategically around a measured area.

Hey hey, things are beginning to look like a mini-ecosystem now!

Potential Drawbacks: Knowing what can be grown together is just as important as knowing what cannot. Certain plants are arch enemies (like beans and onions) that will do anything to hinder each other's growth and productivity. Another issue with companion planting is if the two (or three) plants do not grow at the same rate. A permie pro knows what *not* to plant together.

And a permie pro also knows that there are a lot of opinions out there, and they don't all agree! So utilizing these techniques means researching, and trying things for yourself, seeing what works for your own garden.

Stay tuned, more on all of this in Chapter 10.

7-LAYER GARDENING & FOOD FORESTS

The layered garden principle mimics nature in a tropical jungle. Plants cohab naturally, with some growing taller and others adapting to the jungle floor where there is less light. But you don't have to live in the Amazon; You can apply this idea to any garden to create a mini-ecosystem, or "food forest," that produces an abundance of food with minimal effort.

The "food forest" is sort of the ultimate goal for a permaculture garden. All of these elements lead up to this concept. Tell a fellow permie you're planning your own food forest, and you'll get a knowing smile and nod.

The ideas here overlap a lot with the ideas in guild planting, but are looked at a little differently.

- Guild planting ideas tend to look at the different functions in a guild, or *what* a plant does (this plant fixes nutrients in the soil, that one repels pests).
- Food forest layering ideas tend to focus on the different "layers" of plants, or *where* they are in the whole system (this plant is in the tree layer, that one is in the shrub layer).

Another way to think of these, in terms of the scale of ideas, is this: Food Forest → Guild Planting → Companion Planting. That is, a food forest (the whole unit) is usually made up of guilds (the sub-units), which are built on companion planting concepts (the individual parts). Similarly, a city is made up of neighborhoods, which are made up of certain friendships and neighbors.

These explanations over-simplify, and don't grasp the partnership of these concepts perfectly, but they can help you visualize!

Anyway, in the big picture, these concepts are used together. In one garden area, onions may be recruited to a guild for food and as "repellers" of pests. They would also be located in the herbaceous layer of the food forest.

Who It's For: It's hard to create a food forest inside an apartment, so this method does require a bit of space. However, you can create a thriving layered food forest on only 100 square feet, less than the average backyard!

You can also create food forests in urban spaces. This may require an organized effort and a plot of public land. But it's an excellent way to get the community involved.

Why It's Great: A food forest produces a high yield of food using minimal space and effort. Once established, it can remain productive for years since it has become its own self-sustaining ecosystem. You can grow a wide variety of foods in a small space. Backyard food forests require less water, don't rely on fertilizers or pesticides, and improve soil health.

What You Can Grow: From the top layers of nut and fruit trees to the ground cover of root crops, you can include anything in a layered food forest garden. This includes berries, vines, vegetables, herbs, and more. However, once the upper story is established, you may not be able to cultivate annual plants under their shade.

What It Involves: To start a food forest, you'll first need to remove the lawn and weeds from your yard by sheet mulching (which is done the same way as you would start a no-dig garden). Once your plot is prepared, you can choose the fruit trees, shrubs, and other crops that will grow in your food forest. Food forests require a lot of planning, so this method is not for the faint of heart, but it can pay off dividends in the long run.

It's beyond the scope of this book, but there are 7 "layers" observed in a forest system. Depending on who you ask, some would identify 8 (or even 9). The idea in creating a food forest is to make sure all layers are represented in a symbiotic way, just like in the wild, natural forest. The layers are:

1. *Large canopy / tree layer:* Larger fruit & nut trees. Typically over 30 ft.
2. *Sub-canopy / understory layer:* Smaller/dwarf varieties. Typically 10-30 ft. Dwarf apples, citrus, peaches, etc.
3. *Shrub layer:* Typically up to 10 ft. Blackberries, blueberries, etc.
4. *Herbaceous layer:* Culinary/medicinal plants.
5. *Groundcover / creeper layer:* Plants here crawl across the ground, grow dense, and act as a "living mulch". Strawberries, nasturtium, mint, etc.
6. *Rhizosphere / underground / root layer:* Root crops like carrots, potatoes, beetroot, onions, etc.
7. *Vertical / climber layer:* Climbing and vining plants. They make use of the trees or other vertical spaces like fences and walls. Grapes, climbing beans, snow peas, cucumbers.
8. *(Bonus layer) Mycelial / fungal layer:* In the natural forest, healthy soil means there's a fungal network below.
9. *(Bonus layer) Aquatic / wetland layer:* Ponds, water features, etc. A lot of important plants thrive in the water or at its edge!

These layers all work together in harmony to feed the earth and us, producing a surplus for us to share with many. All the core ethics and principles light up, and all is well with the world.

Potential Drawbacks: Unlike an annual veggie garden, it can take years to establish your food forest, so it's not an instant garden solution for those who want food *now*. And although the food forest will eventually be self-sustaining, it will require a good amount of work and planning in the beginning stages.

MINIATURES

As always, there will be an adept permie out there adapting big concepts to micro situations!

As such, some create "mini food forests" or "mini guilds" in pots! Or small areas. A couple of examples:

- A citrus tree for the tree layer, spinach for the ground cover layer, and sweet alyssum for the herbaceous layer.
- A tomato guild! Tomatoes form a mini "tree" layer, nasturtium for the ground cover layer, and basil and parsley for the herbaceous layer. Depending on the size of your area, you can add a lot more: like borage for the shrub layer, sunflowers for the understory, beans to climb up them, and carrots for the rhizome layer (just plant the carrots more than 6 inches or 15 cm away from tomatoes so as not to impede growth). All of these components bring great guild functions as well!

SUCCESSION PLANTING & CROP ROTATION

Succession planting is a method of using the same garden space to plant multiple crops. It's an excellent way to maximize your square footage and enjoy a longer growing season. In succession planting, you start the next crop right after one has finished.

We will cover this further in Chapter 14.

In the home garden, **crop rotation** means changing the location of annual plants each season. Moving your annual veggie crops from bed to bed with each season, rotating them like musical chairs.

This is another brief mention since we will talk more about this in Chapter 10.

Both of these methods involve working wisely with the soil, reaping the benefits of integration and diversity, and maximizing the yield you obtain. They are great methods to get to know.

CREATIVE PERMACULTURE PROJECTS

Oh, that we had more time and space to dive into the many interesting, resourceful, creative, and fun permaculture projects you could try out!

… But, alas. We simply can't cover them all in this book. If you're looking for some fun projects to add some zing to your permaculture garden, here's a little head start on your research. Try looking up: keyhole beds and mandala gardens, herb spirals, straw bale gardens, hedgerows, banana circles, and chinampas. Just to name a few.

We will touch on a few permie favs in future chapters, even if briefly. These include rain harvesting barrels, pollinator gardens, worm farms, compost bins, and a brief look at berms and swales.

And my hope is that this book will be one stepping stone among many in your permaculture journey. There are so many great resources out there!

WRAP-UP

Well, well, my permie friend! Look at how far we've come.

By now, you've seen that there's more than one way to skin a cat ... er, plant a seed, that is. And I hope you have a fresh confidence boost seeing just how many ways a permaculture garden is possible for people in any space. Your permaculture plan is expanding by the second!

You have many tools in your belt. You can pull from these and use them at any moment in your design process. Oh, look at that porch. Great space for pots. That sunny corner of your yard? You could put your first fruit tree guild there. While you're preparing the soil for that, you could build some raised beds close to the house.

Equipped with all these tools, as well as all the principles, and knowledge you've gained about your space, you're well on your way to creating the garden of your dreams.

In order to do that, we're going to get more intel on your space. In Chapter 4, we zoomed out to see the big picture of your setup. Now it's time to zoom in. *WAY in.*

I know you've been itching to get your hands dirty. Now you finally get to!

That's right, we're going to look at soil! Specifically, we're going to look at *your* soil. This will help you make decisions about which gardening methods to choose.

Then, once we've discovered more about the soil, it will be time to start putting the plan into action with seeds!

PART III

PLANTING THE GARDEN

GETTING YOUR HANDS DIRTY WITH SIMPLE SOIL SCIENCE

Yet soil is miraculous. It is where the dead are brought back to life.

— TOBY HEMENWAY

If you thought dirt was just dirt, my friend, think again! There's so much more going on beneath the surface. There's a whole tiny ecosystem living in each square inch. And just like Toby said above, this is the glorious space where new life comes from things once dead.

Can you feel all the exciting stuff that's happening *right under your feet?*

Well, we're about to look closer, and get down and dirty ... with soil science!

You'll learn about the different types of soil (yep, there are more than one!) and what makes the best soil for growing plants. You'll study the soil in your yard to learn its characteristics. Then, find out what you'll need to do to make it the best environment for your soon-to-be permaculture garden.

This will all lead up to the next chapter, where you'll learn about the different ways to choose and start seeds for your permie maiden voyage.

Kiss your manicure goodbye because it's time to get some dirt under your nails.

WHAT IS HEALTHY SOIL?

Is your soil sickly? Maybe it could use a hearty dose of PermaCulture™. But before you can diagnose it, you need to figure out if your soil is in tip-top shape or if it's feeling a bit under the weather. That's where analyzing soil health comes in.

When we say "soil health," we're referring to the soil's capacity to function as a vital, productive living system. The ability to support plants, animals, and humans now and into the future. That's a big job for a bunch of dirt, isn't it?

Soil health affects the entire environment, including the air and water. But from a gardening standpoint, what we really want to know is: can plants grow in it? And not just grow, but *thrive*. Fertile, healthy soil for thriving plants has three main characteristics. It has good *biological life, structure,* and *nutrients*.

Biological life

Did you know that soil is actually *alive*? The best garden soil is filled with a whole microbiome of living things. Lifeforms from microscopic bacteria and fungi to bigger things like worms and beetles. All of these little guys are constantly eating and pooping to improve soil health.

Structure

Soil is mostly made up of rocks that the elements have pulverized into tiny particles over many years. Combined with organic matter, water, and air, it forms structures that are unique in each plot of land. Soil with *good structure* will have good *drainage* and *airflow*. It will allow roots to easily penetrate while anchoring them securely.

Pore space is the space between each particle for water and air to pass through. An ideal setup for plant life is soil that is 50% pore space, and 50% solids, with equal parts water and air filling that pore space.

Nutrients

Soil nutrients are minerals plants feed on in addition to sunshine. They come from the rocks themselves, the organic matter rotting away in the soil, and water. The best soil is rich in a variety of nutrients.

- The ones *primarily* used by plants are nitrogen (N), phosphorus (P), and potassium (K). This trio is known as "NPK" and these are the **macronutrients** in the soil. They're the main ones we'll cover.
- Plants also need a good balance of **secondary macronutrients** in their soil: Calcium (Ca), Magnesium (Mg), and Sulfur (S).
- Lastly, there are **micronutrients** or **trace minerals** in the soil that also contribute to a plant's growth in smaller amounts, like Iron (Fe), Manganese (Mn), Copper (Cu), Zinc (Zn), Boron (B), Molybdenum (Mo), Nickel (Ni), and Chlorine (Cl).

A lab test is usually needed to determine nutrient levels in your soil. You can usually buy them at a local garden center, or online, and the test results will also point you toward ideal ranges for each nutrient.

Working with the soil

There are other things you might want to look into when examining your soil, which we won't cover in-depth here, like soil salinity (the amount of salt in it), as well as any toxicity or contamination that may be in the soil.

As you work with your native soil to get it ready for the garden, containers and raised beds are great options to get started right away, as mentioned in previous chapters.

Ultimately though, plants grow best right in the ground. By getting to know your own soil, then tweaking and optimizing it according to what you find, you take one of the most important steps in transforming your backyard into a thriving, self-sustaining ecosystem.

You are literally laying the foundation for your dream garden!

SOIL TEXTURE TYPES

When I first moved to my homestead, visiting family and friends would remark on how lucky I was to have such sandy soil. "Not like up in the mountains where you could break a spade trying to dig in an inch." I had no idea what they meant.

Fortunately, I now know that there are three main types of soil: sand, silt, and clay. Soil type generally differs by region. For example, near the coast, our soil is sandier. In the mountains, it's more clayey (yes, clayey is a word and it's fun to say!). And in the fertile heartland of America, the soil is mostly silt.

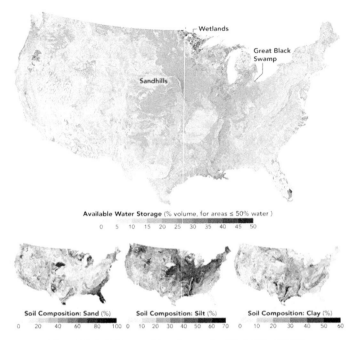

Figure 8.1. Soil Composition Across the US: 1998. *(NASA)*

Let's take a closer look at each type.

Sand

Sandy soils are made up of the largest particles and have the largest amount of pore space. Water drains quickly through sand, which can be a drawback if your soil is too sandy. Sometimes the water passes through too fast for roots to suck up enough. Nutrients are also lost as the water drains away, so sandy soil isn't very fertile. That's why you don't see many plants growing on the beach. Also, if you've been to the beach, you'll know that sand feels gritty.

Silt

The size of silt is between sand and clay. It's made of tiny round, dustlike particles. Small pore spaces between particles means water drains slower than in sandy soil and retains more nutrients. For this reason, silt is often added to sandy soil to reduce the need for frequent watering. Soil is considered silty if it contains 80% or more silt. It feels smooth or slippery (like soap) when wet.

Clay

Individual clay particles are too small for you to see with the naked eye. Since the particles are packed tightly together, they don't drain well, making a bad growing environment for most garden plants. Although clay can be moisture- and nutrient-rich, it holds on tight and doesn't like to share. When wet, clay soil is sticky, and when dry, it can be as hard as a brick. Wet clay particles really stick together and are gluey or sticky in texture (like potter's clay).

Sand particles are 2.0 to 0.05 mm.

Silt particles are 0.05 to 0.002 mm.

Clay particles are less than 0.002 mm.

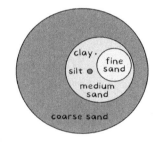

Since each type has its unique properties and size, they each carry their own set of pros and cons.

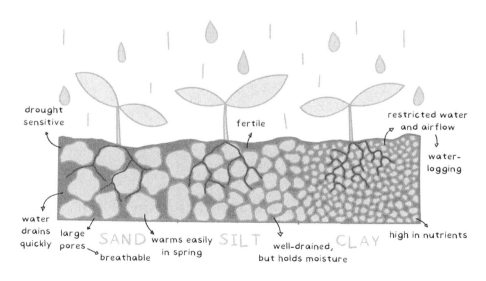

Figure 8.2. Soil Textures and Their Properties.

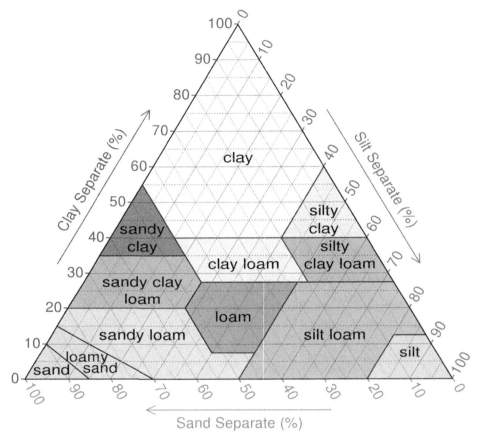

Figure 8.3. USDA Soil Texture Triangle and Textural Classes.

Loam

Soil composition is rarely 100% of one thing. In fact, it's often a combination of all three. You could have clayey sand, silty clay, sandy clay loam, and so on. The summation of a soil's relative proportions of sand, silt, and clay, is known as its **soil texture**.

You achieve the Holy Grail of garden soil with a 40% sand, 40% silt, and 20% clay ratio, which is called **loam**. There should also be about 5% to 10% organic matter mixed in there. Loam feels fine, soft, and slightly damp. Ahhh, loam sweet loam.

Loam is considered the ideal garden soil because it holds moisture and nutrients well and has plenty of pore space for air, water, and roots to pass through. Unless you hit the soil jackpot, you probably don't have the perfect loamy soil. But soon, you'll learn how you can amend it to find that sweet spot.

Those are the main types of soil, and that sweet combo of all three called *loam.*

OTHER SOIL TYPES

There are two other unique soil profiles, which are *less common* but worth mentioning: chalky soil, and peaty soil. Let's take a look.

Chalky Soils

These soils happen on ground where there are big chalk deposits or limestone beds underneath, so they are lime-rich and basic. By "basic" I mean alkaline, or the opposite of acidic. There are a lot of rocks and large grains in this kind of soil, and it drains out quickly and freely. It does have the advantage of warming up quickly in the spring. Large, white stone clumps or a chalky feel can be a sign of chalky soil.

If you're on this kind of soil, you can work with what you've got, and focus on plants that like the quick drainage or alkaline soil. Or you can amend it over time. Either way, improving your soil is always good practice!

Peaty Soils

These are soils found in wetland ecosystems called bogs (where you'd find peat moss). They're mainly organic matter, low on rocks, and hold a bunch of moisture. Kind of like a swamp. It's usually acidic, and it also warms up quickly in spring. Peat soil feels damp and spongy. Rarely is this found in a home garden.

If you happen to live in an area like this, fear not, peaty permie! There are great options for your budding garden. Just look up, "What to grow in peaty soil" or "How to amend peaty soil" and you'll be on your way.

GETTING TO KNOW YOUR SOIL TEXTURE

Get out your safety goggles, kids; it's time to do some experiments! While there are lots of tests you can buy, you can also get to know your soil better with some inexpensive at-home field tests.

Now's the part where you actually get your hands dirty and get to know the soil in your yard. Don't be shy, go ahead and take the gloves off for this! (You thought I was joking about that manicure didn't you?). You'll really want to feel the texture of the soil. The more you do this, the quicker you'll be able to identify different soils. And besides, organic gardeners consider dirt under their nails to be a badge of honor.

> When on international flights, I often find I have the only decently dirty fingernails.
>
> — BILL MOLLISON

And just for fun, here's a cool little side note. As you're out in the sun, taking those deep breaths of fresh air, and working with the earth, guess what? Did you know that soil *may* even have a *natural antidepressant* effect? The friendly bacteria *Mycobacterium vaccae*, commonly found in soil and compost, has been found to light up neurotransmitters which release serotonin (a mood-lifting hormone). In addition to all the benefits of sun, fresh air, and exercise, touching and smelling fresh soil may put a pep in your step! (Paddock, 2007).

So, get ready to smile big, cus we're gonna take that soil and squish it, roll it, dunk it, dig it, and sniff it. Heck, there are even some DIY soil tests that involve playing catch with moist balls of dirt, or throwing it against the wall to see how fine the texture is. When I was a kid, we just called that a mud fight!

This is all very scientific, though, I assure you. We won't do *all* the fun stuff, but we'll find out some basics with these simple field tests. It all starts with:

COLLECTING YOUR SOIL SAMPLE

So. Is your soil clayey with hints of silt? Sandy with a nice sprinkling of loam? The following tests will give you an idea of what kind of ratio you're working with. This is easy to do by feeling the soil in your hands, observing what it does when you wet it and mold it, and measuring how it separates in water.

First, you'll need a sample of soil to test. Go outside and dig up a big 'ol handful of dirt from your garden site. About ½ a cup will do. For best results, get a little deeper here, like 3-6" below the soil surface, to get to the mineral layer.

You'll also want to separate out the **fine earth** to use for these experiments. That's basically all the dirt without the rocks. If you want to get real technical, *fine earth* is all the particles less than 2mm.

So if you wanted to be sure, you would sift out fine earth with a 2mm sieve into a bucket. A standard sink strainer usually has 2mm holes, and a kitchen colander usually has holes ranging from 2.5mm - 3mm, so those would probably work fine for our tests. But in a pinch, you could probably skip the sifting for most of this and just make sure to gather a sample that is fairly free of rocks and other debris.

Now that you've got your soil sample, it's time to run tests! You can just choose one of these, or a couple, or do all of them and compare results.

Also, you can mix soil samples from different parts of the yard to get an "overall" picture, or test a specific spot where you'll be placing a garden bed.

SQUEEZE TEST

Take a small handful of soil in your palm. Drop water slowly onto the soil, kneading it, until it becomes moldable like moist putty.

Now, give it a good squeeze, like you're making a ball with one hand. Now open your hand, and see what happens.

If it falls apart right away, just check: Is it too dry? Add a little more water. Is it too wet? Add a little more dry soil. If you've checked, and it seems wet enough, but still won't keep its form and just falls apart: you've got a lot of *sand* in your soil.

If it does retain its shape, give it a gentle poke.

If the ball retains the shape of your hand like you're in sculpting class, and stays put when you poke it, you've got a lot of *clay*.

If it held its form when you opened your hand, but the poke makes it crumble a bit, congratulations Goldilocks, your soil may be "just right" and you may just have loam!

Let's play with the mud a little more.

Silty and *loamy* soils tend to hold their form for a short amount of time, and they also feel smooth-textured.

So, feel the texture of the moist soil with your fingers. This will give you more clues. If it feels gritty, that's high *sand* content. If it's silky/smooth, that's high *silt* content. If it's plastic/gluey/sticky, that's high *clay* content.

Make some notes, but don't clean up yet! While you're here with this ball of mud, let's run some more tests.

RIBBON TEST

If you could form a ball with the damp soil (you didn't have sandy soil), reroll it into a ball again. Now roll it between your hands, into the shape of a cigar.

Take this mud cigar in your hand, with its end between your thumb and forefinger. Gently start pressing the soil with your thumb, squeezing up and over the edge of your forefinger like a flat ribbon hanging over. Keep pushing out the ribbon until it becomes long enough that it breaks off from its own weight. You'll be measuring this broken-off ribbon.

Lastly, test again for texture. Take a pinch of it in your palm, get it really wet this time, and rub it with the forefinger of your other hand in your palm. Note if it's very gritty or very smooth, or if neither of those is predominant.

How long of a ribbon could you form before it broke from its own weight? (Hint: a longer ribbon means more clay content)

- I couldn't, it just keeps falling apart!: *Sandy*.
- Less than 1 inch: (Gritty) *Sandy Loam*, (Smooth) *Silty Loam*, or (Neither) *Loam*
- 1-2 inches: (Gritty) *Sandy Clay Loam*, (Smooth) *Silty Clay Loam*, or (Neither) *Clay Loam*
- More than 2 inches: (Gritty) *Sandy Clay*, (Smooth) *Silty Clay*, or (Neither) *Clay*

If your ribbon held together a little bit, but has a tendency to crumble, and wasn't overly gritty or smooth: *you may just have loam.*

But let's test a little more first.

SNAKE TEST

For this next one, you'll want to roll a ball of moist soil again. This time about 3 cm in diameter, or about the size of a US half-dollar.

Set the ball down on the ground. Did it fall apart? *Sand.* Did it stay in ball form? Continue on …

Remember when you made snakes out of Play-Doh in kindergarten? You get to use that valuable life skill right here.

Start rolling out the ball into a snake. Does it lose this shape before it is 2.5 in (6-7 cm) long? *Loamy sand.* If not, keep rolling. Does it lose this shape before it is 6 in (15-16 cm) long? *Sandy loam* (or light loam).

If you make a snake about 6 in (15-16 cm) long, time to go to the next step. Try to bend your snake into a half-circle (U shape). If it won't, but instead breaks up, call your friends, cus *you've got loam!*

If you can make a half-circle snake, try to bend it into a full circle. If it breaks up, it's *heavy loam* (or clay loam). If it goes full circle, but the snake is a little cracked, it's *light clay.* If it's a full circle with no cracks, it's *clay.*

Again, if you were able to roll a full snake about half a foot long, but it wouldn't quite bend into a half-circle, congratulations! *You struck loam!* Loamy soil has an ideal mixture of sand, silt, and organic matter and won't need much work to make your plants happy.

But there's one more test if you *really* want to get more "granular" with your results. It's called the:

JAR TEST

Get yourself a large clear jar that's clean, with a lid that closes tightly. The most popular is a mason jar (pint or quart). You'll also need to gather some sifted soil (fine earth), water, a marker, a measuring tape, and a timer.

Fill the jar between ⅓ and ½ up with soil. Remember to use strained fine earth from several inches below the surface. Then fill it *almost full* with water, leaving a little space at the top for shaking up the mixture.

(Optional step): Add 1 tablespoon of dishwashing detergent (preferably powdered). This will help the clay and silt particles separate.

Put the lid tightly on the jar. Ok, now here's where you'll want to have your timer ready, as well as a level spot to leave this jar for a couple of days where it won't be disturbed.

Okay, are you ready? On your mark, get set … shake the mixture vigorously! Do this for about 1-3 minutes, so it becomes a uniform mix.

Once you set down the jar, start your clock! Now the fun part begins. The different components of your soil (sand, silt, clay) will begin to settle at different rates, in different parts of the jar, over the next couple of days.

- At 60 seconds, you can mark the first coarse layer settled at the bottom of the jar. This is the sand layer, which settles first at the bottom.
- At 2 hours, you can mark the next settled layer. This is the silt layer, which settles in the middle, on top of the sand.
- Leave the jar undisturbed and check at the 48-hour mark. Somewhere between 24 to 72 hours, the clay settles on top. 48 hours usually works great. Mark the top of this settled layer. This is the clay layer.
- There may be some stuff floating on top. That's organic matter.

After a couple of days, these layers should be settled, and you should be able to see different layers from the side of the jar. They'll probably be where you marked with a marker at the different points.

Now, get your measuring tape! Measure the height in millimeters of all the solids. This is your total soil.

Now measure the height of each layer in millimeters. Get a calculator, and do this math for each layer:

(Layer Measurement / Total Soil) x 100 = % of that component in the soil.

So if you had a total soil height of 40 mm, and the sand layer was 10 mm, your soil is 25% sand.

There are great online tools that will tell you what kind of soil you have based on your percentages (sandy loam, etc). Just search for "soil texture calculator" and you'll find some great resources. Some will even calculate your percentages based on your jar measurements! (Yay, no math!)

At the time of writing this book, here are two great examples:

- https://agritechcenter.com.np/soil-calculator.html ... Tells you soil texture type based on percentages.
- https://gardentutor.com/soil-texture-calculator/ ... Calculates your texture percentages based on jar test measurements *and* tells you the resulting soil texture type.

So, remember that nifty texture triangle above? If your percentages land you somewhere in the loam area of the diagram, you hit the jackpot!

You can take the findings from all of these tests, compare results, and look for common denominators.

However the results end up, congratulations are still in order. Why? You know so much more about your soil now! Knowledge is power, my friend.

So let's go back in and find out some more.

TESTING MORE SOIL CHARACTERISTICS

OXYGEN: THE SNIFF TEST

Forget what the neighbors might think. Get down on your hands and knees and give that soil a good sniff. If they ask questions, tell them you're doing it for mental health benefits. Then they'll really have questions.

For real though. The scent of your soil can tell you some important things about it. If the soil smells sour and putrid, it's lacking oxygen, which is an essential element for plant growth. Soil with plenty of oxygen and a healthy microbe community will have a sweet, earthy smell.

If your sniffer's not quite up to par, don't worry about it. There are plenty of other tests you can do to get to know your soil. This one's not definitive; it just gives you an idea of soil health. And it gets your face in the dirt, which is always a good thing.

DRAINAGE: THE HOLE TEST

Soil **drainage** is how fast water moves through the soil. It's important because too much water can drown your soil ecosystem, while too little can dry it out. Ideal garden soil will have a good balance of water retention and drainage.

This test is also called a **percolation test**, or "perc test" for short if you want to sound cool and professional to those neighbors that keep checking in on you, wondering what the heck you're doing.

To see the drainage you're working with, grab a shovel and dig a hole that's about a foot deep and a foot wide. Then fill the hole with water. Now watch.

If the water drains out in 10-30 minutes, you're looking at ideal drainage conditions. If it takes less than 10 minutes to drain, you have fast-draining, drought-prone soil. It's probably mostly sand. And if the water takes an hour or more to drain, you have poorly draining soil. It's probably mostly clay.

With too much or too little drainage, plants will struggle to survive. You'll need to do some work to fix the soil or choose plants that grow well in those conditions.

DIY pH TEST

Remember the volcano experiment you did in kindergarten? The one where you got to make a mini eruption by mixing baking soda and vinegar together? It seemed like magic then, but it's simple science, and you can use it to test the pH of your soil.

pH is how acidic or alkaline (a.k.a. basic) a substance is. In gardening, it's important because it affects the types of microorganisms that live in the soil and the nutrients that are available to your plants. Though most plants like soil in the neutral to slightly acidic range, some have specific pH requirements. For example, blueberries, azaleas, and rhododendrons need acidic soil.

pH ranges from 0-14, with 7 being *neutral*. When the pH of something is lower than 7, it's considered acidic, with 0 being the most acidic. Higher than 7 means alkaline or basic, with 14 being the most alkaline. Pure water is neutral, as well as sugar and table salt. Black coffee and bananas are 5, lemon juice and vinegar are 2-3, and battery acid is 0. On the other side, baking soda is 9, soapy water is 12, bleach is 13, and liquid drain cleaner is 14.

Let's get a little more specific for *soil*. The USDA classifies soils that are between pH 6.6-7.3 to be neutral. Most sources agree (along with the USDA) that *most crops and vegetables actually prefer a pH of 6-7*, so the ideal range for most home gardens is slightly acidic to neutral. Nutrients actually become most available to plants in this range. *A pH of 6.5 is pretty optimal for most gardens.*

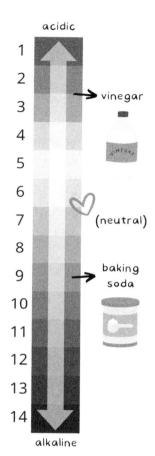

Determining the pH of your soil will also let you know how you need to adjust it for the plants you intend to grow. Remember those blueberries, azaleas, and rhododendrons? They do well in strongly acidic soil between 4.5 and 5.5 pH.

So how do you find out your soil's pH? Well, you can buy cheap "pH strips" to get really specific about your soil's pH. But I know you're eager to conduct that experiment I mentioned!

Without further ado, here is a test you can do with simple household items to find out if your soil is acidic or alkaline.

Go into your kitchen and grab some vinegar and baking soda. In one bucket or bowl, mix a half cup of vinegar with a scoop of soil. If you see a fizzing or bubbling reaction, you're working with alkaline soil. Slight fizzing means slightly alkaline. A lot of fizzing equals higher alkalinity.

In another bucket, mix a half cup of water with a scoop of soil. Then mix in a sprinkling of baking soda. If it fizzes or bubbles, you're working with acidic soil. The more fizzing you see, the higher the acidity.

If you don't get a reaction from either test, your soil is likely well-balanced and neutral. Ah, the wonders of science!

If you saw a lot of fizzing in either test, you might want to test with pH strips to see what you're really working with. A complete professional soil test, mentioned below, also tests for pH.

THE EARTHWORM TEST

Do you speak worm? Well, it's high time you learn, because they have a lot to tell you about your soil. But for now, just observing them will do.

Worms are a fantastic indicator of soil health. If you have good soil full of beneficial microbes, you'll find a lot of them hanging out. But if the soil's health is out of whack, it won't support a healthy worm population. They won't take up residence in soil that's lacking in organic matter, too moist or dry, too compacted, or too alkaline or acidic (neutral is ideal, but they can handle pH 5-8).

And you want these guys around. They're your little underground gardeners. They are experts at soil aeration, decomposition, filtration, and more.

Regular conventional tilling, by the way, can wipe out up to 90% of your worm population. Studies have shown that no-till fields have been found to have 2-3 times the amount of earthworms as fields that are conventionally tilled (Hubbard et al., 1999). Torppa and Taylor confirmed the connection between earthworms and no tillage in a more recent study (2022), and found also that diversified crop rotation (especially including legumes) helped with earthworm populations in fields where reduced tillage did not seem feasible. So three cheers for no-till methods and diversity!

Alright, ready to run your earthworm census?

Get out your shovel again and dig another hole about 1 cubic foot (1' x 1' and 1' deep). Or you can use the dirt from your drainage test hole. Spread the dirt out on a tarp, and sift through it to see how many worms you can find. As a general rule of thumb, there should be at least 10 earthworms per cubic foot of soil. The USDA says 10-20 per cubic foot indicates healthy soil.

How do you encourage more earthworms in your soil? Simply by applying the things you've been learning in this book! Earthworms love organic matter and healthy, balanced soil. Build your soil by layering, adding organic matter, ditching chemicals, reducing tilling, mulching on top to keep the soil moist, etc.

If you build it, they will come.

Professional Soil Testing

All the above tests can give you an excellent starter idea of the kind of soil in your yard. But there's only so much we can do without an actual science lab. That's where professional soil testing kits can come in handy. They can tell you what nutrients and how much organic matter is in your soil, its texture, nutrient levels, pH, and more. They can save time and money in the long run because they point out exactly what your soil needs.

You can pick up a low-cost soil testing kit locally. Try your local garden center or home improvement store, or contact your county extension service. Or you can order them online. Doing the test is as simple as putting a small scoop of your soil in a baggie and sending it off to the lab.

HOW TO ADJUST YOUR SOIL

So you've spent an afternoon with your soil. You've gotten to know it better, and you think this could be the beginning of a beautiful thing. But before you take the next step in your relationship, the soil's going to need to make some changes. Where to begin?

Don't do what I did. As a premie permie, I thought all my soil needed was a good fluffing up. That would make it less compact, add some oxygen, and give it a more productive structure. I got out my handy electric tiller and went to work on it until it looked nice and fluffy, loose and weed-free. I gave it a good watering and thought, *there, now that's some pretty soil!*

In reality, all I did was destroy the healthy microbes living in the topsoil. Within a week, the soil was compact again, the weeds were back, and my seedlings were struggling.

Permaculture isn't about just removing things from the soil and shuffling it around a bit. It's about adding to it in a way that does the least harm. By tweaking it in little ways over time, you can create an environment that's healthy for your plants and your micro-ecosystem. **Amending** means adding to the soil to make it better.

Keep in mind: you don't need *perfect soil* to start a garden. Unless it's in really terrible shape, you can probably start a garden, and keep improving as you go.

And we'll go over some ways to do just that!

Fun fact! Did you know that most of life's problems can be solved with compost? Just keep that in the back of your mind as we explore these common soil setbacks and permie ways to fix them.

THE PROBLEM: TOPSOIL

Topsoil is the top layer of garden soil, usually between 2" and 8" deep, where your plants will grow. If there isn't enough, or if it isn't healthy, plants will struggle to put down roots.

The Fix: No-till gardening is the solution here and in most cases! Adding about 2" of well-rotted manure, mulch, or compost on top of your existing soil can work wonders for the soil microbiome and your plants' health. If you add about 2" each year, it will significantly increase your topsoil depth over time.

Another option is to build raised beds filled with healthy soil. The bonus of this is that you have a controlled gardening plot that's ready to use right now.

THE PROBLEM: DRAINAGE

Poorly draining soil reduces the oxygen available to plants and microbes in the soil. It can cause roots to drown and rot. Meanwhile, soil that drains too quickly can wash away nutrients, cause erosion, and leave your plants thirsty for more.

You want a good, even balance of solids and pore space. Most soil scientists agree that the ideal ratio for plant growth is about 50% solids (40-45% mineral / 5-10% organic matter) and 50% pore space (25% air / 25% water). (Gatiboni, 2022).

The Fix: Regularly adding organic matter, compost and mulch to your soil can improve drainage. We will discuss composting more in Chapter 13 and mulching in Chapter 10. But let's take this opportunity to talk about how the terms compost and mulch interrelate.

Sometimes folks use compost and mulch interchangeably, but they're actually different things with different goals, though they typically work together.

Basically: compost works its way *into* the soil to feed and improve it, and mulch goes *on top* as a blanket. Compost is made up of organic matter that breaks down and feeds the soil, and mulch *usually* is organic matter.

Compost is a mix of varied decaying organic matter (food scraps, grass clippings, leaves, coffee grounds, etc). The mix of carbon-rich and nitrogen-rich materials causes a faster breakdown process. It is added to the soil to boost nutrients and fertility, as well as improve soil structure. When you add it on top of soil, rain and natural processes bring all that good stuff down into the soil beneath it. Compost helps clump together loose soils, and loosens tight soils. It's a wonder drug, I'm telling you.

Mulch is any material that covers *the top* of the soil and it helps to suppress weeds and makes the soil dry slower (i.e. retains moisture). It acts like a "blanket" over the top of the garden (don't you just wanna tuck those cute little carrots in?).

Sometimes mulches are inorganic (like rubber, gravel) but this book will focus on organic mulches, since permies tend to go with these. Organic mulches are usually made of a single ingredient and are usually carbon-rich materials like wood chips, straw, or shredded dead leaves (like the "browns" portion of compost). They actually will also *eventually* break down and enrich the soil, but this is over a longer period of time than the compost mixture.

Some folks regularly throw only compost on top, using it *as a mulch*, and that's a fine choice. But nature doesn't like a vacuum, so that rich, fertile void can quickly fill with weeds. Compost also breaks down quicker and is lightweight, which makes this precious material susceptible to erosion. So many gardeners do *both*.

Basically, when doing both: compost first, then always end with mulch on top.

What about in future years, as you continue to add compost? Some take the time to rake the top mulch layer aside, then add compost and amendments, then rake the mulch back on top as the protective blanket layer. Especially if it's a heavier material like wood chips. Then refresh the mulch on top as it breaks down and more is needed.

But if you want, you can also layer finished compost on top of the mulch to make it easy. Rain and watering will bring those nutrients down through the mulch and into the soil over time.

What about other drainage problems?

If your soil is waterlogged, see if you can find the source. Is there a broken drain or blocked ditch funneling water to the spot? If the water can't be blocked, see if you can divert it away from your garden. You can do this by digging a trench above the waterlogged area, building **berms** (mounds of soil) around your garden, or creating a channel to send the excess water elsewhere (or to a place in your garden where you want it).

You can also raise your garden by building raised beds or adding soil on top of the ground. Or make the best of a boggy area by planting trees and plants that like wet roots. These include willows, magnolias, ferns, and marsh plants.

There's a lot to be said about drainage and directing the flow of water. We'll cover a little more in Chapter 12.

If your soil is too dry, be sure to incorporate a lot of organic matter to improve its water-holding capacity. Again, compost improves soil structure. Also, mulch on top regularly to retain moisture and prevent evaporation.

If possible, redirect streams or drains to bring water to the site. Build a berm or retaining wall at the lower edge of the garden to prevent runoff. Or plant trees and broad-leaved plants that can cast some shade on the dry area.

We talked about some great methods in Chapter 6 and Chapter 7 that could be applied here (layering techniques and in-ground gardening methods).

THE PROBLEM: UNBALANCED pH

The pH of soil affects what types of plants can live in it and what nutrients plants can take from it. Most plants like soil with a slightly acidic to neutral pH (around 6-7). Earthworms do, too!

It's always a great idea to see how you can make the most of the soil you have, and plant species that like your native soil pH. If you really want to plant other ones, you can always grow them in containers. For instance, if your soil is alkaline but you have dreamt of blueberry bushes in your garden, you can have some contained spaces with controlled acidic soil.

However, there are ways to amend your soil pH!

The Fix: If your soil is too acidic, you can raise the pH by adding agricultural/garden lime, dolomite lime, bone meal, or oyster shells. You can buy these natural soil amendments at your local home and garden shop. You can also go the no-waste route and use crushed eggshells or wood ashes from home. All of these solutions also add nutrients to your garden, as you'll see below.

If your soil is too alkaline, you can lower the pH by adding elemental sulfur. If you have access to pine needles or pine sawdust, these can help, too. Some say granite rock dust and other minerals may help. Some also suggest making **ericaceous compost** to amend alkaline soil, which is compost with a lower pH. Composting takes time, but you can make this by mixing high-acid organic materials into your compost like coffee grounds, wood chips from conifers, pine needles, oak leaves, bracken, citrus fruits, and chopped onions.

You will see others amending alkaline soil with iron (ferrous) sulfate, aluminum sulfate, synthetic fertilizers, or diluted sulfuric acid ... but be forewarned: there are some real ecological costs that can come with each of these that you should research if you're considering them.

Note that changing the pH of soil can take time. Think months to a year. So you may want to apply a year before planting. And it might be good to retest after some time to see how things have adjusted.

Again, compost is always a great way to steer any soil in the right direction!

THE PROBLEM: IMPROPER TEXTURE & STRUCTURE

Soil texture and structure determine how well your soil will retain water and nutrients. Also, how well they'll deliver it to your plants. A simple solution is to build raised beds. But if you're determined to work with the soil God gave ya, there are a few steps you can take.

The Fix: So, the thinking often goes: "I don't have enough sand percentage in my clay-heavy soil, so I should just add sand!" Warning: it doesn't work that way. It can have a weird concrete mixing effect if done in the wrong amounts!

It's kind of hard to change your basic soil *texture* (the percentage of sand, silt, and clay). This would involve bringing in a lot of new stuff and presents a lot of economic and engineering challenges. It's not that it's not possible, it's just usually not feasible.

However, you can improve the *structure* (i.e. how the mix is arranged) of any type of soil by amending it. This makes sand retain more moisture and nutrients, and makes clay more porous.

So, the basic overall solution here is to add *organic matter* to the top and keep doing it consistently, season after season. Compost is king! But you can also go with leaves, composted manure, mulch, and even cover crops.

To improve clay soil, try double-dig to work in enough organic material — like composted leaves, bark, manure, or compost — to loosen up the soil. Or, if it's unworkable, add on top of it the no-till way. It's best to do this in the fall when the soil is dry but still workable. Avoid walking on your planting area, as this can make the soil even more compacted.

To improve silty soil, add at least 1" of compost over the garden area each year. Mulch heavily to prevent evaporation and to help the soil retain moisture.

Silty soils can be susceptible to erosion, so if this is you, you might need to use berms or retaining walls to hold it in while you work with it, or plant cover crops to help.

To improve sandy soil, you're going to need to add lots of organic material to bind those particles together. It's best to do this in the spring or fall and add mulch in the early spring to keep the soil moist. Fast drainage can leach nutrients out of sandy soil. You may need to use an organic liquid fertilizer like compost tea to supplement your plants at first.

Another great solution to build sandy soil is to use a cover crop as green manure (see the "recruiting plants" section below), which results in working more organic matter into the soil.

The Problem: Lacking Nutrients

Nutrients determine how fertile your soil will be. Most plants need a good balance of nitrogen, phosphorus, and potassium to thrive. That's why you often see the letters N-P-K on bags of fertilizer. Although you'll need a professional soil test to tell which are lacking in your soil, you can easily make the necessary additions yourself.

The Fix: **Nitrogen (N)** helps plants to capture sunlight energy for photosynthesis. It promotes that lush green color and strong foliage growth. Especially in plants like lettuce, cabbage, greens, and herbs. You can boost your soil's nitrogen level by adding nitrogen sources like aged manure, seaweed, fish, blood meal, alfalfa meal, feather meal, fish meal or emulsion, mushroom compost, or rice hulls.

Phosphorus (P) is essential for the growth and development of plants. It promotes root growth, seed formation, and fruit development. It's especially important for flowering fruits and veggies like tomatoes, peppers, and cucumbers. Adding bone meal, rock phosphate, fish emulsion, animal manure, lime, and seabird guano can increase phosphorus levels.

Potassium (K), also called **potash**, helps plants use water and move nutrients through their cells. It also aids in disease and stress resistance and enhances flavor. Since it helps with root growth, it's essential for root veggies like carrots, radishes, onions, and garlic. You can increase potassium levels by adding wood ashes, seaweed, dolomite lime, oyster-shell lime, kelp, gypsum, rock dust, or greensand to your soil.

Other secondary macronutrients your soil might need include:

- Calcium (Ca), which you can amend with eggshells, lime, bone meal, wood ash, and gypsum.
- Magnesium (Mg), which you can amend with lime, Epsom salts (research before using), poultry manure, and soybean meal.
- Sulfur (S), which you can amend with elemental sulfur.

Once again, most nutrients get a boost from compost, and organic matter is the best way to build soil fertility.

OTHER AMENDMENTS

There are a lot of other fun soil amendments you can research and buy (or even make!), like biochar and mycorrhizal fungi, which will benefit the soil.

Remember you don't have to do it all at once. Don't make the mistake of thinking you have to, which can lead to overwhelm and wanting to quit. Permaculture is about the long game. Enjoy the ride, and stop to smell those roses (and hey, smell some dirt while you're at it!). Aim to make your soil a little better each year, and you'll be doing great.

WHEN DO I AMEND MY SOIL?

In short, adding compost to your soil is pretty much the answer to everything. But when should you do it?

Since organic material breaks down over time, it's best to add compost to your garden beds in the fall. This way, it has all winter to decompose and is ready to use in the spring. But if you're like me and don't think about these things until March, it's okay to add compost in the early spring.

Just make sure it's finished by that time. **Finished compost** has decomposed sufficiently. It looks, feels, and smells like rich earth. Dark and crumbly, with an earthy smell, not smelling like rotting food or any of the original ingredients. If you're composting manure, it should be **well-rotted**, which essentially means the same, and it should look and smell like finished compost, not the original manure. If you made poop not smell like poop, you must be doing something right!

Composting time varies depending on the methods and materials used. Compost can finish in two weeks or two years. More on this in Chapter 13.

Adding an inch or two of compost to your garden each year is the ideal way to build up and maintain soil health.

Apply mulch to your garden in the mid-to-late spring when the ground is starting to warm up. A thin layer will protect seeds and still allow them to work their way through. It's also okay to mulch in early fall. This can be especially beneficial for keeping dormant perennial plants warm over the winter.

Nutrient fertilizers (N, P, and K) are usually added to the soil in early spring. This is before you have planted your seeds or seedlings. You can add nutrients again after harvest to replenish the soil.

A final note. Did you know that there are certain plants that actually replenish and "fix" nutrients in the soil? For instance, "nitrogen fixing" plants can convert nitrogen from the air into a form that plants can use. Others have deep roots that "mine" nutrients from below, bringing them up to the upper layers.

This is where those companion planting principles come in. Which brings me to this amazing idea:

RECRUITING PLANTS TO HELP THE SOIL

> Land, then, is not merely soil; it is a fountain of energy flowing through a circuit of soils, plants, and animals.
>
> — ALDO LEOPOLD

I know it seems backwards. You want to get the soil right to help your plants. But did you know that getting your plants right can also help your soil? Plants not only need good soil … they can also *make* good soil! This is a big permaculture lightbulb moment, so let it sink in, like water into good soil.

Here's an example you probably already know about. Let's say your problem is erosion. True, you may need big structures like dams or terraces where there is heavy erosion on a hillside. But native plants, grasses, and groundcovers fill that space and stop soil from being washed away. Using something like a winter cover crop will end up adding nutrients to the soil as well.

Other plants have big root systems that break up hard soil for you like living aerators. Cover crops can also firm up sandy soil with the organic matter they leave behind. Plants can bring nutrients to the soil to prepare for next season's crops that need those nutrients. Legumes are often used to fix nitrogen, and popular cover crops include clover, hairy vetch, peas, beans, and soybeans.

Winter cover crops can add organic matter to the soil, since they'll be chopped down and left to decompose on top of the ground. A plant grown for this purpose — that is, to turn it into the garden soil to improve soil texture or nutrients — is called a **green manure**. There are certain grasses that are commonly used for green manures, like winter rye, ryegrass, buckwheat, mustards, and oats.

Comfrey is a permaculture favorite, grown in gardens for *many* reasons. One of them is its ability to improve the soil in several ways.

Plants can even *heal toxic, contaminated soil!* **Phytoremediation** is a process that involves strategically using certain plants to remove or reduce toxins in the soil. Date palms, corn, sunflower, alfalfa, certain mustards, and willow and poplar trees are all examples.

If you happen to know there are chemical pollutants in your soil — say, from herbicide or fungicide — cover crops can be planted to *bioaccumulate* the chemicals. Sunflowers, peas, radishes, corn, oats, and wheat are good examples. You'll just need to remove the plants after the growing season and dispose of them somewhere where they won't contaminate the soil any further (like the landfill). If you want to make use of the debris, you could hot compost the contaminated plants, and mark that particular compost pile for only non-edible plants like ornamental grasses and landscaping plants.

Plants are so awesome, and they give so much. They soak up our carbon dioxide and they give us oxygen and food. Here's to you, plants!

Wrap-Up

So now you've had your hands in the dirt, and you're excited to get started right away. You have an idea of what kind of soil you're working with and how you can improve it. Spring is coming, the ground is warming up. And you're thinking, "Wait. So you're telling me I have to wait until I have good soil before I start permaculture gardening? And that this can take *up to a year?* Bummer!"

Hang on, my permie pal! Don't lose heart, because while the outdoor stage is being set, there's a whole food growing party that can happen right inside. As your soil slowly improves, you can begin your garden by starting seeds indoors. Late winter and spring are the ideal times to start. In the next chapter, we'll talk about the best way to start seeds for maximum garden success.

Okay, we're a little over halfway up the mountain. Time for a check-in!

So, have you had any of those juicy "aha!" moments so far? Do you feel more confident, like you've gained a better understanding of your garden and have more tools you can really use? Are you overall more excited about gardening?

True, it may be all that dirt you've been sniffing.

But also, you've made *progress*. Think back to when we first started out. If you've come further at all, that means you've grown! Take a moment and celebrate! (Seriously, do a happy dance, or pump your fist with a big ol *"Yesss!"*)

I have a quick favor to ask, too. If you've enjoyed this book, would you consider leaving a review for it?

I'd sure appreciate it (like a lot). I'll read each one and probably do a happy dance when it comes in. Your review allows me to keep doing what I love, writing and helping others. But not just that! It causes this book to be seen by more people, get on more shelves, and encourage more beginner gardeners.

And then ... more people learn about permaculture, grow their own organic food, help other people, and make the world a better place. Multiplication, abundance ... well, you know the story!

So, if you've been building a treasury of rich permaculture wisdom, consider sharing the surplus, and helping out folks like me and other readers.

It only takes a minute, and we get to spread the message and fulfill those 3 core values together. And we all come out on top! Symbiosis!

Thanks for considering. It really makes a difference! *Now let's go plant some seeds!*

Scan here to review this book on Amazon!

149

STARTING SEEDS THE PERMIE WAY

> Don't judge each day by the harvest you reap but by the seeds
> that you plant.
>
> — ROBERT LOUIS STEVENSON

Infinite abundance can come from a single seed. One tiny seed, barely visible to the naked eye, can feed generations. You plant it. It grows. It produces fruit and, with it, more seeds. Dozens of hundreds of seeds multiply over every season. So much potential in one tiny seed!

Nature makes it look so easy. But in reality, starting your own plants from seeds isn't always simple. Sometimes it's as easy as sticking them in the ground, but sometimes it's not. Needless to say, adjusting soil so that it is at optimal health levels for plants takes time, even a whole year or more.

But that's not to say that you can't start growing food now by using fresh potting soil and containers. Think about the plants you'd like to grow in your permaculture garden as you explore the ways to acquire and prepare them.

ACQUIRING SEEDS

To be a superstar waste-free permie, the goal is to produce your own seeds from plants that you grow each year. This saves money, it's sustainable, and it's super awesome when you think about the potential. It taps into the plant's self-sustaining regenerative power. And, it ensures that you know exactly where your seeds are coming from. But the cycle has to start somewhere, so in the first few years, it's great to buy your seeds.

It's crucial to start with quality seeds. These will be the parent stock that begins future generations of plants. You want to make sure that the seeds have been produced and stored well.

The best place to start is in your own community. Talk to friends or neighbors in the gardening community. Visit local farmers, nurseries, or farm supply stores. They'll have seeds to share, trade, or sell. This way, you'll have a trust-worthy source. And you'll know that the seeds you're getting are acclimated to your particular environment.

Local farmers and gardeners may also be able to offer plant **cuttings**. These are portions of an established plant that are cut off. They will produce new roots or stems when planted. It's like the non-creepy version of cloning. You can grow many herbs and perennials from cuttings.

Companies that sell heirloom, organic, and GMO-free seeds are good places to look. Visit their websites and request copies of their seed catalogs. Also, it's great to ask local gardeners and your local nursery where they buy their seeds.

Heirloom seeds, by the way, are seeds from plants with pedigrees. They've stood the test of time. An "heirloom" is something of *value* that gets passed down in a family, right? You know, like grandma's diamond ring? Well, these varieties of plants have been saved and passed down from generation to gener-ation and they've got a long, strong track record. Typically, heirlooms are clas-sified by having a history of at least 50 years. Others say before World War 2.

Just like a breed of horse or dog, each heirloom cultivar has a long-developed character of its own, depending on where it came from, etc. Heirlooms have been carefully grown and saved through the years for various reasons. Most of the time heirloom varieties were harvested and passed down because they were the most productive or dependable in home gardens, or they had the best flavor, etc. The cream of the crop, as they say.

Also, heirlooms have been open-pollinated. This means you can grow them, harvest their seeds, save them, and reseed year after year, and get the same thing. So they are also the best option to plant for those who want to save seeds each autumn.

In the Supplemental Resources section, I've included a few good places to start looking for seeds online.

STORING SEEDS

To be viable, seeds must be stored properly. **Viable** means capable of working successfully. Or in plant talk, able to **germinate**, or grow. For a seed, this is when it begins to grow and put out shoots after a period of dormancy.

Now with some definitions out of the way, this step's pretty simple: *keep your seeds dry*. Moist environments can let microorganisms like fungi and bacteria in and cause your seeds to mold. You can avoid this by storing them in airtight containers like canning jars. If your seeds are still in their original packets, it's ok to keep them in a regular box as long as the box is in a dry location.

In Chapter 14, we'll discuss seed harvesting and saving at greater length. But basically, if you're working with seeds from plants you have grown, you want to make sure that your seeds are completely dry before storing them away.

This year I opened my seed box to find that most of last fall's pumpkin seeds were covered with mold. When I was prepping them for storage in November, I got impatient and stored them in baggies before allowing them to fully dry out. If I'd just waited another day or two to bag them up, I wouldn't have lost these valuable gems.

As you start out, dedicate an old shoe box or plastic bin as your Seed Storage Vault. Having a place to keep your seeds safe, dry, and organized will help you in the long run. You can even alphabetize them!

PREPARING SEEDS FOR GERMINATION

As you have no doubt already concluded, the word **germination** has nothing to do with germs. I know, misleading, right? It's actually the process that a seed goes through as it turns into a plant. When starting your seeds, consider the way seeds germinate in nature. What are the environmental soil, light, and water conditions? The challenge set before us is to mimic these conditions.

In nature, seeds are prepped for germination in different ways. Sometimes they're passed through the digestive tracts of birds and mammals (a.k.a. eaten and pooped out). They're soaked by heavy rain and snow, frozen by low winter temperatures, trampled on, or sanded down by the wind. Some even have to go through fire to prepare for germination. These fire-activated seeds, which include buckbrush, lodgepole pine, and some eucalyptus species, are completely encased in resin or hard shells that can only be opened by the heat of fire. Luckily, no common garden seeds require this treatment. You can put away the blowtorch.

You can mimic these processes by preparing your seeds through cold stratification, soaking, or scarifying.

COLD STRATIFICATION

In nature, seeds drop in the autumn and overwinter on the ground. This is like a hibernation period for the seeds. When the temperatures rise in the spring, it triggers the seeds to wake up and start busting out of their shells. Most seeds germinate in the 65°F-80°F (18°C-27°C) range.

Cold stratification means exposing seeds to cold conditions to encourage germination. Seeds need a certain number of days below a certain temperature before they're triggered to germinate. Generally around 34°F-41°F (1°C-5°C). Plants from cold climates need *longer times* and *colder temperatures* to germinate.

The seeds for many annual plants can simply be sprinkled over the soil in the spring. But many perennials, wildflowers, shrubs, and trees need cold stratification. It gives time for the hard seed coat to break down so that the tiny plant embryo can emerge.

You can artificially simulate cold stratification by storing your seeds in the refrigerator. This is easily done with a plastic baggie and some paper towels.

1. Soak the seeds for 1-2 hours, then drain them onto a paper towel.
2. Spread the seeds out and fold the paper towel around them. Then, wrap it with a dry paper towel to keep the seeds moist but not soaking wet (you don't want them to mold).
3. Place the paper towels in a ziplock bag with a few pinholes for air. (You can also use a container with a lid, just make sure there are some kind of vent holes for air).
4. Label the bag, and place it in the fridge. Be sure the fridge is set to cool enough (Ideal is 34°F-37°F or 1°C-3°C)
5. If your seeds start to sprout, immediately remove them and plant them in the soil where they're landing, or in a temporary pot if it's not time to plant outside yet. Make sure the little sprout part is pointed up.

Some say a sprinkle of cinnamon around seeds can help prevent mold during cold stratification.

You can also cold-stratify your seeds by mixing them with about a half cup of wet sand, peat moss (or coco coir), or some kind of inert growing medium (i.e. contains no nutrients) like seed starter mix, and placing it in a plastic bag. This method is simpler but isn't as precise for smaller seeds.

Most seeds need at least 4-6 weeks of cold stratification, so start thinking early. If you pull out your packet of lavender seeds in May, it's probably too late. When you receive a new packet of seeds, read over the planting instructions before storing them away. You may need to get them back out sooner than you think!

Make sure that if your seeds need cold stratification, that you find out how long they need before planting, and factor that into your planning in advance.

But Josie, what if I'm lazy/busy/don't have any free fridge space?

Often you can get away with cold stratifying seeds directly in their seed packets. If you see that your new seeds need a month or more of cold stratification, pop the packet straight into the fridge. That butter shelf that you never use is a good spot.

But Josie, what if I'm *really* lazy/busy/low on fridge space?

For most seeds, especially native wildflowers, you can simply scatter the seeds on the ground in late fall and let nature do its work. The drawback to this is that your seeds will be exposed to animals and the elements, so be prepared to lose some. And don't forget where you put them come spring!

By the way, if you want to protect seeds from being dug up, you can cover the area with hardware cloth or a wire screen, bend a few-inch crease in the edges, and sink them like teeth into the ground to hold it in place. Then, when you see sprouts come up, you can just take off the cage.

SOAKING SEEDS

Ok, back to nature. In the wild, seeds are often exposed to wet periods as rain falls and snow melts. This soaking period helps to soften the tough outer coating and supplies a jump start of water to the seed interior. It tells the seed it's time to start germinating.

Soaking is especially helpful for medium-to-larger seeds with thick coatings. This includes beans, beets, pumpkins, sunflowers, chard, and cucumbers. Seeds with wrinkly coatings, like peas, also need soaking to plump up.

On the other hand, tiny seeds like carrots, lettuce, celery, radish, and spinach should not be soaked. They would be a nightmare to pick apart when wet. They're best planted directly.

You can simulate the soaking process right in your kitchen. Fill a cup or bowl with water that is warm but not too hot to touch. Add your seeds to the cup and leave them to soak for 24 hours.

Soaking seeds is also a good way to test if your seeds are viable. Often, seeds that sink to the bottom are good to go. But if they do not sink, but instead float, chances are the seeds will not germinate. You can actually check this after 15 minutes in the water.

Seeds must be planted immediately after soaking. Have your garden bed, pots, or seed starter trays ready to go when you start soaking your seeds.

SCARIFICATION

Some seeds actually need to get beat up a little bit to germinate. Sounds harsh, I know, but these tough little guys need the adversity to grow. How's that for a metaphor?

See, these seeds have developed hard protective coatings as a self-defense mechanism. It prevents the seeds from sprouting too early. It helps them to survive harsh environments and prevents overcrowding. **Scarifying** means breaking down the seed's outer protective coating to speed up germination.

Most native perennials and wildflowers can benefit from scarification and soaking to germinate. Some examples of plants that benefit are sweet peas, nasturtiums, lupine, milkweed, moonflower, and vegetables like winter squash, beans, and spinach. Most vegetable seeds do not require scarification. In general, small, soft seeds do not need scarifying.

In nature, seeds go through the acidic digestive systems of birds. They get trampled on by animals, ground between rocks, and tossed in the wind. But you can scarify your own seeds at home, and you don't even have to eat them first. (Whew!)

You probably already have items lying around your kitchen that will work great for scarification. This includes sandpaper, files, rasps, nail clippers, or knives. To scarify a seed, use your tool of choice to nick the seed coating so that the lighter inside just shows through. But don't get too rough with it; you don't want to damage the seed. Just a single nick will do.

For smaller seeds, rubbing the seed between two pieces of sandpaper works. You can nick larger seeds with a sharp knife or clippers. If you're squeamish about torturing seeds, you can scarify them by pouring boiling water over them and letting them soak overnight (because that's more humane, right?).

As a rule of thumb, scarification then soaking go hand in hand. But if, for some reason, you don't get around to soaking your seeds after scarification, it's not the end of the world. Generally, seeds will still sprout if they're not soaked. It will just take them longer, and the germination rate will decrease.

Just research your plants to find out what their unique seed needs are. "Do cherry seed pits need cold stratification?" "Should I scarify sweet pea seeds?" Ask these kinds of questions, find out what the process entails, and include this in your planning.

WHEN TO START SEEDS

Starting your own seeds at home gives you more choices than if you were to buy pre-started plants from the store. Young plants are often called **starts, seedlings,** or **transplants.** Most stores only carry the usual, popular varieties. The upside is that these varieties are hardy, hand-picked for your climate, and already about a month old. But the downside is that you don't get many choices. It's hard to find interesting heirloom varieties, native perennials, and organically grown plants at your average big box store.

When you start your own seeds, you'll know exactly how they were raised, what they are, and when they were started. And you'll save a lot of money; seedlings can be expensive!

The next question is whether to start your seeds indoors or plant them directly in your garden. Some seeds do best when given an indoor head start. Others prefer to be planted directly in the garden as soon as the temperature is agreeable. Plants like carrots, radishes, lettuce, peas, beets, and pumpkins don't like to have their roots disturbed, so it's best to plant these outdoors.

But starting seeds indoors can give you some advantages. And it's easy to do.

STARTING SEEDS INDOORS

Many seeds can be planted indoors several weeks before the growing season kicks off. Starting your seeds indoors can give your plants a longer time to produce. And in some northern zones, many need to start indoors long before the soil warms up. This gives them enough time to produce in the summer. Tomatoes and peppers are among these.

Most seeds should be started 6-8 weeks before the last frost date in your area. Some should be started as many as four months early. If you're not sure when the last frost is, a quick online search for "last frost date [your town]" will give you an answer. Count back 6-8 weeks from this date, and you'll know when it's time to start.

If you're not sure when to start seeds indoors, the back of the packet will often tell you. It will say how soon to start indoors or if the seeds should be started directly outdoors.

If you're itching for a good table or chart (your favorite!), search for "sowing calendars" or "growing calendars" online, and you'll find a variety of charts showing when to start seeds of different plants, whether inside or outside, when to transplant, and when to harvest. Make sure to include your hardiness zone in your search (e.g. "growing calendar for zone 10"), and you'll find times specific to your area, including important markers like average first frost and last frost. (These are also known as *planting calendars, schedules, or charts*).

If your seeds require a period of cold stratification, or need soaking or scarification, make sure to factor that into your planning and timing as well. For example, cherry pits need about a 3-month period of cold stratification before you plant them. If you want to plant them directly in the ground, the best time is after frost. Let's say that's in March. So you'd want to make sure you had your cherry pits in the fridge by early December to have them ready for spring planting (indoor or outdoor).

Did you know that there are even pits and seeds you can harvest from store-bought organic produce like cherries and oranges? If you are snacking on them anyway, instead of throwing out those pits, start some orchards! You'll want to make sure to research the cleaning, storage, and prep needs of the particular seed type. See if you can grow it in your hardiness zone, and if not, you can always build your indoor collection!

Choosing Containers

To start your seeds indoors, first, you'll need containers. **Seed starter trays,** or plug trays, are the go-to choice for many gardeners. These are large plastic trays that have individual cells (anywhere from 6 to 72) for plants. Starter trays are convenient because they provide individual homes for one or two plants. They often come with a bottom tray for easy watering. It's easy to transplant seedlings from starter trays, and the trays can be stored for reuse.

Peat pots are small starter pots made from a compostable mix of peat moss and wood. They're excellent for starting seeds. They can be planted directly into the ground or into larger pots as your plants grow. These are earth friendly and convenient. You won't disturb the plant's delicate root system when you transplant it.

However, if you want to think sustainable and save money, you don't need store-bought starter trays. You can use biodegradable materials such as egg cartons or toilet rolls. You can transplant these directly into the garden. It reduces damage to tiny roots and increases nutrients available as the container breaks down.

Soilless Seed Starting Mix

Like all living things, plants need water, oxygen, and food to survive. Fortunately, a seed itself has all the nutrients it needs to get a healthy start; no fertilizer is required just yet. It's like the egg yolk is to a baby chick.

But the soil your baby plant calls home is important. The soil should be able to retain moisture, but it also needs good drainage.

You can use compost for the starter mix. However, since seed starting is best done in a near-sterile system, consider first sterilizing your compost. This will kill any fungus, bacteria, or insect eggs that may be in it. You can use the sterilization methods talked about in Chapter 6, like baking the compost or solarizing it in the sun.

Most actually suggest using a *soilless growing medium* for starting seeds. You may remember us talking about this back in Chapter 6 when we went through types of bagged soil. Your knowledge will come in handy here!

You can go out and buy seed-starting mix that is pre-formulated for the job. Or you can mix your own. Here are some common ingredients:

- **Perlite** is a naturally occurring mineral. It's basically volcanic glass that's been mined and heated up. It looks like little balls of styrofoam. It's often seen in potting and starter mixes, and it is USDA-approved for use in certified organic agriculture. It helps with aeration, water retention, and drainage.
- **Vermiculite** is also a naturally occurring mineral. It's also mined and heated up. And it's also approved for organic agriculture/gardening. It looks silvery-gray and flaky. It also improves water retention, aeration, and drainage. Perlite and vermiculite are often both included in starter mixes. They are lightweight, inorganic, and fairly sterile. Perlite is a little better for aeration, and vermiculite wins for water retention.
- **Peat moss.** Ah, Pete. You remember ol' Pete from last chapter? Peat moss forms after many years of sphagnum moss breaking down. It contains fewer microbes (near sterile), is absorbent, and has often been considered ideal for seed starting. However, many have sustainability concerns about using peat moss in gardening, because of its potentially ecologically damaging harvest process, and the fact it renews slowly. So, an alternative can be used:
- **Coconut coir** (or "coco coir") comes from coconut husks, which are taken off before the fruit is sold, so it makes use of a by-product that would normally be tossed. It has similar benefits to peat moss. Some mixes have both peat and coir. Some have one or the other.
- **Azomite powder.** Just throwing this one in here for fun as a bonus amendment. It's rock dust, and carries some sweet micronutrients.

You might see things like rice hulls or sands on starter mixes or DIY recipes.

Sometimes people will mix compost or worm castings in for more nutrients. It's best to sterilize these.

Others still get creative with little boosts like blood meal, bone meal, and feather meal. These add nutrients, but you need to study levels and not overdo it, making the mix too rich for little seedlings.

You can also make your own seed-starting mix from the ingredients above. Do some research and see what clicks, but here are some simple recipes:

Simple: 50/50 mix.

- 50% perlite and/or vermiculite
- 50% peat moss and/or coco coir (moistened)

This could be as simple as 50/50 perlite and coir. Simple, mostly "sterile", and nutrient-free.

A little fancier: ⅓ from each category. Adds compost.

- (⅓) 1 part perlite, 1 part vermiculite
- (⅓) 2 parts peat moss or coco coir
- (⅓) 2 parts "sterile" compost

A little fancierer: Same as above, plus:

- Sprinkle in some azomite, or other amendments
- Add mycorrhizal fungi to the mix
- Try substituting/mixing worm castings with compost

You'll find different ratios suggested by different sources. As long as you find some balance of the basic ingredients, you'll probably be alright.

You may think, why not just use potting mix or potting soil? Well, you can, with some caution. Keep in mind, it can cause problems for tender seeds, and it's best to go with a soilless mix of some kind for the germination process.

However, if you see that potting soil is cheaper, and want to go for it, it can definitely work. There are a few things you can do to help. Make sure to get potting soil that isn't chock full of fertilizer. Sift it down to remove wood chips. Add coco coir to make it more airy. Sterilize it. Think happy thoughts.

Now that we've got our space and growing medium worked out, we can talk about:

PLANTING THE SEED

Okay! When you're ready to plant your seeds, take the steps below. Our focus is on starting indoors, but the following process can be followed indoors or out. If you're planting directly in the garden, skip to step 2.

1. Fill your container to the brim with seed starter soil. Tamp down the soil so that it's compact, then fill the container again. Starter soil is very light and airy, so be prepared for it to get everywhere. You might want to do this outside.

2. Next, make a small indentation on the top of the soil. You can do this with the eraser end of a pencil or your finger. Place one or more seeds in each indentation and cover it lightly with soil.

A good rule of thumb is to plant a seed 1-2 times as deep as it is wide. This is generally ⅛" - ¼" deep. Better to go too shallow than too deep. If a seed is planted too deeply, it takes extra energy for the sprout to reach the surface. This can result in a failure to germinate or a weak seedling.

Some seeds need light to germinate. You can simply place them on the surface or cover them with a light sprinkling of soil. When in doubt, consult the back of your seed packet for a recommendation.

1. Water your seeds carefully with a spray bottle, with a sprinkler-style watering can, or (gently) with the sprayer attachment from your garden hose or sink. Watering with a pitcher can be too forceful and may dislodge your seeds.
2. Water the soil until it is moist. Seeds should be consistently moist but not too soggy. Your soil should be well-draining so that excess moisture can drain out the bottom. If the soil is too wet, seeds can rot away. Usually, once a day is good. Some suggest twice a day, some say once every other day.
3. If you touch the soil and it's dry and easily moveable, it's time to water! If it's dark and wet, you can check the next day.

SUPPLEMENTING LIGHT

"Let there be light!" For real, though, you need to. Once your seeds have started to pop their sprouts through the soil, it's time to get them under some light!

A sunny windowsill is a time-honored way to start seeds indoors. But you can really amp up your results by investing in a low-cost grow light. A **grow light** is an electric light that mimics the sunlight plants need to grow. Although any light can stimulate the growing process, the most effective grow light will provide the appropriate spectrum for plants to photosynthesize.

Photosynthesis is the process in which plants turn light, water, and oxygen into energy. It's how they grow, bloom, and produce seeds.

- Incandescent bulbs are the cheapest lighting option but don't offer a wide color spectrum for plants to reach their full potential. And they can get hot, so they should be kept at least two feet away from your plants. They're best for supplementing daylight to plants that already have a sunny location.
- Fluorescent lights, like the shop light you have hanging in your garage, have long been an economical and easy choice. They have a decent spectrum for germinating plants and don't get as hot as incandescent lights. They're low-cost and easy to find.
- These days, LEDs are the front-runner when it comes to germinating and growing plants indoors. While they're more expensive than incandescent and fluorescent bulbs, specialized LED grow lights provide both the red and blue color temperatures that plants need to germinate, grow, and fruit. They're energy-efficient and don't get hot, which means that you can put them close to your growing seedlings without chances of scorching the lil guys. You can purchase a good-quality LED grow light online for less than $100 (some are less than $30). Plus, they'll last for years to come.

Whether it's on a folding table in your basement or spare bedroom, on a kitchen countertop, or in a specialized grow tent, your grow light should be suspended over your seed starter trays or pots. If you wanna get super fancy, it's helpful to rig it up on an adjustable drop system so that you can adjust the height of the light as your seedlings grow. Or just get a grow light with an adjustable arm. The plants should only be a few inches away from the light so that they don't have to waste energy reaching with their stems and can concentrate on growing strong roots.

Most seeds do not need light to germinate and, in fact, will germinate better in the dark. However, smaller seeds, those that you sow on the soil surface, do need light to germinate. Provide them with **16-18 hours of light a day**. Plugging your grow light into a timer makes this task easy and ensures that you don't accidentally leave your little plants in the dark all day. Since all seedlings (regardless of seed size) need more light than full-grown plants, it's best to leave them on the 16-18 schedule all the way up until it's time to move out.

As you look around your house to scout the location for your little plant nursery, keep in mind: you may be safe from outside pests, but there's something else you may need to watch for. Curious toddlers and pets! Bless their sweet little curious fun-loving hearts.

Involving children in the planting process is such a fun way to give them a sense of ownership in the family garden and teach them about the wonderful world of plants. Just find a good, safe final spot for your nursery, or you might find those kiddos setting all the trapped seeds and soil free. All over the kitchen floor. Trust me.

WATERING

Until your seeds poke their little sprout heads above the surface, you'll need to keep them consistently moist. Light can quickly dry out starter soil, so be sure to check on your babies a couple of times a day. You can cover your starter trays or pots with a plastic covering to lock in moisture and create a humid environment until they've sprouted. This can be plastic wrap, little clear cups, resealable baggies, or some starter trays even come with a clear plastic top that is easily removed for watering. It's like making a little greenhouse!

Once the seeds have sprouted, water them from above. They don't have deep roots yet, so they can't suck up water from below. Gently spray your seedling to keep the surface wet.

After the seedlings have their first sets of true leaves, you can start watering them from the bottom.

What are **"true" leaves**, you ask? They're the second set of leaves to grow on your seedling. They'll look like smaller versions of the mature plant's leaf shape. The first set is called **cotyledons,** and they're actually part of the original seed. They'll eventually dry up and fall off.

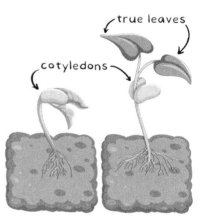

Watering your seedlings from the bottom is easiest done by putting the starter pots in a tray that doesn't have drain holes (starter trays often come with one) and adding about 1"-2" of water to the bottom. Plants wick up moisture from the bottom and control how much they need, so you don't have to babysit them so much. Your little seeds are growing up and starting to make their own choices! After a while, the water in the tray will become low on oxygen, so you should replace it every few days.

Some folks even use a "double cup" method from the very start to avoid over-watering. This involves, as you might assume, two cups. Solo cups work great. The bottom cup has no holes. A few pebbles on the bottom to add space between cups. Then the top cup with drainage holes is placed on top with the starter mix and seeds. This setup creates a little water reservoir at the bottom. It's a great project to look up!

The two main problems to look out for when starting seeds are drying out and molding from excess moisture. If you're worried about mold (it will look like a whitish cotton on the surface of the soil), it's best to let the top surface of the soil dry out before watering again. The best defense against mold is airflow, so you may consider running a fan on the low setting near your seedlings. This will also help to strengthen their stems. Look at you, preparing your little ones for the real world, like a great plant parent!

POTTING UP

Plants are like babies; they're pretty small and manageable when they start out, but as they grow, they take up more space and get more demanding (as any parent of a teenager will tell you). If you've started your seeds in starter trays, you may need to move them to larger containers before it's time to plant them outside. It's like moving to their own bedroom before moving out of the house. This process is called **potting up**. If you've started your seeds in peat pots or cells, this is easy because you can simply plant the entire container. Solo cups are a cheap and effective solution for potting up from starter trays.

Your plant teens will also need some nutrients by this time. You can move your plants into a mix of sterile compost and sand to give them adequate nutrients and drainage, or try a mix like we mentioned above, only put more sterile compost, worm castings, and amendments with nutrients. Or you could opt for a bagged potting mix. In this case, you'd do well to supplement organic fertilizer or compost.

HARDENING OFF

If you've nurtured your baby plants with the right light, water, air, and soil, in about 4-8 weeks, they'll be ready to move outside to their forever home in the garden! But you can't just kick them out of the nest yet. Plants started indoors need some time to acclimate to the outside environment, which is likely colder (plus windier, etc) than that inside your house.

You gotta do some time in driver's ed and ease in with a learner's permit before jumping right into a full-on driver's license, right?!

Hardening off is the process of gradually introducing your plants to the outdoors. It takes about a week. Start by bringing your seedlings outdoors for a couple of hours during the warmest part of the day and setting them in a sunny spot, like on the patio or picnic table. Then bring them back in. Repeat the process each day, adding about three more hours of outside time each day. If the threat of frost has passed, in about a week, your plants will be ready to stay outside full-time.

In the next chapter, you'll learn how to transplant the seedlings into your permaculture garden.

WHAT SEEDS SHOULD I START?

One of the biggest mistakes beginning gardeners make is starting too many plants. It's easy to do! You get excited and want to plant *everything*! And there are, like, 50 seeds in that packet, so planting them all is awfully tempting.

You definitely want to keep that enthusiasm, friend. But just like perfect, loamy soil, you want a good mixture. Part enthusiasm, part wisdom, and part bold action-taking. That's a good, loamy brain right there.

Seeds are tiny; you can fit hundreds of them in the palm of your hand. But seeds turn into seedlings, and seedlings turn into mature plants that can take up multiple square feet of space. When deciding what seeds to start and how many, think about the future.

A full seed starter tray has cells for 72 plants. But eventually, all 72 of those will need to be moved to bigger pots before it's time to move outdoors. Do you have space in your home for 72 5" pots? And, let's be honest, do you really *need* 72 tomato plants?

Okay, maybe you wanna go big! That's great. But before you start shooting from the hip with that seed catalog, there are some questions you should ask yourself. These will help you to better plan your first-year permaculture garden.

- How much space do I have, both indoors and out, for starting and growing plants? What are the space characteristics (sun/rain/wind), and what plants would fill it well?

- What plants will I benefit from? What are the ones my family and I like to eat?
- How soon do I want to produce a yield? Do I want fast-growers like herbs or long-term producers like fruit trees? (A combination of both can be the most rewarding.)
- Do a search for this: What plants are easiest to grow for beginners? (Think: lower maintenance, more resilient). Some examples of great beginner plants are: lettuce, kale, spinach, swiss chard, legumes (green beans, peas), radishes, carrots, beets, cucumbers, zucchini, squash, pumpkins, hot/bell peppers, tomatoes, potatoes, garlic, onion, and hardy herbs.
- Have I incorporated perennial plants into my permaculture garden plan?
- Have I incorporated native plants into my permaculture garden plan? (Hint: ask locals for tips! And not only: "What plants are native here" but "What native plants do *well?*" Think "impossible to kill.") We'll go over perennials and natives more in the next chapter.
- What are plants I'd love to grow that are expensive to purchase at the grocery store?
- What are crops I'd love to grow that are listed on the "dirty dozen?" The dirty dozen are the commercially grown foods found to be most contaminated with pesticides (strawberries, spinach, kale/collard/mustard greens, peaches, pears, nectarines, apples, grapes, bell/hot peppers, cherries, blueberries, green beans)
- Can these plants live outdoors year-round?
- Are these plants that I have the time and capability to care for?
- Could I sell, swap, or give away seedlings if I end up with too many? (This is an excellent opportunity to practice Principles 6 and 8, and some core ethics too!)

We'll talk a lot more about what to plant in the next chapter.

But even now, get out your notebook and make a list of all the plants you'd like to have in your permaculture garden. This can be now in your kick-off season or down the road, so don't be afraid to dream big.

Once you have a list, go through it and place each plant in order of preference. Compare each plant against the questions above. Is it something I will use that fits into my garden plan and that I am capable of caring for in my environment? See which plants check off a lot of boxes. (You may find more answers as you read on).

If you feel overwhelmed, pick three or four plants to start with. This might not sound like a lot, but following permaculture principles, we start small and slow and expand as we go. As your first plants mature, you can find the best sources for your next lot of seeds and make adjustments to your garden as you observe the changes.

Also, your top choices can be the "main" plants you focus on, and you can gather a team of supporting plants around those by using companion planting principles. We will talk a little more about that in the next chapter.

Wrap-Up

Starting seeds for the first time might not always go as planned. Just like counting chickens before they hatch, you can't always assume your seeds will pop up and thrive. That's nature for ya!

But by gathering your equipment before you begin, preparing healthy starter soil, and starting with quality seeds, you can ensure the best chances of success. If you're new to indoor seed starting, I suggest beginning with something simple, like zucchini, bean, or pumpkin seeds. In general, larger seeds germinate the fastest and are easiest to work with.

If you're not sure what food crops to include or what the difference is between a perennial and a native plant, don't worry. In the next chapter, we'll talk about the different types of plants and how they can work together to make your self-sustaining and integrated permaculture garden thrive!

WHAT TO PLANT, WHEN, AND WHERE

It's difficult to think anything but pleasant thoughts while eating a homegrown tomato.

— LEWIS GRIZZARD

He who plants a garden plants happiness.

— CHINESE PROVERB

G rowing plants is just plain awesome. It's fun, it's empowering. And once you get hooked, you find yourself wanting one of everything (or two, or three) at the garden center.

But a little bit of knowledge and strategy can really help you in the long run, both in your selection and care of plants.

When I was still wet behind my gardening ears, I wanted to grow daisies. I did everything right: I ordered the seeds, started them indoors, planted them outside when the timing was right, and tended them well. But by fall, I had a bunch of beautiful foliage and *no daisies*. Discouraged, thinking the seeds must have been duds, I pulled every last plant to free up bed space.

Little did I know: daisies don't flower until their second year. D'oh! What a waste! And this, my friends, is why knowing a little plant background is essential for your permaculture garden success.

We'll start by talking about the types of plants. Then you'll learn when and where to plant them and who they like to hang out with.

ANNUALS, BIENNIALS, AND PERENNIALS

Maybe you've noticed, permies talk about perennials a lot. We love 'em so much that to help us go to sleep at night, we count them hopping over fences and into our yards. One mulberry, two mulberries, three mulberries ... ah, sweet rest.

Maybe you've wondered, though, what does perennial mean? Let's go there.

Plants can be loosely categorized into three families: annuals, biennials, and perennials. The difference basically boils down to their lifespan, or how many years they live. Let's take a closer look.

ANNUALS

The word "annual" means something that happens once every year. So, **annual plants** are ones that complete their entire life cycle in one year. They germinate in spring, bloom and produce fruit in summer, and die in fall. Most of the garden vegetables you're used to are annuals. Edibles like tomatoes, peppers, zucchini, beans, potatoes, pumpkins, and squashes are all annuals.

Annuals are some of the most popular garden and landscape flowers, too. These include marigolds, zinnias, impatiens, begonias, petunias, and snapdragons. Pretty much everything you can buy in six-packs at the garden center is a pack of annuals that were started that spring. Some annuals actually become perennials in warm climates. Flowers like daisies, geraniums, and lantana are examples.

But just because a plant's annual doesn't mean its legacy can't live on. Often, annuals drop seeds that overwinter in the ground and pop up the following spring. When someone says that her garden's full of "volunteers", she doesn't mean it's crawling with Tennessee football players. She means **volunteer plants** or those that have grown from the fallen seeds of last year's crops. This often happens with tomatoes and squashes if you let a few rot on the vine.

169

You may see references to **hardy annuals, half-hardy annuals,** and **tender annuals.** This basically refers to a plant's ability to survive the conditions of the outside world, and it directs you on how to plant the seeds. Hardy annuals can be sown directly outdoors, even early in the fall, because they can survive frost. Half-hardy annuals can just take a little bit of cold, and tender annuals can't really take it. Best to start these indoors or only sow after the last frost.

These terms are really relative to the zone you're in. A plant may be "hardy" in one zone but not in another. And there may be other conditions to be aware of, like heat, drought, or a lot of rain. So in the end, it's always good to know your zone and know your plants.

BIENNIALS

So if annual means one year, then biennial means ... you guessed it, two years! (You're so smart.) **Biennial plants** are those that have a two-year life cycle. They produce roots, stems, and foliage in their first year. Then in the second year, they flower and produce seeds before dying.

Many common garden vegetables are biennials, although they often don't make it to their second year — veggies like spinach, lettuce, collards, cabbage, chard, kale, carrots, and cauliflower. We usually pick them before they have a chance to go to seed because that's when they're at their peak flavor and size for eating. Biennial vegetables that reach their seeding stage are usually too tough or bitter to be palatable. So if you plan to eat them, harvest them before they flower and go to seed.

However, if you want plants again next year, give a few of your biennial veggies a chance to go to seed. Although biennials don't return yearly, they **self-seed** easily. This means that the fallen seeds will overwinter and germinate the following spring. So you don't need to reseed every year if you want to keep your biennials in the same place. They'll create a new army of volunteers all on their own. In this way, they perform like perennials in the garden.

PERENNIALS

Perennials are plants that live for more than two years. With a long-term goal in mind of a self-sustaining regenerative food forest, perennials form the backbone of a permaculture garden. While two years is the starting point, a perennial can live for many more. If given the right growing conditions, long-lived perennials can last 20 or more years. Trees last for decades and even centuries. And what's more fantastic is that perennials are constantly dropping seeds, spreading roots, or multiplying bulbs. So, a well-established perennial garden can potentially last forever!

Unlike annuals, perennials don't die after they produce fruit. They just take a little break. In the fall, after production is done, they store energy and go dormant for the winter. When spring comes, and environmental conditions trigger them, they return to life and start the cycle over again. Hallelujah!

The one drawback of perennial plants is that they're slow growers. Often, the first two years are spent on root establishment. It's common not to see perennials bloom for two or three years (like my poor daisies) or, in some cases, longer. That's why many gardeners incorporate a mix of perennials and annuals in their plans. It's the best of both worlds: fast results and lasting abundance.

Perennials take center stage in permaculture because they're the ultimate survivors. They're resilient, and they give a lot of bang for the buck. Developing deep, enduring root systems, they help restore soil health and reduce water needs. Talk about saving resources! Many perennials perform multiple functions in the garden, such as controlling erosion, providing fertilizer, and repelling insect pests. And they look beautiful, too!

Perennial vegetable crops are a more sustainable choice in agricultural systems because they offer multiple harvests on the same plant. Plant them once and enjoy years of food. Some permie favorites are asparagus, artichoke, garlic, rhubarb, horseradish, and watercress. Fruit trees, berry bushes, and many herbs — like sage, thyme, rosemary, and oregano — are perennials, too.

LONG-TERM PLANNING

So to recap: Annuals live for one year, biennials live for two years, and perennials live more than two years — from three years to hundreds of years. A garden of delicious annual veggies is par for the course in any garden. But as you think about your *long-term goals* and building a regenerative permie garden, give space for some perennials like fruit and nut trees, herbs, and veggies. And fill in the plans with annuals and biennials.

There's another very important category of plant we should talk about.

WHY NATIVE PLANTS MATTER

> There are many things I'd like to change in the world but feel powerless to do so. By planting native plants in my garden, I can make an immediate impact.
>
> — JOHN JANICK

Native plants are ones that grow naturally in your area, without human intervention, and they're uber-important in the permaculture world. Many native plants are perennial, too. Perennial native plants are what permies dream of at night.

Native plants are also known as *indigenous* or *local*. Many species can be found throughout the US, but some are specific to certain regions. So you may need to do some research and observation to find out what's native to your area. Local garden centers, landscapers, gardeners, word of mouth, a book on native plants, your regional native plant society, and the good ol' internet, are all great ways to dig for native plant gold.

Often native plants are overlooked as just "part of the scenery" or referred to as weeds. (And trust me, they hate being referred to by the W word.) But they serve an essential purpose for the ecosystem and your permaculture garden.

NATIVE PLANTS AND WILDLIFE

Native plants are crucial to the ecosystem because they serve as a shelter and food source for the local wildlife. Wild animals and bugs would not be able to survive without them.

Herbivores like songbirds, bunnies, and deer depend on native plants for food. And if there were no native plants, pollinators like bees and butterflies would look elsewhere for sustenance. No pollinators = no new plants. And no new plants = post-apocalyptic wasteland.

Native plants also have a special place above non-native ones (imported from elsewhere) because many local animals have specific requirements. For example, in the US a native oak tree can house 500 species of caterpillars. But an ornamental ginkgo tree (native to Asia) would only host about 5. That's like 100 times the biodiversity!

SELF-SUSTAINING NATIVE PLANTS

Aside from providing food and shelter to the local wildlife, native plants are important to the permaculture garden because they use resources well. Since they are adapted to the conditions, they know how to conserve water and make the best of soil and light. They know how to survive temperature swings, freezing winters, rainfall, drought, and humidity. Non-native plants wish they could be so lucky.

This adaptability makes native plants easy to care for in the permaculture garden. They're low maintenance because they require less water, weeding, or tending. They often self-seed or come back each year as perennials.

If you go back to Chapter 3, I bet you could check off most, if not all of the Permaculture Principles in a garden of self-sustaining native plants. Many are multi-purpose marvels that have edible, medicinal, soil-enhancing, pest-repelling, pollinator-attracting, and aesthetic benefits.

TRANSPLANTING FOOD PLANTS OUTSIDE

If you've nurtured your infant seeds through the final cold weeks of winter, they're probably full-blown plant teenagers by now. They might even be driving you nuts. Don't worry; it's about time to move them outside so you can finally get some peace and quiet. Moving plants to a new location is called **transplanting**.

COOL-SEASON AND WARM-SEASON CROPS

Cool-season crops are those that like cool daytime temperatures (around 50°F-70°F or 10°C-21°C). They're often planted in the early spring or fall and can tolerate some frost. Too high temperatures can cause some cool-season plants to stunt, wither, or bolt. **Bolting** is premature flowering and going to seed. Some cool-season crops are beets, brussels sprouts, lettuce, spinach, and turnips. Many of them can be planted directly as seeds around March-April.

Warm-season crops are those that prefer warm daytime temperatures. They typically shouldn't be planted until after the danger of frost has passed, typically around mid-May. Many warm-season crops can start indoors to give them a jump-start on the growing season, like tomatoes, melons, corn, squash, and peppers.

How to Plant Seedlings

You'll know your little plants are old enough to move outdoors when they have 2-3 sets of *true leaves*. Remember not to count the *cotyledons* as leaves. After a week or so of hardening off, it's time to put them in the garden bed you've prepared.

It's best to transplant seedlings *in the morning* and *on a cloudy day*. This way, the new plant doesn't have to deal with a day of blazing sunlight immediately. Some plants have specific planting requirements, but for the most part, it's simple. You can use a trowel or your hands to dig a small hole just deep enough for the plant's root ball to fit.

Before removing them from their seed trays or pots, give your seedlings a good watering. Then place them in the holes and cover the roots with soil. Plant them about at the soil depth they're currently in.

The exception to this is if you have leggy seedlings. If your seedlings are **leggy** — meaning they have especially long, spindly stems from insufficient light during starting — you can bury them deeper. It depends on the plant, but in general, you can bury their stem up to the first set of true leaves. It will help strengthen their stems and form root mass. This is a common fix for leggy tomato plants, which you can plant even deeper (up to half underground). Just don't bury them when they're still tender and weak, as this may cause the stems to rot in damp soil.

Plants have specific space requirements, usually listed on the back of the seed packet. Often, it's 12"-18" apart. You can use a ruler or yardstick to measure if you want to get really precise. Otherwise, just eyeball it. Remember, permaculture gardening isn't about perfect, straight rows. Your bed may look sparse now, but soon those little seedlings will spread out and fill that empty space.

Give your freshly planted seedlings a watering, and you're done! Good luck, little plants! *(Sniffle)* They grow up so fast.

CARING FOR FOOD PLANTS

Your young adult plants are out on their own and are growing up. Soon they'll be having children of their own! Your role as a plant parent now is mostly maintenance. You know, making sure they're eating and drinking enough water, not falling in with a bad crowd, or getting trashy tattoos on an impulse.

Summer maintenance chores will differ depending on the plant. But for the most part, caring for food plants involves watering, feeding, and weeding.

WATERING PLANTS

Whether veggie plants, herbs, or fruit plants, a garden needs to be watered regularly. Plants should get about an inch of water a week. How frequently you water depends on your soil. Gardens with sandy soil should be watered twice a week, while clayey or loamy soils can get away with once a week. It's best to water your garden in the morning when the sunlight is weakest, and the plants have hours to dry before dark.

Fruit trees and bushes like deep, infrequent watering. If you have sandy soil, water every 1-2 weeks and allow the water to sink in about two feet. You can test this by pushing a shovel or a stick down into the soil and seeing how far up wet soil clings to it. If you have slow-draining soil, water every 2-3 weeks.

Water containers and raised beds more often, as they dry out faster. It might mean watering every day or every other day. Use your plants as a guide. If they're wilting, turning yellow, or the leaves are curling up, they're probably crying for water.

The best way to conserve water in the garden is by applying it directly at the root level. This does three things.

1. Avoids wetting foliage, which could lead to fungus and leaf diseases.
2. Makes water readily available to the roots.
3. Loses less water to evaporation.

Drip irrigation is a method many permaculture gardeners use. It waters plants directly at the root zone. It's the most efficient way of supplying water and nutrients. You can set up a fancy drip irrigation system with plastic pipes or use soaker hoses. These look similar to regular hoses but are covered in tiny holes that allow water to drip slowly into the soil.

FERTILIZING & MULCHING THE PERMIE GARDEN

In the permaculture garden, we wave goodbye to chemical fertilizers. This is because, in the long run, and for a variety of reasons, chemicals cause more problems than they solve and do more harm than good.

But who needs them, anyway? We've got compost! If you worked ample compost into your soil at the beginning, your garden should be good to grow for the season. Compost is king, but there are also organic fertilizers you can use. You can side-dress your crops with more compost or organic fertilizer a few times during the growing season to give them a boost.

Side-dressing is applying a circle of fertilizer around the base of the plant, about 4"-6" away from the plant stems, or just beyond the reach of its widest branches.

Top-dressing is another term used to describe applying fertilizer or compost. This is more of a general broadcast over the entire growing area and is best done in the fall or early spring when the growing season isn't in swing yet. Side-dressing has more to do with feeding specific plants.

Keep in mind, different plants have different needs. Some plants are heavy feeders, some medium, and others actually thrive from being left alone. Tomatoes, squash, cucumbers, corn, and melons are heavy feeders. Legumes like beans and peas, and some herbs like mint, oregano, rosemary, and thyme are light feeders.

We've also talked about **mulching** in previous chapters. Mulching means laying a material over the surface of the soil. It conserves water, suppresses weeds, regulates the temperature of plant roots, and prevents erosion. And it's a great hiding place for helpful spiders that like to eat insect pests. Mix it into the soil at the end of the growing season, and it becomes compost.

You don't have to go dropping your money on bagged mulch. In permie world, there are tons of organic mulch options right under your nose. These include dead leaves (many will say to shred them for best use), seed-free dead lawn clippings, straw, pine needles, hedge and tree pruning waste (a wood chipper is handy here), semi-ripe compost, and shredded cardboard boxes.

Some gardeners say hardwood mulch is good for perennials, whereas straw mulch is a better choice for annuals. Partly because straw mulch will break down quicker.

Mid- to late spring is the best time to put down mulch. After you've transplanted your seedlings, give them a little time to establish. Then add a thin layer of mulch over your garden bed. The plants will add to it by dropping leaves and flower parts as the season progresses.

If you are mulching with something heavier like wood chips, and sowing seeds directly in the soil, consider mulching in the fall, preparing your garden bed for spring planting. This gives the mulch the off-season to break down. Always plant outside seeds directly in the soil *underneath* the mulch, not directly in mulch.

Mulch needs refreshing at different rates, depending on the type. Larger wood chips decompose slower than shredded leaves. Larger wood chips may last years, while you may want to add on more shredded leaves twice a year. In general every 1-2 years, it's good to add more on top, or when you see it getting below that ideal 2-3" thick layer.

Some methods (look up "deep mulch" gardening) recommend a deeper layer of mulch at the top and those who use methods like this swear it keeps the water in and the weeds out. This brings up another topic:

WEEDING

Ah, weeding. Some people find it therapeutic, while others avoid it like the plague. Whichever category you fall into, you'll want to put dealing with weeds on your regular gardening list. Many would say weekly is great. There are a lot of creative things you can do with weeds, and permies love creative solutions. Many weeds can be beneficial!

We'll get more into the weeds in Chapter 13.

In the garden beds, weeds can often compete with your food plants for soil space, nutrients, and water. And plants don't like competition.

The best offense is often a good defense here. Nature doesn't like a vacuum and will fly in to fill bare soil space. So mulching on top of garden beds is a great solution. Also, planting a "living mulch" is great, which is a ground cover plant that covers the soil and suppresses weeds.

If weeds get too out of control, your permaculture garden can soon become overwhelming. That's why we place our veggie beds in Zone 1 on the permaculture design plan. As you walk through your garden to get to your tool shed or your front door, make it a point to deal with any stray weeds *on the way*. They're easier to pull up when they're young (or deal with in other ways we'll discuss later). And if you keep up with them daily, they'll never get out of control.

FINDING THE RIGHT COMPANIONS FOR YOUR PLANTS

Quick, what are Principles #8 and #10? Who can raise their hand first?

That's right! Integrate, don't segregate, and value diversity! Gold stars for you!

These are some of the most important when planning your permaculture garden. That's because they suggest that we grow not just one crop but many varieties, just like in nature.

Look out your window or take a walk through the park. You can count at least four different types of plants growing in one square yard of space.

Like us, plants often grow with companions. They don't like just hanging out with their own kind. That's the difference between *polyculture* and *monoculture*.

MONOCULTURE VS. POLYCULTURE

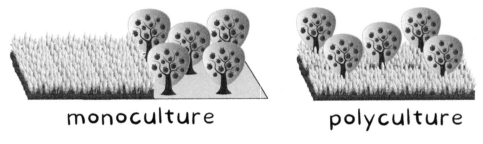

monoculture   polyculture

Figure 10.1. Monoculture vs. Polyculture.

Monoculture gardening and farming is planting only one crop in an area. Most modern industrial farms are monoculture. Monoculture may have advantages on a large scale, or in certain cases like preventing erosion on hillsides. It provides high-demand crops like corn, soybeans, and oats for the masses.

However, this is like putting all your eggs in one basket, and it can be more susceptible to problems, because it's inherently unnatural. If your potato crop develops blight fungus, all is lost. The method carries ecological and sustainability concerns on a large scale, as well.

Polyculture mimics nature in design. In polyculture planting, you combine different plant species in the same growing area. It's an excellent way to optimize and use empty space. Until the dawn of modern farming, polyculture was the dominant farming method used. In many parts of the world, polyculture is still practiced today.

In polyculture gardening, you plant species that complement each other. The plants work together, so you don't have to work so hard. Growing a polyculture is beneficial because it can:

- Give plants better resistance to pests and diseases
- Improve the soil quality
- Increase your yield
- Increase variety and biodiversity
- Mitigate risk and lower your chance of failure
- Maximize space
- Suppress weeds

A food forest is an excellent example of a polyculture. Like a jungle in nature, the layered garden utilizes plants at different heights to optimize vertical space, from the canopy to the root crops. They all work together to benefit each other.

Polyculture is a way to have fun with your permaculture garden design, too. Think about permanent anchors in your yard, like a fruit tree, an established shrubbery, or a pond. You can plan polycultures around these. Consider planting edibles with ornamentals, plants of different heights, plants with roots at different depths, and those with similar water requirements. Experiment! Let things grow, and see how it goes!

The potential drawback of polyculture gardening is that it can be more work upfront to get your soil right for multiple types of plants. And it requires more knowledge and planning. How do you know if an emerging shoot is something you planted or a weed? But in the long run, investing some time to plan with polyculture will actually save time and energy, and improve the soil and yield.

For a little more guidance, let's talk about companion and guild planting.

COMPANION PLANTING: GARDEN BESTIES

When plants are grown close together for the benefit of one or both plants, it's called **companion planting**. Two different species of plants can help each other out by repelling insects, attracting pollinators, improving the soil, or improving each other's growth (or *possibly even flavor*). Or a companion planting may just involve diversifying by planting two different plants with the same growing conditions.

A famous example of companion planting is called the "three sisters". Pioneered by Native Americans, it consists of corn, beans, and squash. The corn provides structural support for the beans to climb. Beans are nitrogen fixers that improve soil quality. And the large leaves of the squash help retain moisture and prevent weeds from growing. They work together in harmony to create a low-maintenance, self-regulating garden.

Tomatoes, basil, and garlic is another example of a supergroup. After all, the three go together so well in spaghetti sauce. The basil and garlic repel tomato pests like aphids, moths, and hornworms. Some also say that growing basil with tomatoes improves the flavor and yield.

Then there are sacrificial plants, such as nasturtiums with cabbage or broccoli. Because they share the same pests, the nasturtiums take one for the team, leaving your veggies unbothered.

Meanwhile, flowers like marigolds and tansy lure in pest-eating bugs and nectar-rich blooms attract pollinators.

Getting to know the best friends and rivals for a plant can take some time.

In Appendix A: Companion Planting, you can find a list of popular garden plants for reference, along with their companions and foes.

While the science behind these concepts is a growing field of research, most of the studies you'll find use words like *intercropping* or *interplanting*. This is partly because "companion planting" can cover a broad range of ideas. Many of the ideas are anecdotal or passed down through generations, but that doesn't mean they're not valuable or real. Just because Granny didn't have studies to back it up, doesn't mean her strategy to plant garlic around the garden to keep pests away wasn't totally legit.

You can find a lot of conflicting information out there about *what goes with what*. In general, certain combinations have shown up consistently as power couples or dream teams through the years, and you'll find those repeated. It's a great idea to compare different charts and recommendations, see what seems really well agreed upon, and make the decision for yourself.

When studying companion planting, it's important to keep in mind what is true about a lot of advice: there are some fundamentals, but every garden is different, so study what works best for yours. There will be some trial and error. And you'll learn and grow, and the garden will continue to get better!

Bringing in flowers and herbs is a great way to experiment with companion planting, by the way. They often bring a lot of benefits to nearby plants.

It is also important to know about:

GARDEN RIVALS: WHAT NOT TO PLANT TOGETHER

While some plant combos go together like Sandy and Danny Zuko, some are best kept apart. They may share some of the same growing conditions, but growing them in the same space can cause trouble in garden paradise for various reasons.

For example, some share common pests and diseases, such as plants in the same family, like tomatoes and potatoes. If one gets early blight, it can easily spread to the other. And since both have the same nutrient needs, growth can become stunted and yield low. For this reason, it's usually a great rule of thumb not to fill a garden bed with plants from one family *only*. Try interspersing some helpful flowers and herbs in between, or other complementary plants.

Some plants compete for water, light, and nutrients. Like a tall plant that blocks all the sun or a needy one that hogs all the water. However, sometimes a height difference can be helpful, depending on the needs of the plants involved. Tomatoes love the sun and are tall. Lettuce does great in the shade, and it's short. Looks like opposites can attract, too!

So choose plant neighbors with *complementary* characteristics, rather than *competing*. For instance, a heavy feeder like corn would go great next to a heavy giver like beans, which supply the nitrogen the corn needs. Corn and tomato, however, are both heavy feeders that would likely compete for nutrients. On top of that, they are both targets for the tomato hornworm and corn earworm.

Some plants are downright toxic to others. **Allelopathic plants** produce chemicals that harm other plants. For example, the walnut tree has a toxic chemical called juglone that can kill plants nearby, and sunflowers can prevent potatoes from meeting their potential.

However, amidst warring Montagues and Capulets, there's often a Romeo and Juliet to make the exception (you know, minus the tragic death part). For instance, some plants aren't as sensitive to juglone, such as various beans, beets, onions, corn, and raspberries. So don't worry, your beloved walnut tree doesn't have to grow alone.

And the sunflower can provide an awesome covering for plants around it, and a trellis for climbers like squash, cucumbers, peas, and beans. Some even *use* the allelopathy of sunflowers to their advantage to keep away weeds in agricultural systems. Check out the findings from this study by Rabat et al. (2017):

> The field, pot culture, and laboratory studies have shown that inclusion of sunflower crops in rotation and intercropping considerably reduced the weed population in the current and succeeding crops.

Wow, so if used strategically, allelopathy can actually be a powerful tool in the garden. It's all in the planning. Let's continue …

While companion planting can boost flavor in some plants, it can ruin them for others. Cucumbers absorb flavors from aromatic herbs like rosemary and sage. I'll pass on that rosemary-flavored pickle, thank you!

At the same time, cucumbers do *well* next to dill. I guess it works in the jar and in the ground!

So you see, there are exceptions to rules and different things that happen with different combinations.

How far apart should you place feuding plants? Well, there's no exact measurement. But it's safe to say that a few other plants should be planted in between the rivals. You know, to help mediate those nasty disagreements.

Looking Beyond Pairings

Inevitably, all the excitement around companion planting can fill us with endless iterations of the question, "Does X go with Y?" This is totally okay, but there may be another way of looking at it.

Perhaps a more effective way of thinking about polyculture, and what to plant together in the garden, is to look *beyond* finding perfect two-plant *pairings*, and *onto groupings* of 3 or more. We can examine the unique benefits that each plant brings to the garden, and assemble a team that loads up on those benefits. Like creating a mini-ecosystem.

So, if you know you want to plant tomatoes, you could definitely look up what are good companion plants for tomatoes, and get some great ideas. Basil, bell peppers, lettuce, marigolds.

To take it further, though, you could also assemble a team of different plants around your tomatoes, to fulfill different powerful roles. Maybe a few of its favorite companions are up close, improving flavor, fixing the soil, suppressing weeds, etc. And then, you have others on the outside perimeter, repelling pests, attracting pollinators, etc.

Teamwork makes the dream work in business and in gardening! And this is where guild planting comes in.

GUILD PLANTING: ASSEMBLING YOUR TEAM

Guild planting is like companion planting 2.0. It creates a community of plants that all support each other. Planning a plant guild is like assembling an all-star team. One that works together like a well-tuned machine. It can sustain the garden mini-ecosystem with little assistance.

The "three sisters" we mentioned above are a type of guild.

A plant guild should include a minimum of three compatible companion plants. Each, ideally, should fill multiple functions. The ultimate all-star plant guild should have at least one of the following:

- An **attractor**. These plants attract pollinators and also beneficial insects which feed on pests. Herbs such as lavender, dill, fennel, borage, and others. Many flowers like salvia, sunflowers, yarrow, coneflower, and daisy, but most flowers will do.
- A **repeller** is a strong-smelling herb that confuses pests. Onions, garlic, and chives are famous for this. Also, daffodils and oregano. Marigold is a permaculture favorite, and many line their beds with it. It's also an attractor and accumulator.
- A **suppressor** acts as a barrier and/or ground cover. It prevents weeds and grasses from moving in and absorbing nutrients. Red clover, pumpkins, rhubarb, strawberries, nasturtiums, squash, garlic, chives, vetch, and comfrey are great suppressors.
- A **mulcher** is a plant that supplies compost in the form of dried leaves or dead foliage (mulch). It incorporates more carbon into the soil and retains moisture, like mulch. These can be perennials that provide a

183

steady supply of mulch. Comfrey is a famous one! Lemon balm, nasturtiums, yarrow, rhubarb, vetch, rye, hostas, and borage also fit the bill.

- A **fixer** (nitrogen-fixer) is a plant that takes nitrogen from the air and deposits or "fixes" it in the soil so other plants can use it. Legumes are famous for this, and green beans, soybeans, chickpeas, and clover are great examples.
- A **dynamic accumulator** is a deep-rooted plant that breaks up soil, "mines" nutrients from down below, and allows for better plant nutrient uptake. Examples are comfrey, chickweed, stinging nettle, strawberries, sorrel, vetch, tansy, supine, chicory, and dandelion. Borage and yarrow also make this list.

There are some plants that play five roles at once! Comfrey, lemon balm, vetch, dutch clover, white clover. These are a few of the powerhouses. Many others play 2, 3, or 4 of the above roles.

Assembling a plant guild might seem overwhelming for the first-time permie. But once you start to notice patterns, you'll be a regular plant coach, assembling all-star teams in your sleep! (While you dream of native perennials).

If you feel up to the task, this is a wonderful way to start a thriving and everlasting permaculture garden. Remember, a guild can be as small as a trio of corn, beans, and squash, or it could be the start of your food forest.

Typically, to design a guild, you pick an "anchor" to be the focus plant in the middle and build roles around it, working your way out. If designing a guild around a perennial like a fruit tree, you can draw out the **drip line**, which is a circle around your tree marking where the canopy of the mature tree will reach. Build your team within this area, trying to cover each role above at least once. Look for some good companions, and mix them up. Draw out your design. Get excited.

Once you have your planting area, use the gardening method of your choice to plant the guild. For instance, cover it with some cardboard or newspaper to get rid of any current weeds, wet it down, and do some layering and composting. Time your planting, and execute!

When designing a companion or guild planting, consider timing. Plants will need to be started at different times to benefit — and not get in the way of — each other. For example, in a three sisters grouping, the corn is planted first to give the beans something to climb. The beans are planted 2-3 weeks later, and the squash a week later.

Mulch the whole area, or where needed. And, since guilds often involve trees:

LET'S TALK TREES

When planting trees and mulching around them, you want to keep the **root collar** (a.k.a. **root flare** or **trunk flare**) exposed. That's where the tree roots *just* begin to fan or "flare out" and where the roots join the main stem or trunk. It's actually a part of the trunk. The bottom of the tree should look tapered out (at least a little) like the trunk is starting to sink its fingers into the ground. Your tree ideally shouldn't look like a telephone pole sticking out of the ground. Burying the root flare can lead to serious health issues later. Many an arborist stay busy doing root flare excavations to save trees planted too deep.

So, what if you're suddenly remembering last year's landscaping job and now you're worried your trees had their root flares buried? Perhaps, now that your permie powers are sharpening, you can even hear your trees whispering to you as the wind blows through their leaves, *"Set us freeeeee."*

Hang on, don't embark on your shovel crusade just yet! Liberation is possible, but just digging could really damage some roots. There are special excavation methods you'll want to research or call an arborist for.

Oh, and let's touch on those "mulch volcanoes" you see around the bases of shrubs and trees. You know, the giant mulch mounds people pile so high that they swallow the bottom 1-2 feet of the tree trunk? Those are a very silly idea. They cause trees a lot of problems and stress. I'd be stressed out too if people buried me up to my knees!

So save the trees. Say no to volcanoes.

SIMPLE CROP ROTATION FOR LONG-TERM PLANNING

As you now know, biennial and perennial plants like to take up permanent residence where you plant them. Moving them would be counterproductive. Each year, you may need to amend the soil to keep it healthy for these long-living plants to thrive. But for annuals that don't mind a transitory lifestyle, crop rotation can be a helpful practice.

In the home garden, **crop rotation** means changing the location of annual plants each season. Moving your annual veggie crops from bed to bed each year does three things:

- It means your plants escape disease-causing fungi and bacteria that have taken up residence in the soil. Maybe in the bed where potatoes grew, a disease like potato scab settles, which can affect the entire Solanaceae (potato) family. Moving the potatoes to the next bed the following year means the new family that comes in won't be affected, and the new bed will be safe for the potatoes.
- This works with pests, too. It confuses the pests that target specific plants, leaving behind larvae that may have overwintered in the soil.
- It also manages soil fertility. Since some plants deplete certain nutrients from the soil, moving them to a new plot gives them a fresh start. And it gives you a chance to replenish the depleted soil, either with nitrogen-fixing plants, soil amendments, or compost.

Crop rotation is recommended because it's a fantastic way to troubleshoot problems naturally. It improves soil health over time and adds diversity to your garden. The best way to practice crop rotation in your permaculture garden is by having several garden beds or plots. Here are some simple tips:

- Avoid planting plants from the same family in the same area of the garden each year. (e.g. *Solanaceae*, the "nightshade" or "tomato family" includes tomatoes, potatoes, peppers, and eggplants)
- Even better, avoid planting an area with plants from the same family more than once in 3-4 years.
- Plant a cover crop in empty spots to improve soil health naturally.
- Keep a log of what you plant each year in a notebook to help you plan.

Feel free to combine crop rotation with companion planting principles by first choosing your main crop rotation crops, and then assembling teams around those, keeping in mind future rotations. In fact, marrying these strategies is a great way to mitigate the weaknesses of using just one.

For instance, growing plants from the tomato family all together in one bed might make the group more susceptible to common pests. Interspersing basil, marigolds and nasturtiums, and other herbs and flowers, could help balance it and counteract this.

A great way to combine strategies is to first put the major vegetable families/groups on rotation, and then assemble herbs and flowers for the companions. It gets a little complex, but it's fun to work out!

Two common ways to rotate crops are to rotate *by plant family* or rotate *by nutrient demands*.

We'll take a look at a popular system for rotating involving 4 garden beds, rotating by nutrient demands. Each group moves one bed over each year, like garden musical chairs.

We'll focus on one main aspect of this plan, which is the use of *nitrogen* in the soil. The rotation starts with nitrogen fixers or "heavy givers" that feed the soil. Then, that same spot is occupied by heavy feeders the following year, which make the most use of the nitrogen. Then come medium feeders, then light feeders, which need the least nitrogen. Then it starts over.

Here is a great 4-year plan based on this idea: Legume (Givers) → Leaf (Heavy) → Fruit (Medium) → Root (Light)

1. **Legumes**: green beans, soybeans, fava beans, peas, edamame, lima beans, chickpeas, peanuts, alfalfa
2. **Leaf (leaf bearers / leafy greens)**: kale, cabbage, broccoli, cauliflower, lettuce, swiss chard, spinach, brussels sprouts, herbs
3. **Fruit (fruiting plants + potatoes)**: melons, eggplant, tomatoes, cucumber, squash, peppers, corn, sweet potatoes, potatoes (the odd one in this category)
4. **Root Veggies**: radishes, garlic, onions, turnips, carrots, beets, celery, parsnip

WRAP-UP

At the end of the last chapter, we went over some questions you might ask yourself to approach that age-old question for gardeners:

What plants do I choose?

I'm gonna say it again because it just bears repeating: *it's okay, you don't have to "get it just right", your plan will change as you go, and it will unfold in stages in coming years.* Have fun with it, try things, and get some dirt under your nails.

With that said, bring out your handy plant list and continue to make notes. You may find you have some new questions now, as well as some new answers. This may lead you to add plants to your list for this year or coming years, or maybe cross some plants off. Ask:

Where are the more permanent spots in my garden plan? What perennials might I want to plant there? Would I want to imagine a guild around them? Would I like to try a crop rotation at some point in the future? What are my "top" plant choices, and what are some of their companions that would do well in my climate and plan?

Are you feeling your team coming together more? I hope so!

Now, guess what? We get to expand your team *even more*. Planning and planting your garden is the first part of the story. The next part is welcoming the rest of the world in.

An ecosystem wouldn't be complete without animal life. At this stage in your journey, you might not be ready to get the family dairy cow, but there are still many ways to make animal life a part of your permie plan. From bugs to birds to bunnies.

In the next chapter, you'll learn about inviting nature in and exploring smaller animals that can team up with your permaculture garden.

PART IV

EXPANDING THE DESIGN

INTEGRATING ANIMAL LIFE

 Life is only half complete if you're not surrounded by animals.

— ME

But when I lived in the city, we couldn't have livestock. Did I let that stop me? Nope. The world is full of animals; you just have to invite them in.

I turned my front yard into a wildflower meadow. It tipped off on a 40-degree slope that was a death-defying stunt to mow, so the meadow was a twofold benefit. The neighbors weren't crazy about it at first, but once they saw it in its blooming summertime glory, they were impressed. And so were the butterflies, bees, songbirds, rabbits, and deer who came to visit.

Anyone can encourage pollinators and other wildlife to share their garden space, even if it's just an apartment balcony. In this chapter, we'll talk about how insects, spiders, and animals play a role in the permaculture garden. Then I'll give you a rundown on the small livestock you can raise in your backyard.

THE ROLE OF INSECTS IN A PERMACULTURE GARDEN

If insects were to vanish, the environment would collapse into chaos.

— EDWARD O. WILSON

Are you icked out by insects? Scream at spiders? Bolt from bees? Well, hang up your hangups because whether you like it or not, bugs play a crucial role in the permaculture garden. By providing food and aiding in pollination, they ensure the continuation of life on Earth. And here's how.

1. Insects Initiate the Food Web

Sixty percent of the world's birds diet on insects. Not to mention the reptiles, amphibians, fish, mammals, and yes, even humans that depend on bugs for food. Without these delicious little creatures at the base of the food chain, many species would poof out of existence.

In the permaculture garden, many beneficial bugs and animals depend on insects to fill their bellies and raise their young. There are creatures out there that are happy to dine on the mosquitoes, gnats, and flies that drive you nuts.

2. Insects Pollinate Plants & Disperse Seeds

Insects pollinate roughly 85% of wild plants and 75% of agricultural crops. In this mutual relationship, the insects get food from pollen and nectar. Pollen sticks to the insects' bodies and is spread to other plants. Voilà, pollination!

Butterflies and bees are the most commonly known pollinators, but many species of moths, flies, beetles, and wasps also serve the purpose. Other insect species help disperse seeds by eating or pushing them along commonly used paths. Ants are great at this.

3. Insects Control Harmful Organisms

Everyone thinks ladybugs are so darn cute. But did you know that they're stone-cold killers? A single ladybug can devour over a thousand aphids in its lifetime. And a wasp? Don't even get me started.

Carnivorous bugs do their part to keep the harmful six-legged pests in check. While they may seem scary (here's looking at you, spiders), they just want to help. Talk about being misunderstood! Spiders, wasps, praying mantises, hoverflies, and assassin bugs (aptly named, right?) all prey on aphids, caterpillars, beetles, and other insects that destroy garden plants.

4. INSECTS CLEAN UP WASTE

Bugs are like nature's tiny janitors. Insects like earthworms, flies, millipedes, pillbugs, beetles, and termites recycle organic matter and give it new life as soil. They eat dead plants, animal bodies, and feces and return it to the earth. This recycling makes the soil fertile and rich in nutrients. It's a dirty job, but somebody's gotta do it. Thanks, bugs!

HOW TO ENCOURAGE MORE INSECTS INTO YOUR GARDEN

If you want to encourage beneficial insects to move into your garden space, treat them like you would a beloved family pet. You'd give Fido food, water, and shelter. So do the same for your insect friends, and they'll be happy to join your garden family.

- *Grow a variety of plants.* Pollinators are attracted to the colors and scents of plants. By growing a variety of plants, you're more likely to draw in a variety of insects. Flowers with compound blossoms and flowering herbs attract pollinators while deterring some pests. Various spring- and fall-blooming plants will ensure your pollinators have food year-round.
- *Plant native species.* Since insects are local to your area, they enjoy dining on the local fare. Native plants will be the most beneficial to them and will thrive in your garden.
- *Grow early-blooming plants.* Pollinators are often the first to wake up in the spring. Planting early-blooming flowers will establish that your garden is the place to be. Alyssum, crocus, and daffodil are some early-blooming flowers. In some regions, peach, plum, and cherry trees are early bloomers, too.
- *Provide water.* Even bugs need water to survive. A bird bath, fountain, water feature, or a simple shallow bowl will provide water for your little garden helpers.
- *Provide shelter.* Leave some areas of your garden "wild" to provide nesting areas for insects. A pile of leaf litter or brush trimmings can host dozens of insect visitors. They'll especially appreciate it in the fall

and winter. Some gardeners buy or build wooden "bug hotels" that serve as homes for various beneficial pollinators and predatory insects. Search for plans online for a fun upcycling project!

- *Avoid pesticides.* Even natural pesticides like pyrethrum can kill both harmful and beneficial insects. When possible, let nature do the job for you.

There are so many flowers, herbs, and other plants you can plant to attract beneficial bugs and pollinators. And a lot of times, they're beautiful! Many gardens will have sections marked specifically as pollinator gardens.

Here are some "attractors" that are permie favorites: comfrey, nasturtiums, marigolds, vetch, strawberry, borage, and lavender.

There are many more, including but not limited to: agastache, aster, bee balm, black-eyed Susan, butterfly bush, chives, coneflower, daffodils, daisy, dill, dutch & white clover, fennel, goldenrod, ironweed, lemon balm, milkweed, oregano, Queen Anne's lace, salvia, sedum, sunflower, tansy, verbena, and yarrow.

OTHER HELPFUL WILDLIFE IN THE GARDEN

While insects have a huge part to play, these two- and four-legged creatures deserve a shout-out, too.

- *Birds.* Like butterflies and bees, birds are efficient pollinators, especially hummingbirds. And by eating berries and fruits, they spread seeds in their poop. Birds are also great pest removers. Adding a bird bath or bird feeder to your garden can encourage native birds to hang out.
- *Lizards, Snakes, & Turtles.* Although many are terrified of snakes, they're great in the garden. They're excellent at catching rodents and not interested in sharing your veggies. The same goes for lizards and turtles who love to dine on insects.
- *Frogs & Toads.* Frogs and toads eat flies, slugs, and other pesky critters. Providing hiding spots like brush, rock, or brick piles will make reptiles and amphibians feel at home. And a pond or water feature is a great way to lure in frogs.
- *Bats.* Mosquitoes suck. In more ways than one. Thank goodness a single bat can devour as many as 1000 mosquitoes in an hour. Bats

also eat moths, who are notorious garden pests, and help with pollination by eating fruit. You can set up bat houses in your yard to invite bats to move in.

ARE YOU READY FOR SMALL LIVESTOCK?

Any stable ecosystem is a balanced relationship between plant and animal species. So, consider incorporating livestock to make your permaculture garden a truly sustainable and self-sufficient ecosystem. Animals process vegetables, grasses, and weeds and turn them into manure that enriches the soil. And they provide food for your family.

Owning livestock allows you to enjoy a fully rounded diet. It provides meat, eggs, milk, and manure to feed plants. You can avoid the skyrocketing prices of meat and eggs at the grocery store. You'll know exactly what's in your food and that the animals were treated well. And once you've tried a farm-raised egg, you'll never go back.

And for our vegan and vegetarian friends, there are so many awesome reasons to bring animals into the garden. Also, certain animals may not work in city or renting environments, depending on your setup. It's always good to ask and see what your options are. Just pick out the parts of this chapter that apply and resonate with you the most!

When you hear the word "livestock," you might think of cows, pigs, and horses. But there are many productive livestock animals that you can keep on less than half an acre of land. Small livestock doesn't take up much space, is easy to manage, and provides multiple benefits.

Let's talk about a few that are possible for backyards of any size.

CHICKENS

In the past few years, changes in regulations have made it legal to keep chickens in many cities.

Chickens provide eggs, meat, fertilizer, and pest and weed control in your permaculture garden. Home-grown eggs are one of the most versatile, delicious, and nutritious foods you can eat. Chickens' unique personalities make them lovely pets. They're adaptable, low-maintenance, and can provide a consistent food source. And there are many breeds to choose from.

But before you buy your first chicks, check your local zoning regulations. If chickens are permitted in your area, there may be laws concerning how many you can keep, how they must be housed, and whether or not you can own a rooster.

CHOOSING CHICKENS

If you're a backyard homesteader, four to six chickens is a good place to start. A mature hen will lay about six eggs a week. She lays one a day and takes off a day or two each week. Factor in the number of eggs your family would like to have each week when determining how many chickens you need.

Rhode Island Reds, Barred Plymouth Rocks, White Leghorns, Buff Orpingtons, and Easter Eggers are the most popular chickens for egg production. These have calm, friendly dispositions, are climate adaptable, and have high egg production rates.

Cornish Rocks are the best choice if you're looking for a fast-growing, beefy bird for meat. These convert feed to muscle efficiently and can dress out (this means slaughtered, cleaned, and ready to cook) at about five pounds in as little as eight weeks.

Many people choose to get chickens as chicks because they're cheaper than buying mature hens. And, yeah, they're *adorable*! You can source chicks from a local farm, shipped from an online breeder, or at a local feed store in the springtime.

While buying adult hens can be expensive, they're ready-to-go egg makers. If you start with chicks, remember that you'll have to keep them in a brooder for about six weeks. A **brooder** is a warm, dry space for chicks kept at around 90°F-95°F (32°C-35°C).

HOUSING CHICKENS

The number of chickens you decide to keep will also depend on your available space. Generally, a chicken should have a minimum of four square feet of coop space and eight square feet of run space. A smaller coop is acceptable if your chickens can free-range around the yard.

Building a coop is the most expensive part of chicken keeping. But, fortunately, it's a one-time cost. Provide your flock with a place to *roost* (i.e. sit on a perch and sleep) for the night, get out of the elements, and keep safe from predators. This could be something you've built from scavenged scraps, a store-bought coop, or a building you already have on your property. Factor this into your permaculture design sketch. Your chicken coop should be somewhere that is accessible to you and that you don't mind visiting once or twice a day.

When planning, you should also decide if you want your chickens to free range (walk around freely) or stay in a confined chicken run. Having chickens in the yard with you is fun, but there can be some drawbacks. Chickens love to dig up seeds and emerging sprouts in the garden. And they're not shy about sharing your vegetable yield.

Some people allow their chickens to free range only during certain times of the year. They're excellent at tilling up the earth at the end of the growing season. Don't worry, they do it right. They only till the very top, aerating the soil while not disturbing the soil life. Others set up protective measures, like fencing or putting mesh over garden beds to keep chickens out.

CARING FOR CHICKENS

Chickens will need access to water and well-balanced chicken feed. But they also love eating kitchen and garden scraps. Chickens are excellent at the no-waste principle. If your chicken yard is located near the garden, you can toss the flock weeds, plant debris, finely mulched grass clippings, and imperfect fruit and veggies. Like pigs, chickens will eat just about anything.

Then they convert all that food into glorious poop. I mean, fertilizer. Chicken waste is such a good garden fertilizer that it's even sold commercially. There's just one holdup: you can't toss fresh chicken poo on your garden. Due to its high ammonia content, it's too strong to apply directly to plants. Depending on your composting method, it will need to be composted for 4-24 weeks.

Manure is considered a "green" in the composting balance along with food scraps, so you'd need to add plenty of "browns" to balance it out. An easy balance is 50/50, or 1:1 browns to greens. Some suggest more browns, like a 2:1 or 3:2 ratio. Leaves, small sticks, shredded paper, dead plant material, straw, and chicken bedding material are all browns.

More on composting in Chapter 13.

RABBITS

Rabbits are the ultimate backyard livestock. They can be raised on rooftops, balconies, and patios if you're short on space. You can keep a pair of meat rabbits on a square yard of space and have a steady meat and fertilizer supply year-round. They're quiet, so they won't bother the neighbors.

And rabbits are meat-making powerhouses. One doe (that's a female rabbit) can produce around 300 pounds of meat in a year. She can produce up to seven litters yearly, with 5-12 babies in each litter. Rabbits can be butchered in as little as three months. And farm-raised rabbit meat is delicious. It's a lean protein with very little fat, a high vitamin content, and less cholesterol than any other meat. Since it's all white meat, it tastes similar to chicken breast and is just as versatile.

But wait, that's not all! Rabbit poop makes an excellent fertilizer. Some of the best! It has four times the nutrients of cow or horse manure and twice the richness of chicken manure. And the best part is that you can spread it directly on your garden. It's considered "cold" manure, so it doesn't need to be composted before use. Some people cage rabbits on the ground and move them around the garden for instant fertilization. However, I don't recommend this on ground you want intact, since rabbits love to dig.

Popular meat rabbit breeds are New Zealand, Californian, and Florida White. American Blue, Chinchilla, and Silver Fox are good multi-purpose choices if you want rabbits for meat and pelts.

GUINEA PIGS

Guinea pigs are another cold manure maker that are popular in permaculture setups. They are pretty low maintenance and bring a lot of benefits like recycling your food scraps and making great friends! They pretty much have the same care requirements as rabbits. And like rabbits, you can eat them (if you can muster up the heart for it)!

WORMS

Okay, so most people don't think of them as "livestock," but worms are a crucial part of the permaculture garden. No, you probably won't want to eat them, and you probably don't want to cuddle them, but they can be just as beneficial as chickens or rabbits. Worm farming is an eco-friendly way to eliminate waste and reinvest it in the Earth as a natural fertilizer.

Vermiculture is the practice of using worms to produce compost. As a bonus, "vermiculture" rhymes with permaculture. So that's cool.

When we talk about "worm farming," we're not referring to the earthworms you find in your yard. Composting worms are called redworms, red wigglers, or tiger worms. They originally come from the Amazon, but you can also buy them on Amazon (or many other online retailers) and have them shipped right to your door.

Worms are exceptional food processing machines. They'll eat anything that was once living, including kitchen scraps, poo, paper, fabric, and even vacuum dust. They quickly process the waste by eating it and pooping it out, converting it into **worm castings**, which look like dark, rich soil-like rounds, and are a nutrient-rich plant superfood that can be added to potting soil or compost. Some even soak castings in some dechlorinated water to brew some **worm tea**, a nutrient-rich liquid fertilizer (this is not tea you want to drink).

FEEDING THE WORMS

Worm farms are a lot like compost piles. Worms like a balanced diet of greens and browns. See Chapter 13 and Appendix C on composting for specifics.

Consider adding a sticker or paper to your worm farm to remind you what to feed them and *not* to feed them. In general, you want to add more food when about half the previous meal has been eaten up.

BUILDING A WORM FARM

You can purchase a pre-made worm farm online or build your own from something like a bucket, tote, or styrofoam cooler. Often, DIY plans (and premade farms) involve several buckets stacked, each for different stages in the decomposition process, and a bottom bucket for drainage.

A worm farm can be as large or small as space allows. You can even keep a small worm farm in the corner of your laundry room or office. So even apartment-dwellers can proudly call themselves farmers! Once you get started, worm farming doesn't cost a thing. It's low-maintenance and is an excellent way to reduce waste while feeding your garden.

You'll want to keep it somewhere with a relatively stable temperature. Somewhere between 55°F-77°F (13°C-25°C) is best. Oh and don't forget holes for air and drainage. Worms gotta breathe too!

WORM TUNNELS

Another awesome project is a **worm tunnel**, or **in-ground worm bin**, which is a hybrid between a worm farm and small compost bin that is planted right in the soil of your garden bed. **Worm towers** are partially buried PVC towers made with similar ideas.

To build a worm tunnel, you can take an old bucket or nursery pot, drill big holes in the side (1"), cut off the bottom, and bury it in the soil like a well. It can even go right in your raised bed. This will act like a compost bin, that worms go in and out of, munching on the stuff inside and also helping the garden around it.

It's best to throw a little finished compost on the bottom to start the composting process, and always have a "blanket" like a newspaper on top of the pile to create a warm, damp environment. You'll want to cover the bucket with a lid (you can use a plant saucer weighted down by a rock).

Basically, you open it, toss composting material inside like food scraps, set the lid on top, walk away and forget about it. The worms and composting do the rest. Nutrients leach into the garden bed around it. After a while, the bucket may fill up with worm castings. At that point, you can dig out the worm tunnel and place it in another spot in the garden.

ASSORTED FURRED, FINNED, AND FEATHERED FRIENDS

Talking about all the livestock options for spaces large and small could take a whole series of books, so I've only covered the top choices for a modest-sized permaculture garden.

Other excellent animals to incorporate into a small-space permaculture plan are quails, pigeons, and bees. **Aquaponics**, or farming fish along with plants, supplies two yields in a single space and can be done in any backyard. This is a really powerful system because the fish fertilize the plants, and the plants purify the water. Symbiosis!

You can incorporate goats, pigs, sheep, alpacas, pheasants, geese, or ducks if you have half an acre. Waterfowl like ducks and geese, of course, will require a water source, but they're excellent at pest control and weeding while providing eggs and meat.

Ducks even scored a mention from Bill Mollison when he famously said, *"You don't have a snail problem. You have a duck deficiency."*

In other words, animals are a great way to balance nature with nature. If life gives you snails, bring in the ducks (natural predators to snails).

And don't forget the value of dogs and cats. Not only are they man's best friends, but they can protect your property from rodent and human pests.

Years from now, maybe your "big dream" slice of Eden involves a diverse array of different animals and plants all working together in harmony. After all, it's nature's way, right?

 What are the main principles underlying Nature's agriculture? These can most easily be seen in operation in our woods and forests. Mixed farming is the rule: plants are always found with animals: many species of plants and of animals all live together.

— SIR ALBERT HOWARD, *AN AGRICULTURAL TESTAMENT*

THINGS TO CONSIDER BEFORE INTRODUCING LIVESTOCK

However, on your way to the big dream, remember: *slow and steady wins the race.*

One of the biggest mistakes first-timers make is buying animals before they're ready. A baby chick might be small, cute, and manageable now, but think a year in the future. It's going to quadruple in size, it's going to need food, and it's going to poop *constantly*. Are you prepared for all this eating and pooping?

Animals can reinvest energy into your garden and help you reduce waste. And eventually, they may yield quite the return on investment. But you also need to budget for them in your bank account and daily workload. Here are some things to think about:

- *Space.* Consider the minimum space requirements each species needs to be happy and healthy. Will you be content to keep animals in cages? Or would you prefer a more flexible method, like free-ranging, pasturing, or mobile housing? Will you need to exclude the animals from certain parts of your space? For example, goats can destroy an orchard in a matter of hours.

- **Shelter.** Your animals will need a place to sleep to be protected from the elements and predators. Do you have existing structures, or will you need to build them? Will the structure be permanent- like a barn- or mobile, like a chicken tractor?
- **Food.** Animals can be a food source, but they must also eat it. And this can cost a lot of money, depending on the breed. For example, you may find buying a frozen chicken cheaper than feeding a broiler up to slaughter age. Weigh the financial, ecological, and personal pros and cons. Think about what foods you'll need to purchase to keep your animals healthy and which ones you can grow yourself or source for free.
- **Water.** As a permie, you want to save and conserve water. But having animals puts a higher demand on the resource. Can you deliver fresh, clean water to your animals every day? Is there a potential catchment system you can construct?
- **Waste.** Fortunately, you can use most livestock waste for compost. But you'll have to have a way to collect it and store it until it's usable. Without regular maintenance, that poop can really pile up. Do you have a way to keep a healthy living area for your animals and keep the smell to a minimum?
- **Companionship.** Most animals are not happy living alone. They need another member of their own species or a suitable companion species to be happy. Do you have the space and resources to keep multiple animals?
- **Time and Care.** Animals need TLC. If you like to vacation, you'll need to think ahead and see if a friend, neighbor, or family member can come to check on the livestock, feed them, and do any regular maintenance while you're gone. They'll need to be the right people, who can feed your animals the right way at the right time. Worm farms can be left unattended for 3-6 weeks if left with enough supplies. Whereas rabbits need check-ins every 2-4 days (some would say 24 hours max), even with plenty of food and water. And of course, the pollinators roam wild. What are the regular upkeep needs of the animals you're considering?

WRAP-UP

Incorporating animals in your permaculture design can be incredibly rewarding. Whether it's wild birds and bugs, chickens, or a whole barnyard full of livestock, experiencing animal life is good for your soul. Listen to the buzz of pollinators at work or the sound of chickens cooing and clucking contently to themselves. It's sweet music. And it's just another way to make your permaculture garden a sustainable, calming place of joy.

Now that we've talked through animal life, we'll talk about another way you can use nature in your permaculture garden, and expand your team even more. Some of its most incredible members are already all around you. Chapter 12 is all about harnessing the power of the elements.

RESOURCES PART 1: WORKING WITH THE ELEMENTS OF NATURE

 If you only do one thing, collect rainwater.

— BILL MOLLISON

Do you remember the '90s cartoon Captain Planet? A flying blue warrior with a wicked mullet and a group of kids called the Planeteers work together to fight the evils of pollution.

Well, as a permie, you're kind of a Planeteer yourself. Like a superhero, you harness the power of the elements to save the world! Or, at least … your own little slice of it.

Water, earth, wind, and sun are central resources in the permaculture design. You might not have a magical ring that compels them to do your bidding (darn), but with a little knowledge and planning, you can use them for the powers of good. As Principle #2 reminds us, we can catch and store energy from natural resources to reduce waste, help our garden thrive, and leave a positive impact on the Earth. Go planet!

Soon, you'll find there are powerful resources all around you, and they may be more abundant than you think. In this chapter, we'll talk about how we can use water collection, wind, and sun in the permaculture design.

In the next chapter, we'll really zero in on the zero-waste principle, and draw power from what many would throw out. We'll harvest hidden stored energy through composting, upcycling, and even creatively working with weeds.

And maybe ... if you listen closely ... somewhere in the distance, you might just hear the words of Captain Planet to the Planeteers:

"The power is yours!"

RAINWATER COLLECTION

Pay close attention, because collecting rainwater is one of the most important practices in permaculture. Remember Bill's bold declaration at the start of the chapter? So quit your day job and get out there with a bucket!

Well, maybe not that extreme. But collecting rainwater is one of the most beneficial and easiest things you can do in your permaculture setup. Rainwater harvesting, also called **rainwater catchment**, is collecting rainwater that runs off of a structure, and storing it for later use. It can be as simple as a barrel under your gutter drain spout or an elaborate gray water collection system with pumps, tanks, and purifiers.

Water is in continuous movement on the planet. It's ceaselessly changing form in what's called the **hydrologic cycle**. Precipitate, collect, evaporate, condensate, repeat. If you wanna get more complex, that "collect" part is where the fallen rain infiltrates the earth, and surface runoff finds its way to ponds, rivers, and oceans. Remember when you pretended to be a little raindrop finding its way to the ocean in Chapter 4? That part.

A common misconception many people have is that there's not enough water available in their area. But in truth, it's more like a shortage of collection. The trick is in capturing that water as it flows through its cycle.

Several rainwater collection systems have great success around the world: things like imprinting, trincheras, gabions, and the Vallerani system. But trying to pack them into one chapter could seriously make our brains hurt. So, for now, let's stick to a couple basics.

RAIN BARRELS: A SIMPLE SOLUTION

Do you stress out about your water bill? If so, rainwater is the perfect natural resource to collect. It's 100% free! It's also packed with minerals and nutrients that your plants love. And collecting it is good for the environment because it reduces pollution in rivers, lakes, and streams.

Check this: a 1,000-square-foot roof can capture 20,000 gallons of water annually. So how can you capture all of that glorious free water? A rain barrel is the simplest solution. And it's an excellent project for a beginning permie. **Rain barrels** capture rainwater that falls from a roof and hold it for later use. They're fitted with faucets, so you can use the water as needed.

You can purchase a rain barrel online, from your local home and garden store, or from your municipality. Or you can make your own. You'll just need a barrel and a few simple supplies from a home improvement store or garden center. You can often find 55-gallon barrels for sale in online classifieds like Craigslist. You could also use an old wooden wine barrel or a large plastic garbage bin with a lid.

And heck, if you just want to *get started and try something,* just stick a 5-gallon bucket where most of the rain is falling off your roof next storm. As the clouds clear, you'll have 5 gallons of rain you wouldn't have otherwise!

Your rain barrel should be positioned at the bottom of an existing downspout on your home, garage, barn, or another outbuilding. The site should be level, and the barrel should be raised a few feet off the ground to make it easy to dispense the water. You'll probably have to modify your downspout so that water flows into the opening of your rain barrel.

You should have a drainage pipe in place to divert overflow. This could be into your garden or another rain barrel. Ensure your rain barrel has a screen over the intake to prevent debris from falling into your water and mosquitoes from moving in.

Rain barrels don't require much maintenance once set up. Use the water as needed so the barrel's empty in time for the next rain event. Inspect your rain barrels monthly to ensure they're secure. Many barrels require you to drain and store upside down in the winter to prevent freezing.

SWELL SWALES TO SLOW, SPREAD, SINK, & STORE WATER

 Life isn't about waiting for the storm to pass. It's about learning to dance in the rain.

— VIVIAN GREENE

One of the best ways to "catch and store" this powerful rain energy is *right in the soil*. You can do this by taking advantage of the way water flows over your land, and strategically redirecting it where you want it to go. Not only can this solve drainage and erosion problems, but it can even *feed and rehydrate the soil*.

Unless your property has been professionally landscaped, water does its own thing when it rains, pooling up wherever nature (and gravity) directs it.

Entire books could be written on the strategic redirection of rainwater. We listed out a few water systems above but here are some more, for all you researchers: from French drains, to infiltration basins, to sunken garden beds, to keylines, and waffle beds (yum!), there are many awesome ways of managing storm runoff.

Maybe the most popular permie solution you'll hear about is the use of *swales and berms*. You'll probably hear these terms as much as "natives" and "perennials" in typical permaculture conversations.

These *earthworks* techniques carry many benefits: they solve erosion and drainage problems, catch and store energy and feed the soil, hydrate the land, create edges and microclimates, and are fantastic places to grow things.

Swales and berms help to *slow, spread, sink* and *store* precious rainwater.

Because there's a whole lot to say about earthworks, I will just cover some basics here. I hope this will help you see if this solution fits your space, and spur you on to research more about it!

A **swale** is a broad, shallow channel at the bottom of a slope used to direct and store runoff. In lay terms: a ditch. If you live in a neighborhood with no sidewalks, you might see swales running along the sides of the road.

Swales are often vegetated, meaning plants are growing in them. As water runs down the slope, it collects in the swale. This provides water to the plants growing in the swale, the slope leading down to it, the berm on the other side, and beyond the berm. A **berm** is like a little artificial hill or bank, made from soil. As a bonus, berm-a-culture rhymes with ... ah well, never mind.

Swales are a swell place to plant water-loving plants, bushes, fruit and nut trees, and all kinds of perennials, herbs, and so on. The berm on the other side makes an excellent no-till bed. There is some strategy involved in optimizing plant choices for the different spots on a swale and berm system, depending on your climate. Read on for more details.

How to Use Swales
Directing Flow and Milking the Water for All It's Worth

So how do you create a swale to control the flow of rainwater in your garden? All it takes is some thoughtful digging. There are some key things to keep in mind while swale-making.

First, swales and berms are not only designed to redirect water around your site like a water park full of slides. They definitely do direct water flow! And they can help change your water flow from an erosive kind to a non-damaging, strategic, gentle flow. And that's always nice.

But they're so much more! This little gem is a function-stacking permaculture powerhouse. Swales and berms are also *planting systems*. They're designed to strategically collect and hold water where it can slowly sink into the soil and feeds it and the nearby plants. It's like a slow-release H2O pill for your garden.

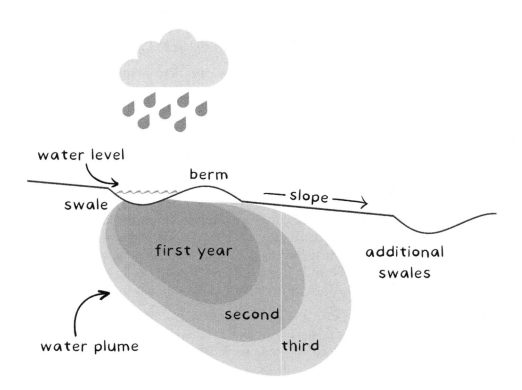

As an important side note, you'll also want to consider the amount of organic matter in the soil of your property, which also greatly affects your soil's water retention capacity. The more organic matter you build into the soil, the more water it will hold onto. Swales don't solve all drainage problems.

You'll need to observe how water flows on your property carefully and sketch out where you'd want swales and berms. Water collected in a swale will soak into the area below the berm, and *downhill* from the swale. This underground well you're building is called the **water plume**, and you know what's cool? Year after year, this plume gets bigger. It permeates more area underneath the surface, replenishing underground aquifers, and watering plants further and further away from the swale. Are you beginning to see the magic of swales?

When you dig a swale, there are a few things to keep in mind. First, the trench should be level for the entire length of the trench, so it doesn't pool at any one part of it.

Also, with this underground plume in mind that we want to create downhill, you could see why a swale at the very bottom of your slope wouldn't really help much to hydrate your yard (although it might still help with drainage issues). For this reason, it's great to dig a swale at a high point, but low enough to catch some runoff. Basically, uphill from a garden. In fact, on larger properties, multiple swales are built, with gardens and guilds in between.

OTHER SWALE CONSIDERATIONS

This may sound a bit like *terracing*. You know, when you have a really steep slope and you build retaining walls to stop the crazy erosion? However, since we are working with dirt here, and since water can be a *powerful force*: swales and berms are not recommended on slopes greater than 15° (about 1:3.75). Steeper slopes could cause a landslide. Which would not be fun. The ideal grade for swales is between 3° and 15°.

Here are a couple of other important structural notes.

You'll want swales at least 10 feet away from a building, and remember water should always be draining *away* from structures.

Also, you want the top 8 inches of soil in the swale to be well-draining. Water shouldn't be standing in the swale for more than a few days.

Finally, you'll want some overflow channels in case it really rains cats and dogs. At the ends of the swale, just cut through the berms about ¾ up, and have that water drain to another place you want. This could even be the next swale down the hill.

BUILD THE BERMS

Alright, so when you finally dig out your swale, what do you do with the soil you dug out? You may have already guessed since you're so dang sharp. One thing you *can do* is use the soil to build a berm right on the other side of the swale. Just mound up the soil on the downhill side of the swale, for the full length of the swale. Congratulations! You just made a swale and berm (sometimes called "berm and basin").

I recommend searching for some how-to's to get some ideas for measuring proportions, and come up with plans that are great for your particular situation. In general, swales are usually about 18 in to 2 ft wide, 6 in to 1.5 ft deep, and however long you can dig them. But swales are different with each space.

PLANTING ON BERMS AND SWALES

It's a great idea to plant on the berm as soon as the swale is complete, especially some ground cover (legumes, etc) on the top. This would prevent erosion and help hold soil in place. It would also start improving the soil, to get ready for the other plants you'll be planting on the berm.

What you plant depends on the climate you're in. Those from drier climates may actually plant a lot in the swale itself, to make the most use of pooled water. Whereas those from wetter climates may only want water-loving plants in the swale, and use different parts of the swale and berm hillsides for different uses.

Typically, this system is used for long-term perennials, which are planted in guilds *on the berm*, to make the most use of the water plume. Also, more deeply rooted perennials like nut trees tend to hold the system in place when they're planted on or immediately below the swale.

Smaller shrubs and trees are great choices for the sides of the berm. Other perennials and herbs are planted uphill from the swale. And annual gardens are often located downhill from the perennial guilds past the berm, making use of the water plume as it continues to expand. There's a whole lot you can do when you consider the varied microclimates created in this system.

Some will use this system as the foundation of their food forest, filling in all the layers using the different areas: uphill from the swale, inside the swale, on top of the berm, on the sides, downhill, etc. This is stacking functions at its best!

CAN I HÜGEL THIS?

Now, I know what you may be thinking. Somewhere you may have noticed the "mound" part of this design and your function-stacking permie brain went, "Aha! I know another place I've heard of mounds!"

You wanted to invite our old buddy Hügel to the party, didn't you? Listen, I love the guy, too. By all means, bring him over. But it's important to consider his strengths and weaknesses before combining functions here.

Remember, hügels are typically built for annuals and short-term perennials because they're designed to break down and collapse on themselves over time. A swale berm is meant to be a more permanent mound for more long-term perennial systems.

It's not that you *can't* place a swale before a hügelmound, but the key here is doing research and thinking toward the future. Otherwise, you can end up with trouble down the line. (Spirko, 2015).

If you tried hügelkultur with bigger logs, following a deeply dug swale, on a particularly steep slope … you could end up with a *log slide* after heavy rain! This is not the kind of perfect storm we want!

So, when working with swales, Google before you Hügel. Know your space, do some digging (figuratively before literally!), and ask some questions. Search online for something like "hügelkultur swales" if you have an insatiable appetite for learning more.

WHEN TO USE SWALES

Swales may be exciting and magical. But ultimately — depending on your particular topography, climate, or other unique factors — they may not be the right fit.

If you're on a steeper grade, it may be better to look into terracing or a different strategy.

Also, if your land is already pretty soggy, you may not need swales, which are meant to recharge the groundwater and hydrate the land. What you could do in this case is a different kind of swale — a *diversion ditch* — which is sloped instead of level across the length, designed to divert water into another place like into a pond or rain gardens.

Hopefully, that gives you a starting point on how and when to use this tool.

As you think of ways to harness the rain on your property, there's one more strategic consideration:

OBSERVE AND INTERACT: PLANTING ACCORDINGLY

You can also take advantage of rainwater by observing your space and planting accordingly. Some plants love having **wet feet**. This means their root systems are tolerant to consistently wet conditions.

Plant thirsty plants where rainfall is more abundant or has a greater flow, like at the bottom of a slope or a low spot in the land. These plants will absorb moisture and prevent it from running off to other areas.

Many native plants are happy to live in wet soil. Examples of wetland plants include black chokeberry, pussy willow, marsh marigold, joe pye weed, hibiscus, cardinal flower, and giant elephant ears.

Likewise, if you have a dry spot in your yard, try planting drought-tolerant plants. Examples include swamp milkweed, butterfly weed, goldenrod, Indian tobacco, trumpet honeysuckle, and several native trees.

THE OTHER ELEMENTS IN YOUR SPACE

While water and earth are garden heroes, there are a couple of other planeteers that are big helpers, too: wind and sun. These natural resources are at work in your garden every day, and harnessing their power is just a matter of proper planning.

Breaking Wind (No Pun Intended)

The wind is a wonderful resource for pollination, spreading seeds and pollen that would otherwise stick close to the parent plant. It provides resistance that young plants need to develop strong stems. Positioning your garden beds where they get ample air circulation also reduces disease. Some even build wind turbines (of all sizes and difficulty levels) and convert that air into power!

But in the garden, too much wind can have its disadvantages. Strong gusts can damage foliage, destroy blossoms, dislodge unripe fruit, and cause chill and moisture loss. If you're working with a windy spot, creating a windbreak can help you tame the beast.

A **windbreak** is any structure that blocks wind from a particular spot. It can be natural or manmade. Manmade windbreaks can be fences or building walls. If you have a little bit of space, natural windbreaks like hedges, shrubs, and trees are an excellent opportunity to add green beauty to your garden. Native hedging plants, in particular, attract local wildlife while protecting your garden.

Or you can combine both by providing a structure that plants can climb. Build a wall from reinforced mesh, lattice, or bamboo canes. Then plant vining plants like ivy, honeysuckle, or Virginia creeper and allow them to cover the structure. Aside from looking gorgeous, this creates a semi-permeable windbreak that proves more effective than a solid wall.

And in an urban setting, this green wall doubles as fantastic privacy screening from those nosy neighbors. P.S. You can use this technique on a balcony or patio: just plant your vines in pots.

A Spot in the Sun

Solar power is an eco-friendly and efficient way to power your home. From passive solar to active solar systems, there are amazing ways to harvest the constant power of the sun. On the smallest scale, you can use solar-powered outdoor lighting or solar-powered pumps for water features. But until you get that government grant for roof-mounted solar panels, you can take advantage of the sun in your permaculture garden by observing and interacting.

Back in Chapter 4, you observed the sun to see how it moved across your property. What areas got the most and least sun? How many hours of sun will your garden get? If you haven't already, apply this information to each plant in your prospective plan. If you're unsure how much sunlight a plant needs daily, you can usually find this information on the back of the seed packet, or the ID tag on a store-bought seedling.

Think about the mature height of plants when mapping out your plot, especially when companion planting. Always plant taller plants on the north side of the garden and shorter plants on the south side. This way, they all can absorb enough light as the sun moves across the sky.

WRAP-UP

Now you've got the power of the elements themselves at your back. You're soaking up the sun. You're directing the wind. You're carving the earth and harvesting the rain. What can stop you?

There's a lot more precious energy we can capture and store, and it's *all around us*. And a lot of times, we don't even know it!

Imagine for a moment that you had little papers show up in the mail constantly with strange symbols on them. Day after day, they show up, and not knowing what they are, you throw them out. One day, you discover they're actually *currency from another country*, and you've been tossing cash all along!

Nooooo!

Well, it may not be straight-up cash, but there's definitely treasure that has often found its way into our garbage cans. And in our garden's economy, it may be worth more than we realize.

In the next chapter, we're going to find out some ways to reclaim that treasure, for our homes and for our gardens.

RESOURCES PART 2: COMPOSTING & GIVING OLD JUNK A NEW LIFE

 One man's trash is another man's treasure.

— FAMOUS PROVERB

You and I, friend, are that second man.

Whether it's learning the art of upcycling old junk, composting kitchen waste, or harnessing the hidden power of weeds, we permies know how to transform "trash" into glorious treasure.

Oh man. Get out your sticker chart. Because this utilizes Principles #2, #3, #5, and #6, and it definitely fulfills Earth Care, on several levels.

Check this out, though. It's not just that this lessens the burden on the landfill (which it does). Nor is it simply about checking off some Permaculture Principle boxes (although that's awesome to do).

This is also about *maximizing potential,* and realizing that sometimes the *best resources* are right under our noses. As a permaculture gardener, you never want a resource to leave your property without making the most use of it!

Look at the forest. Nature has spoken! The leaves fall, decompose, and feed the soil. And forest soil is *rich.* The best, most natural way to feed your garden the nutrients it needs is with that wonder drug called *compost.*

So let's start accumulating wealth nature's way by learning to make your very own black gold.

COMPOSTING ALCHEMY: REDUCING WASTE & MAKING GOLD

Composting is central to a permaculture lifestyle. It ranks right up there with native perennials and water conservation. We've talked about this treasure a ton, and now we get to go deeper. Yay!

Composting is the process of taking organic waste, breaking it down, and recycling it into plant food. Anything that was once living naturally breaks down through de*compos*ition. Helpful bacteria, fungi, worms, and other tiny creatures assist in this breakdown. When the composting process is complete, we call the product **finished**, **mature**, or **stable compost**. This means it's ready to use in your garden.

As organic matter breaks down into compost, it activates those three key macronutrients (NPK) that are essential to plant growth. It holds onto these nutrients (and others) and supplies them steadily to the plant's root system. It increases soil health and fertility. It increases water retention. It makes the Earth happy.

So can you grow plants in straight compost? Not really. Although compost contains all the nutrients that plants love, it doesn't have the soil structure to retain water and stability. Some low-spreading, acid-loving plants like squash can thrive in compost alone. But most plants prefer a balanced mix. Compost should be added as a layer of top dressing in garden beds, about 1-3 inches. Or you can mix it in with the soil at a ratio of about 10%-25%.

WHAT CAN AND CAN'T BE COMPOSTED

Practically any organic (living) matter can be composted. This includes kitchen scraps and lawn debris.

But there are some things that can cause some trouble if you toss on the compost heap. Waste such as meat and dog poop (and dung from other carnivores) can become infected with E. coli, salmonella, and listeria bacteria. This, in turn, can contaminate your entire batch of compost. It runs the risk of spreading the bacteria to your plants. These materials can also attract rodents and make your compost smelly.

However, it is possible to compost these things separately in a pile specifically earmarked for landscaping. It's a great way to get rid of all that dog poop! Just don't put it on anything you intend to eat.

Check out Appendix C for a helpful list of things you *do* and *do not* want to add to your compost.

COMPOOPST

It happens. Everybody poops.

If you really wanna go "zero waste", livestock dookie is actually a power-packed, nutrient-rich composting ingredient. Manure has been used in agriculture ever since the first farms.

In general, it's recommended to only use manure from *herbivores* — and not *carnivores* — in your main compost pile, for the reasons listed in the previous section.

And, let's talk about it. *Humanure* (you can probably guess what that is) requires *very* specific considerations and treatment that you'll need to research if you're just that committed to the zero waste game.

Some of the most poop-ular animal manures for composting include: cow, horse, sheep, goat, alpaca and llama, chicken, turkey, duck, goose, rabbit and guinea pig, gerbil and hamster, and worm.

You'll want to make sure the manure is well-rotted (i.e. composted) before putting it in the garden. Manure is like fine wine ... er, maybe not ... but you get the point.

As we learned in Chapter 11, some animals produce "cold manures," which have a higher ratio of carbon to nitrogen. These animals include cows, sheep, llamas, alpacas, rabbits, and guinea pigs. Theoretically, you could put cold manures right into the garden. Best practice with all manures — whether hot or cold — is still composting.

While manure is typically *brown* in *color*, it is highly nitrogen-rich, so it is actually considered a *green composting ingredient*. So it needs to be balanced with carbon-rich "brown" materials to compost. More on "greens" and "browns" in the next section.

Well, friends, that's the scoop. I think Elizabeth Von Arnim said it best:

The longer I live the greater is my respect for manure in all its forms.

— ELIZABETH VON ARNIM

BROWNS & GREENS

As I've alluded to several times at this point, the list of things that can be composted is broken down further into "browns" and "greens".

At last, here we are, for a more detailed look.

Brown materials are made up of any organic matter that's rich in *carbon*. These are usually things that are dry, hard, and fibrous. Brown compost is more resistant to decay, so it breaks down slowly in your compost pile. Some examples of brown materials are dead leaves, twigs, pine needles, straw, bread, corn stalks, dryer lint, cotton, shredded paper, cardboard (minus the waxy coatings), wood ash, and sawdust.

Green materials are fresher and wetter than brown compost. They are recently dead materials that are high in *nitrogen* and break down quicker. Some examples of green materials are grass clippings, vegetable and fruit scraps (best to use materials that weren't cooked in oil), plant trimmings from your annuals and perennials, annual weeds that haven't gone to seed (more on this later), seaweed, lake weed, tea bags, coffee grounds, and manure.

If you want, you can help process bigger chunks by grinding, shredding, or chipping them down. A blender, paper shredder, leaf mulcher, or lawnmower with a catching bag all come in handy here. The finer your material, the faster it breaks down. This is really more useful with certain browns and hard stuff, which take longer to decompose (eggshells, twigs, paper, cardboard, etc). Usually, you can just toss greens in as they are.

BALANCING THE COMPOST CHEMISTRY

Gardeners differ on the ideal ratio of browns to greens in your mix. Some would say 2-3 times the browns, and some suggest that a 4:1 brown-to-greens ratio works best. Whether 3:2, 2:1, 3:1, 4:1, etc, it seems to be the case that ratios tend to favor more browns. Although a few would argue that the balance is better with more *greens*.

The easiest thing to do is aim for an even mix in your compost: 50/50, 1 to 1, half-and-half greens to browns. Then, play with the recipe. So, *basically*, for one handful of green materials, make sure you add one handful of brown materials. Feel free to try boosting your browns (or greens), and observe what happens to your bin over time.

You're probably fine just aiming for 50/50.

But, if you want to get more specific, let's make this whole balancing act a little more interesting.

So, a handful isn't always a handful, as some materials are weighted differently in their ratios. Some green materials are more nitrogen-rich than others, and some brown materials are more carbon-rich than others.

Actually, each composting material contains a unique amount of both carbon and nitrogen. Technically, all of these materials have more carbon than nitrogen. But the whole greens/browns classification comes in at the dividing line of 30:1 carbon to nitrogen.

A material is typically categorized as a "brown" when it has a higher carbon content than 30:1 in its carbon-to-nitrogen ratio. A material that is categorized as a "green" is actually still higher in carbon than nitrogen, but being more nitrogen-rich than other materials, its carbon-to-nitrogen ratio falls *below* 30:1. So:

- Is the relative carbon amount *higher* than 30:1 C:N? Generally, that's a *brown*.
- Is the relative carbon amount *lower* than 30:1 C:N? Generally, that's a *green*.

Some *green* materials are "greener" and sway the balance more toward a green-heavy mix, and some *brown* materials are higher in carbon and sway the balance more toward a brown-heavy mix.

Here are examples of greens, from lowest to highest nitrogen richness.

- Potato peels are 25:1 C:N, coffee grounds are 20:1, vegetable scraps are 15-20:1, grass clippings are 15-25:1, sprouts are 12:1, hair/fur is 10:1, soybean meal is 6:1, and manure can be the greenest, ranging from 5-25:1 (poultry comes in at 6:1, cow 18:1).

Here are examples of browns, from lowest to highest carbon richness.

- Nut shells are 35:1, leaves are 60:1, corn stalks are 75:1, straw is 40-100:1, pine needles are 80:1, shredded paper is 175:1, and wood chips are 400:1, sawdust is 300-500:1, and shredded cardboard is 350-500:1

THE GOLDEN RATIO FOR BLACK GOLD

So, what's this 30:1 number that keeps coming up? Well, *this* is what all this balancing talk boils down to.

See, scientists have found that somewhere between 25-30 parts carbon to 1 part nitrogen is the *perfect ratio* for the *best, fastest decomposing compost mix*. At this C:N ratio, things really start to heat up and create an ideal environment for the creation of sweet black gold. So, *technically speaking*, the best compost mix *overall* is when the whole heap is about 30:1 C:N.

But hang on, if you're getting overwhelmed and wondering if you'll need a calculator and a scale and have to keep track of all this, don't worry, there are *much* easier ways!

The birds and squirrels aren't out there on the forest floor measuring out ingredient ratios (at least I don't think they are), and it all works out.

These are just guidelines. You don't have to keep it right at 30:1 C:N. Your compost needs 4 basic things: Greens, browns, water, and air. It will decompose with a decent mix of greens and browns somewhere within the "ballpark" of ideal.

Best practice is to also keep it moist and aerated, but there are even methods that don't monitor these (more on that below).

One way to keep balance is to think in terms of handfuls (2 handfuls of X green is balanced with 1 handful of Y brown). I've made a helpful table in *Appendix C* to help you balance ratios in easy handfuls.

THE EASY WAY

But guess what? Even if you just want to just toss things in and not think too hard about it, you'll probably do just fine by aiming for a 50/50 mix of greens and browns without worrying about particular ingredient ratios.

Then, just check in on the compost every so often. You can do a few simple tests to check on the balance, by keeping an eye (and nose) on the compost pile.

Sniff it

First, smell it (I know how much you like sniffing the dirt). If it smells acidic, sickly sweet, or rotten, or like ammonia, or like nasty trash, it might be heavy on greens or need a good turning or aerating.

Wait but ... doesn't nasty trash smell like ... nasty trash? You'd think, but a well-maintained compost bin actually has a deep earthy smell to it. If it smells rank, add some browns to the mix, and turn it/aerate it.

Eyeball it

Also, if it looks too wet, it may need some browns in the mix. It should be moist, but not soggy. Turn it and add browns.

If it looks too *dry*, maybe it's too brown-heavy and needs some nitrogen-rich greens, or it could use some water. Either way, add some green materials and some water, and turn it.

COMPOST HAPPENS

At the end of the day, composting is a matter of trial and error and letting nature do its thing. In the wild, it's really this simple: *compost happens*. If you handle the basics, you'll be on your way to black gold in no time.

So how *do you* do the composting? I'm glad you asked. Let's talk about:

COMPOSTING METHODS

There are a variety of composting methods you can use both on large and small scales. Much of the choice will depend on the amount of waste your family produces and how much space you have.

OPEN-AIR COMPOSTING

Open-air composting is the easiest and most common method for recycling home and garden waste. In an open-air system, organic material is broken down by the naturally occurring organisms that feed on it. An open-air compost bin can be any size, so this method is perfect for people who live in small spaces.

Some examples of open-air composters are:

- A plastic trash can
- A wire cage stabilized by four posts
- A corral made from pallets
- A Gedye bin
- A series of composting bays made from corrugated metal and wood (this is for large-scale composting and requires a bit of space)
- A simple pile in the corner of your yard

Cold composting vs. hot composting

Start your compost bin directly on the soil so worms and microorganisms can easily join in. Add brown and green compost to the bin in an even mix. This is often referred to as **cold composting**. You simply add to the pile and let nature do its thing. Stop adding to it when your bin is full, or the internal temperature reaches 80°F-90°F (27°C-32°C). While this is mostly hands-off, it's best to still water it down to keep it moist.

You can speed up the composting process by turning your pile every 3-4 days with a pitchfork, shovel, or your hands. This will aerate it and mix the outside ingredients to the inside. I've found a pitchfork to be the most effective, and it makes me feel super farmy. This method is called "**hot composting**" because the oxygen allows for the decomposition and microbial activity inside the pile to create heat. In hot composting, temperatures should reach 115°F (46°C) or more. It should feel uncomfortably hot in the middle. Just don't turn your pile every day. This can disrupt the microorganisms at work in there.

Cold composting is more hands-off than hot composting. On the other hand, cold composting can get stinkier, take longer, and attract pests.

With the open-air method, compost is usually ready to use in about 4-6 months. It can take up to 1-2 years, or you can have it in a month or two. It will all depend on the materials used in your compost, how much work you put into it, and how "finished" you want it to be.

If you do hot composting by turning the compost regularly, have a good balance of greens and browns, and keep it moist like a wrung-out sponge, you'll have finished compost quicker.

When is my compost finished?

Finished compost should feel fine, soft, loose, and crumbly. It looks like rich soil, dark brown to black in color. And it has a slightly sweet smell, like fresh, rich earth after it rains.

You can test it further by sealing some in a resealable plastic bag. Open it up after 3 days. If it smells sour, it needs to mature some more. If it's sweet and earthy, it's ready to do its job!

THE TUMBLER SYSTEM

Like the open-air method, a compost tumbler is a closed barrel or bin rotated regularly to mix the composting ingredients inside. This can speed up the decomposition process by introducing oxygen to the mix. Compost tumblers are usually considered cold composting, though you can heat it up by getting your greens and browns balanced in that ideal range.

There are many models of compost tumblers you can buy. Their compact sizes make them perfect for small yards, and they have a subtle look that doesn't scream, "there's a rotting pile of trash in here!"

Or you can make your own using some DIY plans. You can use the same kind of plastic barrel you would for rainwater catchment. Any tumbler should have holes for aeration. Tip: if you add screening material over the air holes, you can keep the flies out.

Add brown and green materials to your compost tumbler every day or two until it is about ¾ full. Turn the tumbler about 3 times a week. Tumblers produce finished compost in around ten weeks, though with a lot of attention, you can have finished compost in a month.

WORM FARMING

Worm farming is also called **vermicomposting**. We discussed it in Chapter 11, so you already know what wonders these little wigglers can work in the garden. While worms can be put to work in any compost situation, creating a specialized vermiculture setup can help break down compost quickly.

You can also make worm tea. Read below about compost tea (which is closely related) if you're considering it.

However, farming worms is a bit more work than standard composting, and it doesn't produce compost on as large a scale. Since worms are living things, they must be fed regularly, even when you're out of town.

They need to be kept out of the sun, rain, and frost and are known to escape when the conditions aren't right. But, if you're up to the task, worm-keeping is an excellent way to reduce waste in even the smallest spaces, creating rich garden fertilizer known as **worm castings**.

BOKASHI OR EMO COMPOSTING

EMO stands for "effective microorganisms." In a closed composting system, these waste-eating microorganisms break down organic matter much quicker than in any other composting method. **Bokashi** composting is a popular method of using EMOs. In Japanese, bokashi means "fermented organic matter."

The Bokashi method fills a small bucket with compost, and EMO inoculant is added (a powder you buy in little packets). The powder is usually mixed with wheat bran or molasses that the EMOs use for food. It's similar to adding a little bit of sugar to yeast when making bread.

You can buy a Bokashi kit or make your own Bokashi bucket. It will need an airtight lid (because Bokashi is a process of **anaerobic fermentation**, meaning *no oxygen*) and a drain spout at the bottom to remove the liquid produced.

When layered and left to sit, the mixture in your Bokashi bucket quickly begins to ferment. Within ten days, it's ready to go in your garden.

So why am I mentioning this weird sciency composty thing? Because it's excellent for people who live in apartments, condos, dorms, and other small spaces. A standard Bokashi bucket is about 12" x 16", so it fits neatly under your kitchen sink. It's a wonderful way to recycle kitchen scraps when you don't have outdoor space. You can dig the finished compost directly into your garden. And the "Bokashi tea" it produces is perfect for houseplants.

SHOULD I MAKE COMPOST TEA?

Similar to worm tea, some gardeners talk about the use of *compost tea*, which is basically water that has come from steeping finished compost in water.

Important Note: Compost tea *is not* the liquid that drains out the bottom of your tumblers or tubs from water filtering through *unfinished compost*. That liquid is called *leachate*, and it could contain stuff that's toxic to your plants. Best to pour that back into the compost bins.

Making compost tea involves a specific process. So does worm tea, but the processes are sometimes different so you'll want to look them up. Most recommend "brewing" compost tea by aerating it with an air pump that bubbles the tea. This is *aerobic compost tea*, as opposed to *anaerobic*. Aerobic means it's made with added oxygen.

But does this process help much more than just placing the compost right on top of the soil? The jury is out on this one. Remember, human energy is a resource too! If it is a lot of extra effort for not much gain, it may not be worth it. Also, homemade compost tea can sometimes lead to problems if not brewed correctly.

Some swear by the stuff. Others say the best thing to do is to simply plop finished compost right on top of the soil and let it be.

If you want to try brewing some tea, go for it. Just do some research and make the decision that best serves your garden and you!

CREATIVE COMPOSTING IDEAS

IN-BED COMPOSTING

Yes, we permies love composting, but no, I don't mean snuggling up with your pile next to where you sleep.

By "in-bed" I mean in your *garden beds*. As we've discussed before, some people put composting columns right inside garden beds, like the center composting cage in a keyhole bed design, or those in-ground worm bins.

These are great ways to stack functions and get creative with your composting, with a method that's mostly hands-off.

KEEP A TUB OF BROWNS ON HAND

I have found it really helpful to have a tub with a lid right by my compost pile, filled with a shredded brown material of some kind. I've used sawdust, shredded leaves, or shredded paper. I keep a little scoop in the tub, like a cheap quart measuring cup, or old milk jug with the top cut off.

This is because, most of the time, I've got a steady flow of green materials coming in. Kitchen scraps, coffee grounds, manure, plant clippings, etc. Whenever I dump my under-sink bucket of greens into the main compost bin, I can just scoop some browns to balance the greens. Easy.

SOURCING FREE COMPOSTING MATERIALS

Maybe, like me, you find yourself so excited about compost, you wonder what kind of resources you can harvest in your neighborhood. You can call local shops, or knock on neighbors' doors, and you'll often find that they're more than happy to give away their surplus of rich composting ingredients.

Here are some ideas that you can ask about, several of which I've used!

- Spent coffee grounds from coffee shops
- Fruit pulp and food scraps from organic smoothie shops & nutrition stores that juice
- Spent grains from breweries
- Sawdust from wood shops (just be sure you can gather dust from only untreated wood)
- Rock dust from countertop and other rock-carving companies (this is more of a soil amendment, but cool to note)
- Recycled paper and cardboard from recycling centers and other printing/packaging places that would have it
- Piles of dead leaves from yards, streets, shops, etc.
- Manure from places or folks with livestock

People are ditching stuff everywhere, and I'm sure you can think of many more places where you can source free compost food (plant & food scraps, wood chips, etc). All you have to do is ask!

I knew of an organic juice shop that was happy to fill up a tub with fruit and vegetable pulp for a weekly pickup from a local gardener. The gardener would pick it up, replace it with a second tub for them to fill, and swap the next week. He'd take that nutrient-rich pulp home to his compost pile each week.

That's permaculture at work, baby!

OTHER WAYS TO USE JUNK

Without a doubt, there is a certain satisfaction that comes from getting nutrient-rich garden food from something that might have otherwise ended up in the landfill.

Not all junk can be thrown in the compost bin. But that doesn't mean it can't be reused.

Done eating your fried chicken and left with bones? You can make chicken/bone broth, which is healthy for you. And you can clean, dry, and grind up those bones into bone meal, which can help soil deficient in phosphorus and calcium (best absorbed in acidic to neutral soil).

Did your milk spoil? Did you know that queens used to take milk baths to improve their skin? Sour milk can be great for your skin! If you can stomach it, look up how to use it for a facial or foot soak and embrace your inner royal.

What about that milk jug? You'd be surprised how many cool projects come from used plastic jugs. From self-watering containers to mini-greenhouses to in-ground worm bins, these things can come in handy.

Upcycling means using an item in such a way that creates a product of higher value than the original. Just search "ways to upcycle [your junk item]" to have some fun with stuff you might otherwise throw out.

A FUNNY THING HAPPENED ON THE WAY TO THE COMPOST ...

You know what's fun? Learning the art of upcycling *on the way to the compost bin*. Some things will end up in the compost, but you can get some cool uses from them beforehand!

Take a banana for instance. You eat the insides as a nutritious treat, and then you're left with a peel. You already know you can compost it, and that's great! But wait, *there's more!* Before you compost that banana peel …

- Make a "fertilizer juice" out of it by steeping it in water for a day or two. (Add tea leaves and oats for extra nutrients). Use the strained water for fertilizer.
- Refresh the skin on your face. The fleshy inside of the peel is moisturizing and nourishing to your skin. So go on and wipe your face with it!
- Whiten teeth. Yeah, you guessed it. Rub that fleshy inside right on your teeth. Some say it can help remove stains and whiten teeth!
- Boil some banana peel tea. Slice it and steep it! This stuff is great before bedtime, as it contains stuff that is relaxing.
- Some yummy recipes actually use banana peels.
- Feed your animals. A lot of livestock will eat the scraps like this right up! Just make sure they're organic or washed off.
- Clean with it. These things can wipe dust off of houseplants, as well as polish shoes and even polish silver.

So the next time you're eating a banana at the gym for your post-workout snack, embrace the awkward looks and rub the peel across your teeth and face, and pack it away for the compost later. "Is that the same weird guy who sniffs his backyard?" Yes, and proud of it.

MAKING THE MOST OF THINGS

Here's the big picture. Remember the old phrase we learned growing up? "Reduce, reuse, recycle." It's actually in that order on purpose. See what you can go without. Then, what you can't, see what you can reuse for something else. Then, what you can't, take to recycling. Then, what you can't, the last resort is the landfill.

If you do recycle, it's best to ask your local recycling collector what their requirements and processes look like. Some only take certain kinds of materials (e.g. only certain plastics), or need materials prepared in a certain way to use them. You don't want to end up wasting your effort (or theirs), so a little upfront research helps here!

Okay. There's one more "junk item" you've heard me mention a few times now. In gardening circles, it's usually not a fun word. And yet, here I am using it in a positive way? Well, brace yourself as we talk about an interesting, perhaps challenging idea you'll hear about in permaculture circles …

WEEDS CAN BE YOUR FRIENDS

 Weeds are flowers too, once you get to know them.

— A. A. MILNE

Oh, that hateful "W" word. So many people judge plants before getting to know them, calling them weeds and tossing them aside like yesterday's garbage. But if you shift your perspective — by putting on those permie glasses you've grown so fond of — you just might find that they can be helpful in your garden.

Weeds have a role to play in the ecosystem. Just like Bill's wise natural farmer friend from Japan, Masanobu Fukuoka said:

 Weeds play an important part in building soil fertility and in balancing the biological community.

Often, we want to rip those suckers out because they compete for nutrients and soil space. But permaculture is about working with nature, not against it, right?

In fact, you may even hear some permies say, there's no such thing as a "bad plant" … *only good plants in the wrong places.* Whew. May sound like a stretch to some folks. Maybe some plants need plucking. But let's take a fresh look, and see where we can get creative.

HEY! WHAT'S THAT WEED DOING THERE?

Weeds can be good indicators of what grows well in your garden. What's more, since they're often native, they attract greater biodiversity. Sometimes what is considered a "weed" by one farmer or gardener, is actually a treasured plant to another.

For instance, you may have noticed comfrey being mentioned several times in this book. It has actually been considered a weed for a long time. However, it's a permaculture favorite for many reasons. It is a powerful perennial herb with medicinal properties. Because of the many companion planting benefits it provides, it's a favorite addition to plant guilds. And that's just the start of what this misunderstood plant can offer you.

Cottonwood trees are considered an invasive weed by some. But these gorgeous giants provide dappled shade and great habitat for wildlife. They can be nutritional and medicinal. They grow fast and tall, so they are great for providing a windbreak and privacy. Not to mention they're beautiful. If you've ever heard the gentle fluttering lullaby of their leaves rustling as the wind blows through them — like the sound of a waterfall — you'll wonder how anyone could call them a weed!

So hey, get to know the plants that show up in your soil. Maybe they're useful. Maybe they're trying to tell you something.

See, weeds can also be great indicators of what your soil is like, and what it *needs*. They were drawn to that spot of soil for a reason. Certain pH levels, certain amounts of minerals or nutrients, high or low moisture in the soil, and compaction can all attract certain weeds. You can use these signs to replace these weeds with similar plants, or use the weed-given knowledge to amend your soil. Don't shoot the messenger!

Crabgrass, for example, grows in nutrient-depleted soil (especially low-calcium soil). Dock shows up in poorly drained, wet soil. Mustard usually means your soil is dry, sandy, and high in phosphorous.

Dandelions can indicate poor and compacted soil, but guess what? Not only are they sending up a signal flare to amend your soil, but they're helping you do the job! They are accumulating nutrients and fixing nitrogen, and their tap roots are aerating the soil. Plus, they're edible and medicinal. More on these dandy little guys later.

And how about stinging nettle? This is nature's "plant your garden here" sign, since it grows in nutrient-rich, high-quality soil with good aeration. It brings tons of value, too. It's an attractor, repeller, mulcher, dynamic accumulator, and with the right guidance, it can be medicinal and edible.

Here's another thought as you look upon your weed kingdom. What if we didn't see weeding as a chore? Instead, what if we saw it as *nutrient harvesting?* Let's look at ways you can work with this idea.

THE LAW OF RETURN

Weeds balance soil health. Those with deep tap roots dig deep and break up loose soil like little plant shovels. They also mine nutrients from deep down below and bring them up into their leaves. When they break down, they leave those nutrients in the topsoil.

In gardening, **The Law of Return** states that nutrients taken from the soil must be returned to the soil. For example, a plum tree extracts nutrients in the summer and replaces them by dropping leaves in the fall. The Law of Return kinda makes you think differently about pulling weeds and carting all those nutrients away. You don't wanna break the law, do you???

Instead, you can often return the weeds to the earth using the chop-and-drop method (see below), which involves dropping the stems and leaves right back where you pulled them from. As they decompose, they'll return their nutrients to the soil. They will have stewarded the soil for a time just like a ground cover, and will have added organic matter.

Another benefit of returning weeds to the soil is that it maintains the nutrient balance. Pulling weeds and replacing them with a load of compost is good, too. But let's see how we can use them directly.

CHOP 'EM N' DROP 'EM

No, it's not one of Bruce Li's lesser-known kung-fu moves. **Chop-and-drop** is a gardening process, and it's exactly like it sounds. You chop dead plant material and drop it on the ground. It's like a lazy way to compost by letting the dead plants decompose right at the soil level.

Annuals and non-woody perennials die back when growing season wraps up. We gardeners will usually rip 'em up and toss them in the trash. Then all that valuable potential fertilizer is hauled off to the dump. What a waste!

Chop and drop is a way of reducing waste and recycling it back into the earth. This takes a page from nature's handbook. In nature, leaves, branches, and dead plant material fall to the ground, slowly decomposing and turning into rich, fertile soil. You can do the same thing in your permaculture garden.

Chop and drop is as easy as it sounds. But you should follow a few guidelines before you go hacking at your unsuspecting garden. Soon, you'll be chopping 'em and dropping 'em like a permaculture black belt nature ninja.

- Chop and drop is best done in the spring and fall, when *precipitation* is greater than *evaporation*. This could differ by location, but it's best not to do it during dry times, like in the summer.
- You can chop and drop any plant if you're just doing yard cleanup in the fall. But some, in particular, are excellent for the system. These produce a lot of plant material, have deep tap root systems, and fix nitrogen in the soil. Some examples are pigeon peas, nasturtium, lupine, lemongrass, and moringa.
- Most of the time, when you chop and drop, you don't need to bother pulling out the roots. Leaving them in the ground will help stabilize the soil and slowly add organic matter as they decompose. Sometimes, gardeners will pull weeds that are especially pernicious.
- Put in the extra work when chopping and dropping, and you'll reap the benefits. You could simply cut all those spent cucumber vines, dried-up tomato plants, and sunflower stalks. But it'll look like a mess. And it will take longer to break down. So as you go, chop up material into smaller pieces before you drop.
- Some gardeners cut back plant material before it goes to seed. But if you choose not to, you can cover the dropped material with a layer of fallen leaves or leaf mold. This can smother the seeds and prevent them from germinating in the spring.
- If the plant you cut has a disease or parasite you're trying to eliminate, it's best to do something else with it to stop the spread.
- You can also chop and drop woody plants like trees and bushes. Just cut them up small and drop them on the ground. They'll work as lovely wood chip mulch.

BREWING WEED TEA

Weed tea, like worm tea, isn't something you want to drink. It's a delicious beverage for your garden. Making **weed tea** (a.k.a. **weed soak** or **weed fertilizer tea**) turns weeds into nutrient-rich liquid fertilizer. It's a favorable option if you're not a fan of dropping dead weeds onto your perfectly maintained raised beds.

You can use any weeds to make weed tea, but ones with deep taproots that mine nutrients from deep in the soil are a bonus. Dandelions and dock are two examples. Making weed tea is also a great way to use weeds you don't want to compost, like grass clippings or ones that have gone to seed.

However, it's best not to use toxic plants like nightshade, pokeweed, or poison ivy in weed tea intended for edible plants.

To make weed tea, you ferment pulled weeds in a bucket of water. To start, fill a lidded plastic bucket with weeds until it's about ⅔ full. Make sure to pack the weeds in tight. Fill the bucket with water. Rainwater is much preferred over chlorinated water. Some use a brick to hold the weeds down under the water. Some will say to cover with a loose lid (not airtight) and leave it alone. Others say to cover it with a screen material and stir it daily to keep it aerated.

To speed up the fermentation process, you can add a spoonful of preservative-free fermented food like sauerkraut, yogurt, or wine. This introduces beneficial microbes that will break down the plant material. Also, leaving it in the sun will speed up the process.

Allow the weed tea to ferment for a week or two. Warning, it will be stinky, so try not to get it on your hands/clothes/dog. You can strain out the plant debris by pouring the tea through cheesecloth. To use the weed tea, dilute it with fresh water in a 1:10 ratio. You can pour it directly on plants at the root zone.

After straining out the tea, you dry out the solids for composting if you want. This brings me to:

FOOLPROOF WEED COMPOSTING

People are often nervous about composting weeds. Won't spreading the compost just put the troublesome weeds right back in your garden? Not if you compost them properly by removing or deactivating the roots and seeds. Almost all weeds can be composted. Here are some tips:

- Pull weeds when they're young. This is before they've had a chance to develop deep roots or seed heads. You can toss these directly on your compost pile.
- Dry 'em out. In the hot summer sun, you can desiccate — or dry out — weeds by laying them on concrete, metal, or asphalt: roots and all.

After 2-3 weeks, the roots will be baked hard and ready to toss on your compost pile as a brown material.

- Bag large quantities of weeds in compostable paper bags. Fill them with weeds, then leave them where they'll be out of the way, like behind a shed. This method can take a long time (2-3 years), but it takes zero effort and rewards you with usable compost.
- Heat 'em up. Place the weeds in a clear or black plastic bag, seal it up, and let it sit in the hot sun for about a week. This will destroy the seeds (but it can get a little slimy).
- Try hot composting. Hot composting will destroy weeds' roots and seed heads so they can't propagate in the compost. However, the compost must be hot enough (about 135°F or 57°C), so this option doesn't work in most composting situations.
- Avoid composting plants you know are diseased. Composting can kill the spores, but temperatures have to be very high, and most home composts don't heat up that much. If you won't be hot composting, best to send these away instead. You can burn them too. Sending/burning is also best for especially invasive weeds.
- Sometimes, certain poisonous weeds are not recommended for compost or tea, such as toxic ones like bindweed, and poison ivy/oak/sumac. Research methods of getting rid of these and where to put them.
- Plants treated with chemicals like pesticides or fungicides can just be thrown away.

FORAGING FOR EDIBLES

Many native plants that are commonly known as weeds have culinary uses. **Foraging** is seeking out, identifying, and collecting wild plants for food. Common edible weeds in your own garden include chickweed, lamb's quarter, plantain leaf, and dead nettle. Try them in a salad or soup!

You can put dandelion in salad, or make dandelion leaf tea or dandelion root tea, and reap many nutritional and health benefits.

On that note, you can also use weeds for medicinal purposes. No, I'm not talking about *that* kind of medicinal weed. I'm talking about the native plants used to cure ailments for hundreds of years. These include plants like California poppy, blackberry, dandelion, and milkweed.

Permaculture is usually about trial and error. However, this is one time you *really* want to do your research. ***You should always be 100% sure before consuming any wild plant***. It's best to be sure it wasn't sprayed with chemicals, and you'll definitely want to check the species. Buy a book on edible wild plants in your locale, take a course, do some online research, or consult your local naturalist (you know, that guy in the shack) to learn more about wild edibles.

GETTING INTO THE WEEDS

The best way to get into your weeds and know how to move forward is to *get to know them specifically*. Most permie gardeners will use a combination of techniques to "observe and interact" with their weed population, depending on which weed it is, and how it is growing in their particular setup. As such, you can make lists of which weeds you're going to let grow, which you'll eat, which you'll chop and drop, and so on.

To identify plants, you can take pictures of them and show local gardeners and nursery staff, and see what they can tell you. Also, there are smartphone apps nowadays that will identify a plant by simply snapping a picture of it!

It's understandable to want to keep your garden beds filled with only the plants you want there. Especially in your primary beds in Zones 1 and 2. There is typically a greater need for management here, even if it includes a few beneficial companion weeds that you've grown to love.

To keep others out, the best offense is a good defense. Weeds fill empty voids. Mulch and plant weed-suppressing companion plants and ground covers, so there's no space for weeds to fill.

What next? First, see what weeds may actually be beneficial to simply let grow. Maybe they're edible, medicinal, or help the soil and aren't aggressive. Maybe they're good companions, or they attract beneficial insects.

In some cases, maybe they're great ground cover to hold space in soil — and even work the soil — that you're not yet ready to cultivate.

If they aren't any of these things? Try chopping and dropping. See if you can leave roots in for their benefits to the soil. If they're persistent perennials, or particularly invasive, try pulling and dropping. You can leave them on the surface to dry out and act as mulch, or let them compost on the pathways between beds.

If leaving them on the soil surface still causes problems, pull them, then dry them out on hard ground, and/or add them to weed tea or compost.

Then again, some plants make tasty treats for your livestock, even if you don't want to try the above methods. You may not like the thistles, but your goats might!

What about diseased and contaminated plants and debris?

Maintained hot composting will kill *most* disease in plants. Now, composting must reach higher temperatures to kill off fungal spores, and most home composts don't reach this without a lot of special attention.

If you're aware of the disease, and still want to compost, it's best to hot compost. Otherwise, the plants are best hauled off as yard waste, sent to a commercial composting facility, burned, or buried underground.

But if you don't get around to any of that? Don't worry about it, this stuff happens in the wild all the time, and nature will take care of it over time.

Also, when dealing with weeds that have been clearly *chemically contaminated*, it's usually best to send these off.

IRRECONCILABLE DIFFERENCES

There may be times that you feel you've really done all you can do to get along nicely with a weed, and it's just time to part ways.

People try to tell you how pretty poison ivy is, how the birds eat its berries, and that you can even eat the young leaves and build immunity. (Who wants to volunteer first?)

Well, maybe it's got its place in nature, but it is *not* making your garden a happy place. In times like these, there are eco-friendly ways of getting rid of weeds, which don't harm the soil.

- Suppressing them with layers of cardboard or newspaper.
- Solarization. You can use any light barrier on top to solarize the soil, like a tarp or plastic. Just be sure to remove non-biodegradable materials after the weeds are dead. Depending on different factors like material used and weather, this can take 2-8 weeks.
- Some people bust out the flamethrowers and torch weeds!

- You can also research eco-friendly organic herbicide alternatives. Spraying a highly-concentrated vinegar mix is a go-to for post-emergent, and spreading corn gluten for pre-emergent. **Caution:** Wear protective gear when working with high-strength horticultural vinegar, as it can be dangerous. Read instructions carefully, and make sure not to spray a frog or any wildlife that might be hiding under your plants.

In the end, you've got to weigh the options and do what's best for you and your garden. It's a good idea to check with locals to see what plants are too invasive, or best avoided in your area.

At the very least, this is always true: *weeds give you valuable information.* They're nature's messengers. Before you pick a method of handling them, see if you can harvest the valuable yield of *knowledge* they are giving you.

No matter what you choose to do with them, permaculture is all about shifting perspective right? Whether looking at your garden, or at life itself, perhaps this little phrase will be all the more inspirational to you now:

 When you look at a field of dandelions, you can either see a hundred weeds or a thousand wishes.

Wrap-Up

Wow! At this point, you've learned so much about what it means to be a permie! Give yourself a pat on the back!

Now is an excellent time to revisit your original permaculture plan. Are there any new elements that you can add? Are there areas that need windbreaks? How can you introduce a simple rainwater collection system?

Where is the best place for a compost heap? What are the different plants that spring up naturally in your soil, and where does each go in your plan?

Your permaculture plan may be in full swing already. Seedlings will soon become food. You're tweaking elements to improve outcomes with confidence. Maybe you're getting excited about what to plant next.

The final step in your permie journey is learning how to harvest and preserve food so everyone can enjoy your yield.

PART V

THINKING AHEAD

HOW TO FEED YOURSELF & YOUR FAMILY FOR A WHOLE YEAR

> We're only truly secure when we can look out our kitchen window and see our food growing and our friends working nearby.

— BILL MOLLISON

Not to sound all "end of days" here, but food security is a real concern for many. Many are shifting to a homesteading lifestyle as a solution. And permaculture seeks to follow the map written in nature's code, to a place of abundant, enduring security; all the while leaving the Earth in great shape for the next generation. Sounds pretty exciting, as well as timely.

You may recall the inspiring words of Toby Hemenway back in Chapter 1, about permaculture giving us a toolkit to move from *fear and scarcity* to *love and abundance*.

Maybe Mollison's and Hemenway's vision seems like a far-off utopia for many people. Feeding a family of four with only homegrown produce may not seem realistic for someone living in the city. However, you'd be surprised what you can do with urban gardens, in community spaces, and on rooftops, balconies, patios, and even indoors. You've been training your mind to see *potential* and *possibilities*, and nature has a whole lot to give when we learn to work with it.

Wherever you're gardening, you can get the most out of what you've grown by harvesting and storing it properly. This way, you can supplement your diet with fresh, organic foods throughout the year. You might even have some left over to share.

So how do you make your permaculture garden work to the max? We'll start by discussing the importance of succession planting and greenhouse gardening to extend the harvest period. Then we'll cover harvesting tips and how to collect seeds and store them for the following season. Finally, we'll look at how to preserve different homegrown food for a full pantry!

HOW MUCH FOOD DO WE REALLY NEED?

When starting out, it's easy to get overly excited and want to plant everything. And 50 of everything! But this overzealousness can result in waste if you're not up to the task. Fruit can rot on the vine because you don't have time to pick it. Valuable veggies can get tossed in the compost bin because you can't eat them fast enough. I mean, eggplant is good but come on, you can't eat it seven days a week!

It's not that this is downright terrible. You can share the surplus with fellow humans or the livestock can have a feast. But your time and energy are valuable resources, and you want to *maximize* them by thinking ahead.

So, when you make your garden plan:

- Consider how much the family currently eats. Are you strictly vegetarian? Do you like two veggie sides with every meal? Do you have teenage boys (better triple your estimate)?
- Consider what your family likes. If nobody's a big fan of broccoli but loves cauliflower, it makes sense to start more cauliflower seeds. And while blooming okra can be beautiful, if nobody's going to stomach those slimy pods, it's probably best to decline. And yet … *Fun fact!* Research is showing that when kids help in the garden to grow fruits and vegetables, they're much more likely to eat them, and try a wider variety. (Davis et al., 2021; Moore & Ellis, 2022) Well lookie there, your permaculture garden may finally get little Sally to eat her peas!
- Think about how you can keep the excess for eating throughout the year. Do you have the means and skills to freeze, preserve, and store food? Do you have the space?

- Make a plan for how you'll share extra food. You might not be able to get it to all the starving children across the planet, but I bet there are people in your community who would appreciate some fresh produce or canned goods. Can you swap extra produce with other gardeners? Could you sell at a local farmer's market? Donate to a food drive?
- If you really want to be prepared, and have the capacity for it, take your baseline calculation for your needs, and then double it. This will help mitigate any loss you might experience through weather, pests, etc. Again, it's good to have a plan in place for what you'll do with the surplus.

With these considerations in mind, you may be wondering:

How Much Garden Space Do I Need?

It's the burning question on everyone's lips. But unfortunately, there's no definite answer. Since different crops take up different amounts of space, it depends on what plants you want to grow. Furthermore, do you want a 100% self-reliant off-the-grid garden or a simple kitchen garden to supplement your meals with fresh produce? There are too many variables to answer with a one-size-fits-all number.

With that caveat, the general consensus is that you need *100-200 square feet of space per person for a self-sustaining garden.* So if you have a family of four, that's 800 square feet.

If properly planned and harvested, this will allow you to grow and preserve a harvest that feeds everyone year-round. This is considering your yield will go as planned (which we know rarely happens). As stated above, you may need to plant more than you think you need.

A true survival garden should include a variety of plants for nutritional completeness. These should consist of proteins like beans and nuts, carbohydrates like potatoes and fruits, vitamin-packed plants like spinach, spices, and medicinals like herbs. Make space for a variety of foods you're interested in eating. After all, man cannot live on potatoes alone.

Of course, only some have this much space. And as a beginning permie, you don't want to throw out your Costco membership card just yet. In your first year, start with a single crop you'd like to try and preserve for a year's worth of food. Something easy like green beans or zucchini.

243

PROLONGING THE GROWING SEASON

Even if you never can the first green bean, you can still enjoy fresh produce for over half the year. Strategic planning allows you to extend the growing season to get three or more harvests in a single year.

SUCCESSION PLANTING

Succession planting is a method of using the same garden space to plant multiple crops. It's an excellent way to maximize your square footage and enjoy a longer growing season. In succession planting, you start the next crop right after one has finished.

This is where knowing your cool- and warm-season crops is essential. If you start your garden in the spring with cool-season crops (radishes, lettuce, spinach), those crops will be finished when the summer heat kicks in. Once you've cleared that bed, you can plant warm-season crops in their place. Then, if you live in a moderate climate, you can plant another batch of cool-seasoners when those are spent. Three crops in one season in the same spot! Bam!

For example, you may grow peas in March, then replace them with green beans in June. Or you might grow spinach in the spring while starting tomatoes from seed indoors. The spinach will be ready to move out in May, and your tomato seedlings will be prepared to move in.

Relay, or **staggered planting**, is a type of succession planting in which you plant the same crop but harvest at different times. For example, planting a few lettuce seeds every two weeks. This way, you have a steady supply and not an overwhelming amount all at once. Beans, peas, radishes, spinach, and corn all do well with relay planting.

If you want to try succession planting, here are two helpful things to keep in mind.

1. The time from planting to harvest for each plant. You may need to start seeds indoors to ensure they're finished in time for winter.
2. Companion planting principles. Ensure you aren't planting a crop near one of its enemies or after a crop that depleted the soil nutrients that the new one needs. In this way, it's almost like short-term crop rotation.

SQUARE FOOT GARDENING

We discussed this method earlier, so I'll only touch on it briefly here. Square foot gardening is an excellent way to maximize your yield in a small space. It can provide enough food to supplement a family's diet throughout the growing season with some left over.

Remember, in square foot gardening, you divide a raised bed into 1-square-foot sections using a grid. A different crop is planted in each square.

You can find charts online that tell you exactly how much you can plant in each square foot. As we saw in Chapter 5, plants are categorized by size in a square foot garden. Here's a brief look:

- *Extra large (broccoli, cabbage):* one per square foot
- *Large (leaf lettuce, swiss chard):* four plants per square foot
- *Medium (bush beans, beets):* nine plants per square foot
- *Small (onions, carrots):* 16 plants per square foot

So, for example, if a family of four needs 4-6 broccoli plants to keep the broccoli train rolling, you would need 4-6 square feet of garden space. For most plants, you'll need about two squares per person.

When combined with succession planting, square foot gardening is an excellent way to use your space best. However, if you're not crazy about math, this method might seem like a headache. You can always pass it off to your 10-year-old as an extra-credit math project.

GREENHOUSE GARDENING

Who loves a garden loves a greenhouse too.

— WILLIAM COWPER

A greenhouse is an excellent way to extend the growing season, through the entire year in some places!

Do you have space for one in your design? Well, there are different options, and benefits and drawbacks with each. This basic info can help you decide if a greenhouse is in your current or future permie plan.

Greenhouses cut back on seasonal planting restrictions and allow you to produce food all year round. However, they aren't for everyone due to space, time, and funding demands. Consider these pros and cons.

BENEFITS OF HAVING A GREENHOUSE

- Since a greenhouse is generally 20-30 degrees F (11-17 degrees C) warmer than the outside temperature, an unheated greenhouse can extend the season by about 4 weeks. (A heated one can lengthen it by 8 weeks).
- You can grow food year-round in a greenhouse in many locations, especially if it is heated.
- Lower risk of weather, insect, and animal damage to crops.
- Greater opportunity to make money selling produce, especially if you are producing during the off-season.
- A greenhouse has aesthetic appeal in your garden. And it's a great place to hang out on cool days.

DRAWBACKS OF HAVING A GREENHOUSE

- High startup and operating costs, depending on size and design of the greenhouse and if supplemental heat and cooling are needed.
- Risk of diseases spreading faster in a confined space.
- Lack of pollinators in the enclosed environment, so pollination may have to be done manually.
- Requires more maintenance than a traditional garden, including more watering since rain is not a factor.
- You must constantly monitor greenhouses for signs of pests or disease. Problems must be dealt with right away.

The pros and cons of having a greenhouse can differ from person to person. There are workarounds and solutions for the drawbacks listed above. You can open the doors to let in pollinators during the day. You can automate watering with drip irrigation. More is discussed below.

If the size of a greenhouse is holding you back, think again. Not all greenhouses have to be walk-in structures. You can have a mini greenhouse in a kitchen window! Remember the clear plastic cover we put over our seed starting tray? A greenhouse can be many things!

GREENHOUSE DESIGNS FOR ALL SPACES

Before we go on, what exactly is a **greenhouse**? It's any structure made from a transparent material (this could be glass or plastic) that's used to grow plants. They're also called **hothouses** or **glasshouses**. The enclosed structure creates a controlled, humid environment that reduces heat and moisture loss to extend the growing season.

Greenhouses come in all shapes and sizes, so a large garden isn't required. It may be as small as a tabletop terrarium, a standard 10' x 12' shed, or as large as a warehouse. Where does your space fall on this scale? Here are a few greenhouse ideas for spaces large and small.

- **Wood-framed greenhouse.** These traditional greenhouses are made with a wooden frame and have walls and a roof made from glass or plastic film. They may have different designs, like gable, flat arch, or lean-to. They come in many sizes, but you will need yard space to build one. A rooftop will do, too. Popular sizes are 10', 14', and 32' long. You can often buy these as kits if you don't want to do it all yourself.
- **Arched PVC or tunnel greenhouse.** Although these also take some space, greenhouses made from PVC pipes with plastic covers are lightweight, simple to build, and less expensive than wooden frames. You can buy these in kits of many sizes, like 10' x 7' or 20' x 10', but beware, many are flimsy and won't stand up to heavy snow or high winds. In a tunnel greenhouse, plants are often grown directly in the ground.
- **Geodesic dome (a.k.a. Geodome) greenhouse.** Geodomes are lightweight yet secure dome-shaped structures that resemble modern geometric art. They're all the rage with permies. Thanks to the design, they absorb lots of light, have lots of growing space, and are stable under heavy wind and snow. Although these, too, can be built in various sizes, you will need outdoor space to construct one. And they can take some major math skills to design.
- **Upcycled window greenhouse.** Not all greenhouses have to be walk-ins! If you have some DIY skills, you can transform six old windows into a cute mini greenhouse. Using windows is an excellent way to repurpose materials, and you can design one to fit in the smallest of spaces, like on a patio or balcony.

- **Mini greenhouse.** Some mini greenhouses are simple shelving units covered in a plastic enclosure that can fit on a balcony or patio. Others are small enough to set on a tabletop. These are great for starting seeds in the spring or keeping potted plants warm in winter. Want to use this principle with some upcycling? Cut off the top of a soda bottle, take off the label, and place it upside-down over a plant. Mini greenhouse!
- **Cold frame.** Essentially, a cold frame is a box with a transparent roof. It protects cold-hardy plants from frost and severe temperatures in the early spring and late fall. It can be any size. I modify my smaller raised beds into cold frames in the early spring by laying old windows over them.
- **Cloches.** A cloche is a transparent dome that's usually only large enough to house one or two plants. It's often used to protect garden plants from the elements. For example, if an unexpected cold snap is coming through, you can cover your newly planted seedlings with cloches overnight. They're also ideal for humidity-loving plants. A cloche can be as simple as a plastic water bottle or milk jug with the bottom cut off.

WHAT MAKES A PERMACULTURE GREENHOUSE UNIQUE

Like a permaculture garden, a greenhouse is a mini ecosystem that has its own living organisms and environmental conditions. Building one is more than just a way to extend the growing season. It's an opportunity to express the permaculture principles.

A greenhouse is an excellent place to maximize diversity with companion and guild planting. In the enclosed space, you become more aware of each garden element's impact on the ecosystem. When working properly, each plant provides multiple functions. There are a lot of edges to use in a greenhouse. And while maintaining a greenhouse might take work, a permie looks at it as a few more hours to enjoy all that garden life inside this beautiful sanctuary.

While greenhouses are enclosed, they're an excellent way to embrace nature. Bacteria and insects are still at work in the soil, and you can invite pollinators and beneficial insects in by opening the windows or doors on nice days. A greenhouse is a beautiful place for you, your family, and neighbors to enjoy the outdoors, even on cold winter days. Breathe the oxygen-rich air, exercise, play, or just relax.

HARVESTING YOUR YIELD

Ah, we are here at last. The harvest.

Think of a garden as a three-step program. First, you plant the seed; next, you tend the garden; then, you reap the rewards. And how rewarding it is! You'll never forget the taste of the first tomato you planted and picked yourself.

And if you harvest and save seeds, the rewards can multiply.

As a general guideline, cool-season crops like lettuce and radishes mature quickly and are ready to harvest about two months after you plant them. Warm-season crops take a little longer. It may be up to or more than 100 days from planting to harvest. Most summer crops are picked through September, depending on your zone. You can always refer to the back of your seed packet for a quick estimate.

Picking fruits and vegetables seems like a no-brainer. But harvesting your crops at the right time can provide the best yield and quality. While each plant has its individual needs, here are some general guidelines.

IT'S ALL IN THE TIMING

When it comes to harvesting vegetables, bigger isn't always better. A three-foot-long zucchini might look impressive, but it tastes nasty. You should harvest crops at specific stages to ensure the best quality, texture, and flavor.

Many vegetables, like lettuce, cucumbers, peas, and potatoes, will be the most tender when they're still immature. Others, like tomatoes and watermelons, should be picked when they are fully ripe but before they've begun to spoil.

You should harvest perennial vegetables before they've had a chance to flower. If you wait until that point, they'll taste tough and bitter. The same is true with culinary herbs like oregano and basil. Their leaves will be the most flavorful before they've flowered.

Root vegetables like turnips, beets, potatoes, and onions should be harvested when they're about the size of a golf ball. This is about 6-8 weeks after planting (10-12 weeks for potatoes). A good rule of thumb is that the leaves will be darker and the stem thicker when a vegetable is ready to be pulled.

As always, look up the specifics. "When should I pick/harvest my [fill in the blank]" is a great question to search.

STAY OUT OF THE RAIN

Avoid harvesting crops in wet weather. Working your garden in the rain can encourage the spread of bacteria and mold in disease-prone crops like tomatoes, cucumbers, and squashes. Listeria bacteria that live in moist soil can attach to root crops and low-growing veggies when it rains. And wet crops, especially grain, won't keep as long. So give your plants at least 24 hours to dry before picking them.

So what do you do if you know a storm's a' brewin'? If you have any ripe or nearly ripe tomatoes in your garden, get out there and pick them now! Excess moisture can cause tomatoes to swell and split. The same applies to melons, plums, peaches, pears, and nectarines.

HARVEST OFTEN

Harvesting crops is like popping corn. Once that first kernel pops, the rest will start taking off. It's essential to check your garden daily during the harvest season. That three-foot zucchini might have only been three inches long a few days ago. Okay, maybe closer to 10 days, but a lot can happen fast when the garden gets poppin'.

Harvesting frequently will ensure you get the best quality fruits, vegetables, and herbs. It will also increase your yield as plants can put more energy into the newly developing fruits instead of pouring it into the mature ones.

EQUIP YOUR TOOL BELT

A lot of fruits and vegetables can be harvested by hand (that's the most fun way to do it!). You can simply pluck beans, peas, leafy greens, and most fruits from the vine. However, some have a harder time letting go. Have you ever tried to pick a pepper and ended up pulling off half the plant? I have.

For plants with thick or tough stems (cucumbers, zucchini, peppers, eggplants, pumpkins), it's best to cut the stem where it joins the branch or vine. Pruning shears, kitchen scissors, or a sharp knife work well for this. This prevents you from damaging the plant or picking off more than you intended.

When harvesting, root crops like carrots, potatoes, beets, and radishes may also need some TLC. Gently loosen the soil around the plant with a trowel or a garden fork. This will prevent you from yanking the green off of the root.

HARVESTING HERBS

When planting culinary and medicinal herbs, think about the part you will eat. The leaves, the flowers, or the seeds? Some are multi-purpose. You may assume that mass harvesting is best done at the end of the growing season. But by then, many have depreciated in flavor and value.

- Harvest foliage herbs, like basil and oregano, just before they flower for maximum flavor.
- Harvest flowering herbs, like chamomile and calendula, when the blooms just open.
- Harvest herbs grown for seeds, like coriander and fennel, when the seeds have matured and dried. You'll know they've dried because they will turn brownish in color and easily fall from the plant when shaken or rubbed.
- If you just want to harvest herbs for an instant burst of flavor in tonight's dinner, you can pick them any time.

It's best to pick herbs in the morning after the dew has dried but before the sun heats them up. This is when they're most flavorful. You can use your fingertips to pinch off fresh leaves, stems, and flowers or a pair of herb snips or hand pruners.

COLLECTING AND STORING SEEDS

Harvesting your own seeds from your garden is the best way to ensure you'll continue to have more plants each year. Talk about food security. And it's free! If you collect seeds from your most successful plants each year, you'll never have to pay for seeds or seedlings again.

Harvesting and storing seeds varies from plant to plant, but it's pretty straightforward. It just takes some planning and observation (and by now, you're a pro at observing nature). Here's a quick Q&A to get you started.

WHAT SEEDS SHOULD I COLLECT?

You can collect and store seeds from any plant, including vegetables, fruits, trees, shrubs, and herbs. Only collect seeds from the healthiest, most vigorous plants. This ensures that you're collecting the best quality seeds.

WHEN DO I COLLECT SEEDS FROM FLOWERS?

Are you a fan of flowers and want to spread more of that colorful pollinator-inducing beauty next year? Seeds are generally ready to collect about two months after flowering. For most plants, you must wait until they've fully matured or "ripened." If seeds are collected when immature, they will not germinate well. However, if you wait too long, they'll disperse before you have a chance to collect them.

You'll know seeds are ready to collect when the seeds change color. They'll turn from green to brown, black, or red as they dry out. Now's your chance! Cut the seed heads from the stems and put them in a shallow box or tray. You may have to gently crush the seed heads or pods to remove the seeds. This applies to popular flowers in the sunflower family, like coneflowers, marigolds, and zinnias, and members of the legume family, like lupine, sweet pea, and wisteria.

HOW DO I COLLECT SEEDS FROM VEGETABLES & FRUIT?

Harvest seeds from fruits and veggies when the fruit is fully ripe but not yet rotten. Carefully separate the seeds from the **flesh**, which is the part of the fruit that we eat. For example, with a pumpkin, you'll want to remove all of the stringy "pumpkin guts" from the seed.

Different seeds benefit from different cleaning methods to remove the guts. Some just need a good rinse. Others may benefit from an additional step of *fermentation* (like tomatoes and members of the squash family). It's best to research how to clean and save your particular seed type.

For those that just need washing, you just place them in a bowl of water. As you may recall, by the way, the viable seeds will sink to the bottom of the bowl, and the dead ones will float. You can separate the pulp from the viable seeds with your fingers. Then, pour out the water, pulp, and dead seeds, holding onto the washed viable seeds.

Fermenting is also very helpful for some seeds, removing thick gel, decreasing the chance of disease, and increasing germination rates. This process mimics nature since fruit naturally falls to the ground, rots, and ferments.

To do this, follow these steps:

1. Take all the seeds and pulp and put them into a jar.
2. Fill the jar with just a little water, about half the amount as the seeds and pulp.
3. Store the jar somewhere warm (75-85°F) for 1.5 to 5 days.
4. When you see bubbling or a white mold-like film, the fermentation has started. This is yeast, and it smells sour. At the sign of first fermenting, let the film build for about a day.
5. Then, pour all the jar's contents into a bowl of water, and do the washing process described above.

When fermenting seeds, you'll want to watch for that white film regularly, since you don't want your seeds to accidentally germinate.

After washing (or fermenting then washing), pat the seeds down to dry. Then, you'll need to dry the seeds out thoroughly, as described below.

How Do I Prepare Seeds for Storage?

Regardless of the plant type, seeds need a chance to dry out before storage. Any moisture left inside the seed can cause it to mold or rot.

Lay seeds out on a piece of waxed paper, plate, screen, tray, or some kind of non-stick surface. Spread them out so they're not covering each other.

There are several ways to go about this which people recommend.

- Some will say to dry them in a shaded spot because the intense sun can degrade or kill the seeds.
- Others will say choose an inside spot in the indirect sunlight.
- And others recommend drying them directly in the sun for a faster process, but not during intensely hot times (12 pm-2 pm). Note: If you choose to sun-dry, bring your seeds in at night to avoid moisture from nighttime dew.
- Lastly, other people will recommend using silica gel to dry seeds out, or drying them in a bag.

I think a great, safe method is drying them out in the open air, indoors, in a dry location (not humid). You can use indirect sunlight if you'd like. A light breeze or fan is also helpful to make the drying process go faster. Every day or two, give them a stir to make sure they dry evenly. Seeds can take 1-3 weeks to dry out.

To see if it's done drying, poke it with your fingernail (or bite it). It should feel hard. You're aiming for *al dente*, as the Italians say. If it "gives" or leaves indentations like it's still moist or spongy at all, it needs to dry more. Dry seeds are hard and brittle and should snap in half (and not bend) when you try to break them. If you have a moisture meter, they should reach 5%-8% moisture content before storing.

Make sure to remove any **chaff** (a.k.a. the **husks** or **pods**), the material surrounding a seed. There are a variety of methods that work to separate seeds from chaff, depending on the type of seed. Crumbling between your hands, using rolling pins, swirling in a bowl, sifting through mesh, threshing, and the ancient method called *winnowing*. Again, research your seed type for better direction here.

How Do I Store Seeds?

After your seeds have been properly cleaned, dried, and separated from the chaff, they are finally ready for storage!

Package seeds in labeled paper packets or envelopes. Never use plastic baggies, as these can trap moisture (if you remember my pumpkin seed story, you understand). Store your seeds in an airtight container and keep them in a cool, dry place. You may add a desiccant, like the silica gel packets you find in bagged beef jerky or medicine bottles, that will help keep the container dry.

For most plants, seeds will be fine in storage until a suitable planting time, such as the following spring. Properly harvested and stored seeds can last for 2-5 years. Even longer if kept in the fridge.

Start gathering seeds this year, and soon you'll have quite the collection!

PRESERVING YOUR HARVEST

In the early days, people preserved food because they couldn't pop over to Walmart if they ran out of peanut butter. Today, food preservation is popular in homesteading and prepping circles because it ensures food security. It's an excellent way to stretch your harvest and ensure you have access to your homegrown food for months.

So how do you keep your bumper crop of summer strawberries from going bad? And how can you enjoy them in the middle of December? This is where preserving steps up to the plate. **Food preservation** is any process used to safely prepare food for long-term storage. The benefits of preserving food include:

- It enables you to enjoy out-of-season fruits and vegetables and share them with others.
- It keeps food at its best quality and minimizes pathogenic bacteria (those things that grow on food as it gets old).
- It saves money. No more buying canned corn at the store!
- It reduces waste, especially when you have an overabundance of a crop.

Preserving doesn't just mean your Granny's peach preserves (which, by the way, taste great in oatmeal). Fruits and vegetables have different properties, so some work with particular methods while others don't. Luckily, you can preserve many garden crops in multiple ways. The three most common are freezing, dehydrating, and canning.

FREEZING

Hundreds of years ago, people discovered that freezing food halted deterioration in its tracks. In its quasi-cryogenic state, the food stayed exactly how it was because bacteria couldn't reproduce in sub-zero conditions. Thankfully, we no longer have to ship frozen blocks of ice across the country. We have a handy home device called a "freezer" that does all the work for us.

Freezing is a preservation method that's easy, low-cost, and accessible to anyone. Here are some other benefits of freezing food:

- Foods retain their nutritional value longer than any other preservation method.
- Frozen foods can last forever (like that wooly mammoth found in Alaska).
- Freezing is the quickest and easiest preservation method.
- Cooking with frozen food is simple.

What Crops Can I Freeze?

Fruits and veggies that are firm and low in moisture are the best candidates for freezing. Veggies include carrots, cauliflower, corn, broccoli, green beans, peppers, squash, and winter greens. Fruits include berries, plums, peaches, nectarines, and other stone fruits. Herbs also freeze well. Just chop them up and add them to ice cube trays filled with water.

Vegetables and fruits with a high moisture content don't freeze well. They'll be mushy when you thaw them out. These include cabbage, celery, cucumbers, lettuce, melons, mushrooms, and tomatoes.

Homegrown fruits and vegetables are best frozen as soon as possible after harvesting. This is when they're freshest.

How Do You Freeze Foods?

All you need to do is prep your harvest properly before its cryogenic slumber. Rinse, sort, and prepare it. Trim off roots, stems, and damaged spots. You can save yourself time in the future by chopping, slicing, or peeling the foods now.

Many crops do best if **blanched** before freezing. This means scalding them in boiling water for a minute or two, then plunging them in ice water. This stops enzyme action and preserves the food's texture, color, and flavor. It's not essential for safety but rather for quality. Some veggies that are best blanched before freezing are asparagus, broccoli, beans, and winter squashes.

After prepping and thoroughly drying your fruits or veggies, spread them out on a sheet pan and pop it in the freezer. You can bypass this step, but it will separate your food into nice pieces instead of one big frozen chunk. Once fully frozen, the food is ready for freezer-safe storage bags or containers. Make sure to label it before putting it to bed!

DEHYDRATING

Even more old-school than freezing, dehydrating food for preservation has existed for thousands of years. It was done in the hot sun back then, but today we have new-fangled dehydrator machines that make the job quicker and easier.

Drying or **dehydrating** food is the process of removing moisture so that mold and bacteria can't grow. Reducing the moisture content to around 10%-20% preserves flavor but prevents decay. Although we're familiar with dehydrating to make delicious beef jerky, the process can also be done with fruits and veggies. The benefits of dehydrating foods are:

- They don't need to be refrigerated; just stored in a dark cabinet is fine.
- They're easy to store and portable, so they make a quick, healthy snack on the go.
- Dehydrating foods takes minimal equipment. All you need is a dehydrator or an oven. Or you can harness the power of the sun and do it outdoors. You'll make Bill so proud.
- Most fruits and vegetables retain all of their vitamins and minerals when dehydrated. In fact, since you're removing much of the water from the fruit, you're getting a more concentrated dose of the good stuff in each bite! Some examples of nutrition-packed foods to dehydrate are bananas, figs, plums, dates, beets, and green beans.

WHAT CROPS CAN I DEHYDRATE?

You can dehydrate practically anything, even your little brother's goldfish (so it can live on forever as a mummy).

This includes herbs, seeds, nuts, sprouted grains, and meats. Vegetables that dry well include beans, carrots, celery, corn, mushrooms, onions, peas, potatoes, and tomatoes. Fruits that dry well include apples, apricots, bananas, blueberries, cherries, cranberries, pears, peaches, plums, and strawberries. These can be dried whole or as yummy fruit leathers (like a homemade Fruit Roll-Up™).

Like freezing, dehydrating food is best done soon after harvest, before it shows signs of aging. Choose fruits and veggies at their peak ripeness for the best flavor.

HOW DO YOU DEHYDRATE FOOD?

Prepare foods for dehydration by following the same process as freezing. Ensure the pieces are chopped up uniformly to dehydrate at the same rate. Small foods can be dehydrated as-is. Aim for about ¼" - ½" thickness.

To dry out food in the sun, lay it on a mesh screen or rack. Then cover it with another screen to keep the bugs out. Set it in a spot with long periods of sunlight and temperatures above 86°F (30°C). This method can take several days and is the least controlled. You might have to do some experimenting to get it right.

An electric food dehydrator, on the other hand, is practically foolproof. If you plan on doing a lot of preserving, you should definitely spring for one of these babies. You can get a good one for under $100, and it will be well worth the investment.

To use the electric dehydrator, lay out the prepared food on the racks, then turn on the machine. It's that easy! All machines have different settings, so refer to your user's manual for specific temperatures and times.

You probably guessed this, but there are also great ways to use an oven to dehydrate food, whether full-sized or even a toaster oven. You'll want to search for specifics online since directions vary according to food and oven type. But in general, this operates much like the dehydrator, with your oven on the lowest setting. Plan on it taking somewhere between 6-10 hours, with intermittent checking and flipping food.

After thoroughly drying and cooling your food, you can store it in plastic baggies, canning jars, freezer containers, or vacuum-seal bags. And don't forget to label it. You don't want to accidentally eat Goldie.

CANNING

Can you can? Yes, you can! People often shy from canning because they fear food-borne bacteria. While this is possible, food will last for decades if it's appropriately canned. And it's really quite simple.

In the **canning** process, you put food in jars or cans and heat them to a high temperature to kill any existing bacteria and stop enzyme activity. It creates an anaerobic environment (no oxygen) and a vacuum seal so nothing can get in. Bacteria can't live without oxygen, so your canned green beans are safe to live on for generations.

Canned foods can last forever, although they will start to deteriorate in nutritional value, color, and flavor. It's best to eat canned goods within two years. Some benefits of canned foods are:

- They can be stored anywhere. No need for refrigeration.
- They retain their flavor well.
- You can eat canned goods directly; no thawing, cooking, or rehydrating is necessary.
- Canning offers unlimited possibilities. It's more than just boring canned green beans and tomatoes. Jellies, jams, condiments, salsas, pickles, and more! Canned goods add variety to your pantry. And they make great gifts or farmer's market products.

What Foods Can I Can?

Like dehydrating, canning offers many possibilities. Fruits, vegetables, and meats are all candidates (get it, *can*-didates?). Tomatoes, green beans, corn, and cucumbers (pickled) are some of the easiest, most versatile choices. Tree fruits, berries, and grapes are all excellent as spreads or canned whole for pies.

Some low-acid foods must be amended (by adding salt, sugar, or vinegar) before they're safe for canning. Others, like pumpkin and potatoes, can not be safely canned if mashed or pureed. That's because they are too dense to transfer the heat needed to kill bacteria. So leave the pumpkin puree to the professionals at Libby's.

As with all preservation methods, foods are best canned soon after they are picked. This will ensure the best flavor and freshness. You don't want to risk tossing a rotten fruit into your canning jar. This could cause contamination.

How Do You Can Food?

Canning isn't hard, but it does take more time and care than freezing or dehydrating. And while canning your own produce saves tons of money versus buying from the store, there is some equipment you'll need to start out.

- Water-bath canner or large pot with a secure lid
- Jar rack that fits inside the canner
- Jar lifter
- Funnel
- Headspace measuring tool
- Magnetic lid lifter
- Canning jars

In case all this fancy jargon makes it seem like you need an entire canning factory, don't worry. These are actually mostly small-sized items. Some kits are available online, and some companies manufacture 3-in-1 tools to cover multiple functions like a combination magnetic lid lifter + bubble popper + headspace measuring tool. With a little prep and practice, you'll be doing the can-can like a pro in no time.

You can look up the best canning methods online or read through dozens of great canning books to familiarize yourself with the process. To save page space, I'll settle for a crash course here.

1. Fill your canner or pot with water and bring it to a boil on the stove.
2. Thoroughly wash and sanitize your canning jars, lids, and rings.
3. Prepare your fruits or vegetables according to how they will be canned.
4. Using a canning funnel, load the foods into your jars. **Cold pack** canning is when you pack food raw, then pour boiling liquid over it. **Hot pack** canning is when you wholly or partially cook the food first.
5. Check the headspace (the space between the top of the food and the jar lid) with your handy tool. It usually should be between ¼" - ½". Then use it to remove any bubbles from the jar.
6. Wipe the jar lids clean, place a jar lid on top, then screw on a lid ring.
7. Place jars in your canner so they are evenly spaced and not touching.
8. Return to a boil, put on the lid, and start a timer. **Processing** time — the time it takes to kill bacteria and stop enzyme activity — is usually between 10 and 30 minutes.
9. When the time is up, remove the jars and allow them to sit, undisturbed, for 12-24 hours.
10. Finally, check your seal by pressing the center with your fingertip. If there's no give, you've done it! That means you have a good seal. Your jars can be labeled and stored away for later.

If you're a canning newbie, start with something easy, like corn, tomatoes, or green beans. These don't require any ingredients besides the vegetable and water (plus salt to taste). You can pack these directly into jars, cover them with boiling water, and process them.

Ensure that you've harvested enough produce to make steaming up the house worth it (never fun in the middle of August). Aim for at least 4-6 jars, or enough to fill your canner. If you follow a recipe, ensure you have enough to fulfill it.

WHAT ABOUT PICKLING?

Pickling is a type of canning in which foods are preserved in a brine made of salt and vinegar rather than plain water or syrup. You pack the foods in canning jars, then pour a boiling brine over them. The brine kills bacteria and other microorganisms.

Pickling is an excellent way to preserve vegetables with high water content, like cucumbers and zucchini. And it's great for adding zingy flavor to other-wise dull veggies like asparagus, cauliflower, and beets.

And the best part is that pickled foods don't *have to* be canned. If you're still squeamish about canning, you can pickle your produce and store it in the refrigerator. Pickles will keep in the fridge for two or three months. You just can't store them in the cabinet if they haven't been processed.

OTHER PRESERVATION METHODS

Though we've covered some of the most popular methods, there are a variety of other ways to preserve your food. These include: storing food in a root cellar (cold cellar), salting & curing, sugaring & making jellies or preserves, and vacuum packing.

WRAP-UP

Harvesting and preserving your yield is where all three core ethics of perma-culture come alive. You are now gardening in a way that cares for the earth (earth care). You're feeding your family and others (people care). And you can take the extra and give it away, swap it, or even sell it (sharing the surplus)!

What started by simply looking out your window has, or will soon, turn into something extraordinary.

But what happens when things don't go according to plan? You planted 20 seeds, and only two germinated. Or an army of aphids has moved into your strawberry patch. Curveballs can and will happen, but that's okay! We are nimble, adaptable permies!

Our final chapter covers potential problems when growing your own food and addresses ways to resolve them in the permaculture way.

15

TROUBLESHOOTING IN YOUR PERMACULTURE GARDEN

 When we work with nature instead of trying to impose our will, the solution is often found within the problem.

— DAVID HOLMGREN

Whoa. That's deep. Like wise-old-philosopher-with-a-sweet-long-silvery-beard deep. Take a minute to absorb it.

A partnership with nature is both the beauty and the beast of permaculture gardening. Nature might let you have a say, but it won't let you forget who's really in charge. And because of this, permaculture gardens don't always go according to plan.

No need to panic! Even the card-carrying veteran permies face setbacks. Gardeners plan, and nature improvises! But take Cool Uncle Dave's advice — counter by pulling a trick from nature's own hat. That's how you dance the dance.

This chapter will discuss natural, organic, permie ways to deal with pests, diseases, and other problems in the permaculture garden. We won't be able to cover all the possible problems. But for the beginning permie, this should help fill out your tool belt.

DEALING WITH PESTS THE ORGANIC WAY

Hey, permie, permie, put aside that pesticide! The birds and the bees don't want to deal with that killer chemical cocktail. And spraying nature with a faceful of insecticide is no way to start a positive relationship.

Permaculture gardening follows many of the same routes as organic gardening. Though there may be some unique characteristics, there's a lot of overlap, as both seek natural ways to deal with pests in the garden. Both frown upon manufactured pesticides because they:

- Leave toxic residue on edible plants that we ingest.
- Harm the beneficial insects that we want in our gardens. Even so-called organic pesticides like pyrethrin harm pollinators like honey bees and butterflies.
- Create a toxic environment when they leach into the soil, waterways, and groundwater and bioaccumulate in living organisms.

Often, insect pests build a resistance to synthetic pest controls, so farmers must rotate through different chemicals. It's a frustrating cycle that's not cost-effective or getting to the root of the problem. So how do you get rid of crop-munching bugs without chemicals?

FIGHTING BUGS WITH BUGS

In every ecosystem, one organism feeds on another. It's the food chain, baby. And nature has already given us a solution to every pest problem. Just look for the organism that eats it. Introducing beneficial insects to control the pest population is the best biological pest control method.

We talked a bit about beneficial predatory insects earlier. These ones prey on other insects, often the pests that are preying on your veggies. Some examples of helpful garden predators are:

- Ladybugs to control aphids
- Persimilis predatory mites control spider mites
- Parasitic wasps (parasitoid wasps) control moth egg parasites and pest caterpillars (don't worry, these aren't the kind that sting and bite humans and guard hives fiercely)
- Mantids feed on flying insects

- Spiders feed on grasshoppers and moths
- Green lacewings, minute pirate bugs, ground beetles, and big-eyed bugs are general predators

You can purchase some beneficial insect predators at garden centers or online, like ladybugs, praying mantis egg cases, green lacewing eggs, and parasitoid wasp pupae. Introduce them to your garden first thing in the morning and at least once a year.

And if your financial manager won't allow bugs in your budget, you can lure in the free kind: plant native and pollinator-friendly **insectary plants** (plants that attract beneficial insects). Pincushion plant, bee balm, dill, rudbeckia, and buckwheat are popular options. Dedicate a bed for them or scatter them about your garden. Ground covers and mulches like straw or bark provide a welcoming habitat for spiders and beetles.

OTHER NATURAL PEST-CONTROL OPTIONS

But what do you do when the ladybugs are too full to eat another bite? Creating an uninviting or outright restricted environment can also keep pest insects out of your garden. This might be with physical barriers, like netting, glue traps, or glue bands around tree trunks.

When spending time in your garden, you can manually remove pests from plants. Large bugs, like stink bugs and caterpillars, can be picked up and disposed of. However, the smaller ones aren't that easy to pick off.

There are some earth-friendly alternatives to chemical pesticides for those tiny bugs that swarm by the dozens. You can whip up many of them with ingredients you already have at home. Here are some natural pest control solutions that won't harm your garden.

- *Dish soap.* You can use gentle dish soap to combat aphids, mites, whiteflies, and beetles. Create a plant-safe solution by mixing about 1 ½ teaspoons of dish soap with a quart of water. Put it in a spray bottle and apply it on the tops and bottoms of leaves where insects appear. Repeat every 4-7 days. You can also use a bucket of soapy water when manually picking large pests, like squash bugs, from plants. Simply drop them in the bucket, and they won't be able to fly out.

- *Vegetable oil.* When combined with dish soap, vegetable oil coats the bodies of bugs like aphids, beetles, thrips, and mites. This oil coating blocks air holes, so bugs can't breathe and eventually suffocate (yikes!). Mix one tablespoon of dish soap with one cup of vegetable oil to make a spray. Add two tablespoons of the mixture to one quart of water in a spray bottle. Apply to plants every 4-7 days.
- *Hot pepper spray.* Add two tablespoons of powdered red pepper, cayenne pepper, or paprika to one gallon of water. Put the mixture in a spray bottle and apply it to plants to combat spider mites and aphids. This solution also repels deer (and it tastes great on tacos!)
- *Beer.* Placing a shallow bowl full of beer in your garden will attract slugs, snails, and the neighborhood winos (you know, the insect kind). They'll fall in, perish, and can be removed in the morning. But what a way to go!
- *Vinegar.* The smell of vinegar repels slugs, snails, ants, flies, and moths. Mix one part apple cider or white vinegar with three parts water to create a plant-safe spray. However, you should only apply it to the base of the plant, as the vinegar can dry out the leaves and cause them to wilt.
- *Garlic.* It's not just for vampires! Garlic will repel various pests like aphids, ants, beetles, caterpillars, flies, mosquitoes, and slugs. Add 2-3 crushed garlic cloves to a tablespoon of vegetable or mineral oil. Let it sit for one day, then strain out the garlic. Add two cups of water and a few drops of dish soap to the garlic oil and put it in a spray bottle. Apply to plants weekly. (Note, companion planting garlic also deters pests!)
- *Neem oil.* Neem oil is a natural oil that comes from the neem tree. It is commonly used to kill insects like aphids, beetles, caterpillars, whiteflies, thrips, spider mites, and nematodes. It's available in ready-to-spray and concentrated forms that you can buy at your local garden store.

When using a natural pest spray on your garden, apply it early in the morning before the sun hits to avoid burning the leaves. When trying a new pesticide, apply a small test spray to a few leaves to ensure your solution isn't too strong. Check back the next morning to determine if there were any ill effects.

COMPANION PLANTS FOR PEST AND DISEASE CONTROL

Adding diversity to your garden can increase yields and stop common problems before they start. It's just another reason why integration is so crucial in permaculture.

We talked about companion planting back in Chapter 10, so you know how vegetative besties work together to enhance growth and improve the soil. And like good friends, they protect each other, both from neighborhood bullies and insect pests. Just like some plants attract beneficial insect predators, others repel bad bugs with their odors (which are pleasant smells to us).

Here's a list of the most common flowers and herbs that are natural insect repellants in your garden. Dedicate areas to these phenomenal pest fighters, intersperse them with your veggies, or use them as borders. This can be around containers, in garden beds, guilds, and the whole yard.

INSECT-REPELLING FLOWERS & HERBS

- *Alliums* repel cabbage worms, carrot flies, slugs
- *Basil*: asparagus beetle, carrot fly, flies, mosquitoes, whiteflies
- *Borage:* aphids, asparagus beetle, tomato hornworm
- *Catnip:* ants, aphids, cabbage loopers, cockroaches, Colorado potato beetle, flea beetle, Japanese beetles, squash bugs, weevils
- *Chives:* aphids, carrot flies, cucumber beetles, Japanese beetles, spider mites
- *Chrysanthemum:* ants, beetles, mosquitoes, nematodes, roaches, silverfish, ticks
- *Dill:* aphids, cabbage loopers, spider mites, squash bugs
- *Garlic:* aphids, bean beetle, fleas, Japanese beetles, potato bugs, spider mites
- *Geranium:* corn earworms, leafhoppers, mosquitoes
- *Horseradish:* aphids, blister beetles, caterpillars, Colorado potato beetles, whiteflies
- *Lavender:* bean beetles, cabbage moths, carrot flies, ticks
- *Lemongrass:* mosquitoes, whiteflies
- *Marigold:* most insects, including bean beetles and nematodes
- *Mint:* ants, aphids, cabbage moths, bean beetles
- *Nasturtium:* known as a "trap crop", it draws pests away from your

crops and to itself, such as ants, bean beetles, squash bugs, and striped pumpkin beetles

- *Rosemary:* bean beetles, cabbage moths, carrot flies, mosquitoes
- *Sunflower:* as a trap crop, it draws away aphids
- *Tansy:* ants, beetles, cabbage moths, Colorado potato beetle, cutworms, flies, squash bugs
- *Thyme:* cabbage wasps, cabbage worms

PLANT DISEASES

TELLTALE SIGNS YOUR PLANT HAS A PROBLEM

Is your plant coming home at all hours of the night? Has bloodshot eyes? Smells oddly of cigarette smoke? It might have a problem.

While you sit your plant down and give it a lecture on the dangers of boozing and drugs, you might wanna also check it over for common plant diseases. Just like humans, plants get diseases. And they can be especially bothersome for beginning permies who are trying to garden the natural way.

While native perennials tend to be more hearty, many annual vegetable crops and fruit trees are susceptible to diseases. They're mainly caused by **pathogenic organisms (pathogens)** like bacteria, viruses, fungi, and protozoa. And they're often spread by insects, but can also be transmitted by infected seeds or transplants, water, contaminated tools, and humans.

How can you really tell if your plant has a problem (other than checking its pockets for suspicious plastic baggies)? Look for common telltale signs, like discolored or withered leaves and blemished fruit.

Let's go over a list of the most common plant diseases and ways you can prevent or treat them.

BLACK SPOT

Black spot often happens in cool, moist weather and is especially prevalent in roses. This fungal disease may not outright kill plants, but it weakens them and makes them susceptible to other diseases. It appears as small black spots on foliage, which eventually turn yellow and fall off.

Since black spot fungus *overwinters* (meaning it lives through the winter) on diseased canes and leaves, cut them back before winter. You can make a tablespoon of baking soda mixed with a gallon of water and a few drops of dish soap into a spray to reduce the spread of black spot.

DAMPING-OFF DISEASE

Damping-off disease affects young seedlings. It's most problematic in humid conditions and is caused by soil-borne fungi. Infected plants will look thin and threadlike near the base of the stem. Leaves will look gray-green to brown and wilted. You'll sometimes see fluffy white cobweb-like growth on the soil.

Unfortunately, you can't treat damping off, but you can prevent it. Always use new pots or those disinfected to prevent the spread of fungi. Use fresh, well-drained soil and avoid overwatering or overcrowding seedlings. Adequate ventilation is also crucial. Make sure your plants aren't cooped up in a spot that doesn't get any airflow (like in a bathroom, basement, or grow tent). You can even use a fan set on low speed to provide air in stagnant spots. And be sure there's plenty of space between plants.

DOWNY MILDEW

Downy mildew is caused by a fungus and often occurs in wet weather. It affects many ornamental and edible plants like lettuce, broccoli, cauliflower, and grapes. It appears as yellow spots on the upper sides of leaves and a white or gray mold on the bottoms.

While prevention is the best course of action, you can treat downy mildew with a copper fungicide spray. This is one of the only fungicides currently approved for organic gardening and seems to be effective against downy mildew and late blight.

POWDERY MILDEW

Powdery mildew is similar in cause and appearance to downy mildew. The difference is that the entire leaf, stem, or flower will look covered in a powdery whitish growth rather than yellow spots. It's common in apples, grapes, cucumbers, peas, and other plants.

Powdery mildew should be treated in the same way as downy mildew. You can treat the fungus with copper fungicide or the baking soda spray described under "black spot."

FUSARIUM WILT

Fusarium wilt is a soil-borne fungus, and it often affects beans, tomatoes, peas, and asparagus. It's especially active in the hot summer months. Infected plants will look stunted, and their leaves will turn yellow, wilt, wither, and fall off. It usually appears first on the lower leaves and moves up along the stem.

There are some biological fungicides (like Mycostop™) that are approved for organic gardening, and safely protect plants from the wilt that Fusarium causes.

As with all incurable diseases, prevention is the best action here. Follow the tips below.

MOSAIC VIRUS

The most common forms of mosaic virus seen in the garden are tomato mosaic and tobacco mosaic, which affect tomatoes, peppers, potatoes, cucumbers, lettuce, and others. It appears as a mottled yellow and green on the leaves. Leaves will often be curled and distorted around the edges. Some plants will exhibit stunted growth or deformed fruits.

Unfortunately, mosaic virus has no cure, so prevention is key. Since the mosaic virus can live in soil for a long time, removing affected plants is essential.

RUST

Rust is easy to identify because it appears as rusty spots on leaves and stems that progress to turn reddish and black. It affects many types of plants, including trees, shrubs, and grass.

You can treat rust with the baking soda solution used for "black spot." You can also treat affected plants with neem oil or a weekly dose of sulfur dust (which also happens to help with leaf spot and powdery mildew).

AN OUNCE OF PREVENTION

Unfortunately, many fungal and viral plant diseases can't be cured. They can only be prevented. Here are some tips for preventing plant disease from taking up residence in your garden:

- Choose resistant plant varieties whenever possible.
- Also, companion planting principles can help resist the spread of disease.
- Create good circulation by avoiding overcrowding plants. Stake or prune them as needed. Clear away tall weeds to allow optimal circulation at the ground level.
- Immediately remove affected plant parts and dispose of them. For some diseases, you must remove the entire plant, roots and all. DO NOT compost diseased plants.
- It's usually best to water the soil and not the foliage of plants. Wet foliage is more prone to diseases. While you can't avoid the occasional rain shower, try to use drip irrigation or water only at the soil level.
- However, this doesn't apply to every plant. Some aren't really susceptible to fungus, like brassicas, and actually watering the leaves can help wash away caterpillars and aphids.
- Water early in the morning so that plants can dry out during the day.
- Disinfect pruners and other tools used to cut diseased plants after use. You can use straight rubbing alcohol or diluted bleach water (a 1:10 ratio of bleach to water is great). Rinse after.
- If purchasing plants from a garden center, carefully inspect them for signs of diseases or pests.

STAY ENCOURAGED

Look. If disease strikes, it can definitely feel frustrating. This may be the most important advice of all, though. Feel the frustration, and then move forward as an *even more seasoned gardener*.

Remember those cool permie glasses? Put them on, change perspective, and encourage yourself: *These things happen.* And it's definitely not the end of the world, or your garden. Nature's pretty tough and resilient, and she's been handling stuff like this for a long, long time. These things typically work themselves out over the next couple years.

If pathogens find their way into your garden, *it doesn't mean you or your garden have failed*. Try on this context instead: This is a fantastic opportunity to learn, grow, and come back stronger. And that applies at least 2 permaculture principles. Which is awesome.

ISSUES WITH PLANT GROWTH

If only life were like a video game. You could just choose fully grown, beautifully healthy plants and place them where you wanted them. Voilà! An instant Garden of Eden. Sigh.

Until you find Jack's magic beans, this will never happen in real life. Before you have lush, productive plants, you need healthy plants to put in your garden. While planting a seed seems straightforward, many problems can arise from seed to fruit. Poor germination, wilting seedlings, spindly plants, and more can wreck your garden dreams fast.

But don't give up! There are some simple solutions to these common gardening problems.

FAILURE TO LAUNCH

The Problem: If you've purchased your seeds from a reputable seed company, they should have at least an 85% proven germination rate. So why are none of your seeds germinating?

The Fix: If more than one variety of seeds isn't germinating, chances are your environment's to blame. Start by checking your soil. It should be evenly moist until germination, not too wet or dry. Seeds also need a specific temperature to germinate. This is usually between 68°F-86°F (20°C-30°C). If the soil is cold, they may not become active.

If you're starting seeds outdoors, outdoor conditions become an issue. Insects, birds, or small mammals could be eating your seeds. Make sure your beds are protected from such pests.

Some seeds might just be too old. How long have your seeds been in storage? Were they prepared and stored properly? This can be an issue if you're using your own seeds from last year's crop.

Finally, give your seeds some time. They won't necessarily pop up on the germination day noted on the package. They might need a few extra days if the conditions aren't perfect. Wait a week or so before starting over.

PREMATURE TERMINATION

The Problem: Your seeds have germinated, and you're so excited! But now, one by one, they all seem to be withering up and dying. What's up with that?

The Fix: The problem's usually in the soil, so this is the first place to make changes. Ensure that your soil isn't too damp or too dry. Evenly moist is the golden rule. If the soil is too wet, it can cause root rot, which makes your plant die where the stem meets the soil.

Damping-off disease can be another significant issue, so start your seeds in fresh, clean seed starter soil. Preferably, this is a soilless mix. You can always sterilize soil or compost, too. As you'll recall, this can be done by solarizing it in the sun, or by spreading it on a baking sheet and popping it in the oven at 180°F-200°F (82°C-93°C) for 30 minutes. Reference Chapter 6 for more details on how to sterilize soil.

Never fertilize seedlings in the first part of life. This is like giving steroids to an infant. Or steak. You'll want to wait until you see the first set of true leaves, as a good rule of thumb. Even then, you'll want to start very small. Dilute liquids in water, etc. You know, baby food in baby-sized bites.

If starting seeds outside, pests can be an issue. If you notice insect invaders, use an organic pesticide.

LEGGY BABIES

The Problem: Your seedlings have long, skinny stems with few leaves. When they're growing spindly, as if stretching for the light, we call these "leggy" plants. This problem is common with tomatoes, peppers, and other veggie seedlings.

The Fix: Legginess indicates that your plants aren't getting enough light. If you're starting your seeds with natural light, it may be time to call in an electric grow light. If you're already using a grow light, move it closer to the plants. Position LED or fluorescent grow lights 2"-4" above the plants.

Leggy seedlings may also be a result of overcrowding. Thin seedlings to give them enough room to grow. **Thinning** means removing crowded seedlings so that the healthiest ones have room to develop stronger roots. Pluck out the weakest-looking seedlings, giving the remaining ones an inch or so of "leg room." Water only frequently enough to keep the soil moist but not soggy. And remember never to fertilize young seedlings. Too much nitrogen can cause spindly plants.

STUNTED GROWTH

The Problem: You know that plants don't grow overnight, but come on. This is taking too long! Your plants look healthy, but they seem to be growing at an unusually slow rate.

The Fix: Some plants are just slow growers. But factors like lack of light, heat, and nutrients can also cause stunted growth in young plants. Ensure your plants are in a location where they're getting enough light. If the springtime temperatures are still low, cover your plants at night with row covers, cloches, or a cold frame.

If your plants are over a month old and have been moved to the garden, it's time to supplement them with compost or liquid fertilizer. Your soil may lack some nutrients they need to thrive, so you may need to test it and amend appropriately.

Pests and diseases can also cause slow growth, so inspect your plants for signs.

CODE YELLOW

The Problem: Plants are supposed to be green, right? So why are your tomato plants turning yellow?

The Fix: Leaves turning yellow is a common issue for many plant varieties. It could be a sign of a lot of things, so you'll want to get your seed packet and go through a checklist. Check the water needs, the light needs, the type of soil it needs, etc. Make sure you're following those guidelines.

You can also do an online search for, "Why is my [plant] turning yellow?" You may find more plant-specific signs that point you to the cause. Signs of a *nutrient deficiency* may look a little different than signs of *over-fertilization,* though they both involve yellowing.

The *leading* reason behind yellow leaves is too much or too little watering. Test the moisture level with your finger, by sticking it down a couple inches into the soil (or a couple knuckles deep). In general, you'll only want to water when it feels dry.

How's the soil? Have you tested it? Is the pH the right level for your plant? Is it too compact? Does it lack nutrients? Have you fertilized too much? These factors can cause yellowing.

And if your plants aren't getting enough light (or getting too much if they're partial shade plants), you may need to move them to a new location.

FRUITLESS ENDEAVORS

The Problem: Your plants have grown up healthy and strong. They look great, lush and green. But the summer's almost over, and you've only harvested a handful of tomatoes. What gives?

The Fix: Many factors can cause a poor yield in vegetable and fruit crops. The temperature can be an issue, so be sure to only plant varieties that are appropriate for your growing zone. Test your soil to ensure your plants get the nutrients they need and not too much nitrogen. Keep the soil evenly moist.

If your plants are perennials, they might not be mature enough to produce. Give them more time and keep nurturing them. They may produce a better yield next year. Lack of pollination can also be a problem. Attract pollinator insects to your garden to ensure plants get the attention they need.

It could be that certain critters have gotten to your fruit. You know that phrase, "The early bird gets the worm?" Well, sometimes the early bird gets the blueberry, too. Look for animal droppings and fruit with beak-sized holes or carvings out of them.

I know, I know, permies love nature. But we can still put up some healthy boundaries in this relationship. Yes, it's always nice to share some of the surplus with the local critters when you can. But, consider the yield you're setting out to obtain, and need to protect. Then, bring in the fences or barriers you need, so you can invite wildlife into your garden while reserving some areas for VIPs.

Bird netting can be a great option for birds and small animals. There is also finer mesh that keeps out insects. Make sure your mesh size is not too large. Otherwise, birds can get their heads stuck, and we're not trying to do that. If your finger just barely fits through, that's a good size. Also, white netting can be seen better than black netting, so white is nicer for the birds. Also, woven netting is stronger than extruded netting, so it's harder for animals to chew through.

COMPOSTING PROBLEMS

Composting for natural fertilizer is a huge part of permaculture gardening. You want to start your permie plan the right way. But, like planting seeds, composting isn't always as simple as it looks. Organic matter is supposed to rot naturally, right? So why isn't this working?

Top-notch composting takes some practice. Without the proper maintenance, a compost pile can quickly become a smelly trash mound. Learning how to deal with common composting problems can help you make the most out of your garden with organic, homemade fertilizer.

We talked about composting extensively, so you may recognize some of these problems and fixes already. Ultimately, the solutions to compost issues usually boil down to the following:

- Only compost the stuff that should be composted.
- Keep the right balance of greens and browns.
- Keep the compost moist, but not soggy.
- Keep the compost aerated, by turning it. Depending on the method, this can be flipping with a shovel or pitchfork, turning your tumbler, etc.

INSECT INVASION

The Problem: You wanted to invite beneficial insects into your garden, but this is ridiculous. Your compost pile is crawling with flies, maggots, and ants!

The Fix: Flies lay eggs in decaying organic matter. When adding to your compost pile, chop up plant material into small pieces and cover kitchen scraps with a layer of soil to keep the flies from finding them. Cover your entire compost pile or bin with a fine mesh screen to keep insects out.

If ants are in your compost pile, it's probably too dry. Add water to keep it moist. If tasty kitchen scraps are sitting on top, cover them with a layer of soil or brown ingredients. Never compost meat, fat, or oil since this can attract rodents and flies.

GARBAGE STANK

The Problem: Your compost pile is starting to smell like the dumpster behind that burger joint on a hot summer afternoon.

The Fix: Healthy soil should have a sweet, outdoorsy aroma. Deep and earthy. It shouldn't smell like sewage or ammonia (or decaying fish or stale pee). A foul or rotten smell is usually the result of poor air circulation. Aerate your compost by turning it more with a shovel or pitchfork. If your compost smells strongly of ammonia, or sickly sweet, or acidic, there's probably too much green material. Add more brown material to balance it out, or even soil.

Overall, if something smells off, you can't go wrong just adding more browns and aerating.

HEAT LOSS

The Problem: The inside of your compost pile is as cold as a polar bear's toenails. And that's no way to transform trash into natural fertilizer!

The Fix: Cold weather and a lack of proper compost materials can prevent compost from breaking down into fertilizer. If your compost pile isn't hot in the middle, it usually lacks nitrogen. Add more plant matter and other green material to heat up the mix.

Covering your compost pile, especially in the cold months, can also help. You can insulate it with straw bales or cover it with a sheet of black plastic. The black color absorbs sunlight to heat up your pile while protecting it. You'll still want to keep it moist and aerated. Take the cover off for rain or watering, and to turn it every now and then.

Also, compost gets "hot" because of microorganisms having a party inside, literally breakin' it down. They need oxygen to do that! Make sure you aerate by turning it or shaking it up. Depending on the method, a couple times a week is usually good.

UNINVITED VOLUNTEERS

The Problem: You're noticing weeds and plants sprouting up in your compost.

The Fix: Many a healthy compost pile sprouts the occasional weeds. If there aren't many sprouts, simply pull them up and toss them back on the pile. Dry them out first if you really wanna be sure. If they're plants you want (like tomato volunteers from rotting tomatoes), you can dig them up and transplant them.

We discussed weeds in your compost pile at length in Chapter 13. But here are some basics. If you are adding them to the pile, pull them before they've had a chance to go to seed. Or you can soak them in a bucket of water for a few days before adding them to your pile. Drying them out first is a good idea. Turn your compost often to keep it warm (above 145°F or 63°C). Hot compost will kill seeds before they can germinate.

MOISTURE IMBALANCE

The Problem: Compost that's too dry won't decompose. Compost that's too wet turns into malodorous sewage. How do I achieve moisture zen?

The Fix: Your compost pile is like Goldilocks. It needs everything to be *just right* to be happy. If your compost pile is too dry, add plenty of water as you construct the layers. Add more green materials like lawn clippings and kitchen scraps to moisten it up.

If your compost pile is too wet, it probably has too much fresh green material. These materials have a high water content, so add some brown material like cardboard and straw to balance it out. Turn the pile while adding browns to improve drainage and aeration.

WRAP-UP

Prevention is always better than cure, and many problems can be prevented by observation. You can keep your maintenance tasks low simply by spending time in your garden, observing and interacting.

Remember what Bill Mollison said about ducks and snails? You can always have this question in the back of your mind: If I were nature, how would I handle this situation? As you look at a problem with permie glasses, you might just find the "solution within" it.

I use my garden-scouting time as the perfect excuse to wander around my happy place. Under the guise of "troubleshooting" I'm taking in my mini-ecosystem's beautiful sights, sounds, and smells.

Need a break from the world (... or your spouse)? Tell 'em you need to go outside and do some *very important research*. As a bonus, chopping weeds is great therapy. Smelling fresh soil on your hands is a prescription for happy vibes. Sunshine is the best energy drink. The garden is the place to be.

No longer do we need to see weeding, pest removal, and plant maintenance as chores. Instead, we can see them as a way to spend time perusing and building our little slice of paradise.

When you go into your garden with an open mind, heart, and eyes, you almost always end up finding the answers you were looking for.

And sometimes, you find the answers you weren't looking for.

 I like gardening. It's a place where I find myself when I need to lose myself.

— ALICE SEBOLD

CONCLUSION

 If you've never experienced the joy of accomplishing more than
you can imagine, plant a garden.

— ROBERT BRAULT

You started with a single seed.

Or maybe it was a packet or two. After all, variety is the spice of Principles #8 and #10.

You planted that seed, nurtured it through germination, fed it organic compost fertilizer, and held its hand when it was going through that rough breakup with the corn next door.

Finally, you harvested it and shared the delicious results of your hard work with your loved ones. Maybe you even had extra to preserve, donate, or sell at a farmer's market.

Guess what? Do you know that you successfully practiced the core ethics and principles of permaculture by looking at gardening from a new point of view? You partnered with the Earth to produce a yield that you and those around you could enjoy. All in one short and busy year, you accomplished quite an amazing thing.

Congratulate yourself! Many people look at gardening as a mystifying concept. It's something they admire but don't think they could ever do themselves. They think green thumbs must be something you're born with.

To grocery shop is human, to grow food divine.

Now that you have the basics of permaculture gardening under your belt, perhaps growing food isn't such a far-off concept. When you follow nature's map and observe the well-tuned machine of the Earth at work, things start to click and fall into place. Look at your thumbs. Do you see a little bit of green starting to show?

Whether you're a first-time horticulturist or two credit hours away from that permaculture doctorate, hopefully, you're looking at the world in a whole new way. From start to finish, there are many advantages — for your planet, your community, and your soul — to a permaculture lifestyle.

- You now know that anybody can achieve a permaculture mindset, whether you live on a 500-acre ranch or in a 500-square-foot studio apartment. Living a low-waste, self-sustaining lifestyle doesn't require a country locale, just a shift of perspective.
- You know how to work with your unique space and plan your permaculture design. You're able to incorporate techniques to maximize the use of space, utilize renewable resources, and increase your yield.
- You are pretty much a soil scientist at this point. You know how to test your soil, you know how important good soil is, and that this can take time to achieve. Until then, you know how to use containers as the ideal planter for many fruits, vegetables, and flowers. In many ways, these are easier for beginning permies to control. And when the time is right, you know a *lot* of gardening methods you can use for the right situation.
- You know how to pick plants and raise 'em right! You know the power of perennials and natives, and how to strategically plan and organize your annual gardens, too. You're a plant matchmaker and team-builder, and you know the power of diversity. While you may grow mainly food crops, you know how to surround your garden with beneficial herbs and flowers to transform it into a thriving ecosystem.
- You've become one with the animals. Well ... at least you know more about 'em! If you aren't ready to introduce livestock into your space,

that's perfectly okay. As much as they have to offer, mouths to feed are a big responsibility. Maybe start with something small and manageable, like worms or a few chickens. Until you're ready, you can invite wildlife into your little permaculture ecosystem by creating the ideal environment for critters like butterflies and ladybugs.

- You've grown your capacity to use your resources and work with what you've got. Capturing water, sun, and wind. Reusing and upcycling, with kitchen, yard, and building materials. You know the power of composting, and you've even befriended all the weeds. Well ok, maybe you haven't gone *that far* yet, but you certainly understand them more, and know how to milk that milkweed for all it's worth! Overall, you know that there are resources *all around you* that can be used for your permaculture garden.
- You know how to harvest and preserve your yield, and even extend your growing season, so you can enjoy your yummy garden through the year.
- You're equipped to overcome some common permaculture gardening obstacles you may encounter throughout the whole process. And, when you reach one that stumps you, you know you can find the answer you need to grow and adapt, like the nimble, resourceful permie you are.
- You also know that a perfect permaculture garden doesn't happen overnight. Naturally, if you attempt to go from your current situation to a completely self-sustainable one in one season, you're going to be overwhelmed. Even if you take it slowly, mistakes will be made. And that's okay! In fact, Principles #4 and #12 embrace this! But if you look at what you have at the moment, make small, achievable changes, and plan for the long term, you will be well on your way to a more productive, self-sustainable lifestyle.

And someday, you may look upon your space, and realize that you have indeed transformed it into a thriving ecosystem, and you've brought the forest home.

You don't need anything more than your own two eyes to begin your permaculture journey. Leave your stresses behind and go enjoy your outdoor space. Seriously, right now. Go on, get out there!

If you haven't already, take your handy dandy notebook and observe what's going on around you. Once you take the time to look around, it's as simple as starting your design.

Think about what you want, what you need, and how to leave a positive impact on this planet we get to steward. The dream may be big. But it happens one backyard at a time. And it starts with one raised bed, one container, or one pot on a windowsill.

In fact, the dream starts with one little seed.

By the end of this book, you have the tools you need to put your permaculture plan into action. Start with a project or two. A compost bin under your sink. A raised bed with two or three companion plants. A rain barrel by the gutter. Some seedlings on the windowsill.

Now that you have a basic understanding, maybe you'll want to dig into some of these topics deeper. I encourage you to search the online forums, read books, find local permaculture and gardening groups, and connect with others on a similar journey. You may even want to take a course or get your Permaculture Design Certificate (PDC). Get after it!

Most of all, though, go build that beautiful garden.

And don't forget that you already know *so much*. This journey isn't about "knowing everything before you start" (Hint: you never will, so that idea will leave you stuck). It's about learning enough to embark on your great garden experiment and learning more and more as you go along.

While you're at it, take People Care and Sharing the Surplus to the next level by *sharing what you've learned*. There are many others who can benefit from the knowledge inside of you. And, more importantly, glean from you the reassurance that they can do the same. Remember how the idea of permaculture started as a seed for you? Well now it's grown into a fruit-bearing tree! Go spread the renewable resource of knowledge like the Johnny or Jill Appleseed that you are!

Who knows, maybe you'll write the next book!

One of the best ways to share the knowledge is by sharing a review for this book on Amazon. That way, more people will see and have access to *Permaculture Gardening for the Absolute Beginner*, which means more will be able to begin their own permaculture journeys. Together we can help each other grow our dream gardens, and leave a positive impact on our world.

Bill Mollison would be so proud. The Earth's pretty happy about it, too. Can you feel it smiling? Mmm. That's the warmth of partnership right there.

You know I'm not gonna leave you without one last quote from Papa Bill.

 I can easily teach people to be gardeners, and from them, once they know how to garden, you'll get a philosopher.

— BILL MOLLISON

Whoa. Looks like you've got more to tell your friends than simply, "I've become a gardener." As you stroke your long, silvery philosopher beard, think of this.

We started this journey by looking at the power of a single seed. A seed grows into a plant, and just think back to all the phenomenal things we've seen that plants can do. They bring life to us, other plants, the animals, and can even heal and revive the soil itself. And on top of that, those little superheroes are filled with *a bunch more seeds!* There are entire life-giving forests inside of *one tiny seed.*

Kinda makes you think differently.

Well, since you're already rubbing banana peels on your face and sniffing dirt for fun, I'm sure you'll have no problem with this one. The next time you pass by a vegetable, or fruit, or herb, or a little flower ... just say to it,

"Wow. There is far more potential inside you than I have ever realized."

And then ... the next time you pass by the mirror, take a good look into it, and say the same thing.

Because, well ...

It's true.

THANK YOU FROM THE PUBLISHER

Wow, what a journey we've taken together. We hope you enjoyed it! If you did, would you consider taking a brief moment to review this book?

As a small independent publishing company, we rely totally on the support of our readers. Every review means a lot, and we read and take each one to heart.

Not only does your review allow us to keep publishing more inspiring books, but it's the main way this book gets seen and therefore considered by more people who are eager to start their own permaculture journey. You help us and them, and we all help the world. Teamwork!

Thank you for being the best part of us and helping us build a community where we grow together, and discover *all we need to live life to the full.*

With deepest gratitude - *All We Need Publishing*

Scan here to review this book on Amazon!
www.allweneedpublishing.com/qr-pgab

Free Stuff!

Wanna join our super-cool reader team and get access to free stuff? Stuff like our fresh-off-the-press ebooks, new audiobooks as we produce them, and other inspiring materials ...

If you're interested, just visit this website:

www.allweneedpublishing.com/readerteam

All We Need
PUBLISHING

🅰 amazon.com/author/allweneed.publishing

🅖 goodreads.com/allweneedpublishing

🆅🅱 bookbub.com/profile/all-we-need-publishing

🅵 facebook.com/allweneed.publishing

🅞 instagram.com/allweneed.publishing

🅟 pinterest.com/allweneedpublishing

SUPPLEMENTAL RESOURCES

PLANT DATABASES TO SEARCH FOR PLANTS

The Lady Bird Johnson Wildflower Center

This is an awesome free online resource. You can search for *native plants* in your area (North America), and filter down results by lifespan (annual/perennial), light and water needs, how long they retain leaves (evergreen/deciduous), plant habit (tree/shrub/etc), mature plant size, plant family, and more.

- https://www.wildflower.org/plants/

Plants For A Future (PFAF)

Here is an another amazing free online resource for finding plants. You can get even more detailed here, searching by what you want to do with a plant (fix nitrogen, various medicinal/edible uses, etc), hardiness zone, and so much more. Great for US, UK, and more.

- https://pfaf.org/

Other Plant Databases

Gardenia Plant Selection Guides by Zones, Types, and Characteristics:
https://www.gardenia.net/guides/plant-selection-guides

National Wildlife Federation (NWF) Native Plant Finder:
https://www.nwf.org/nativeplantfinder/

USDA "PLANTS" Database:
https://plants.usda.gov/

WHERE TO PURCHASE SEEDS

There are a variety of places you can find online that sell organic, non-GMO seeds, as well as heirloom seeds. Asking your local nurseries where they buy their seeds is a great place to start.

Here are some great options, used by many organic gardeners:

- *Baker Creek Heirloom Seeds:* www.rareseeds.com
- *Botanical Interests:* www.botanicalinterests.com
- *Fedco Seeds:* www.fedcoseeds.com
- *High Mowing Organic Seeds:* www.highmowingseeds.com
- *Johnny's Selected Seeds:* www.johnnyseeds.com
- *MIGardener:* migardener.com
- *Peaceful Valley Farm Supply:* www.groworganic.com
- *Seed Savers Exchange:* www.seedsavers.org
- *Southern Exposure Seed Exchange:* www.southernexposure.com
- *Territorial Seed Company:* territorialseed.com
- *True Leaf Market:* www.trueleafmarket.com

You'll also find sellers on Etsy.com selling their homegrown organic seeds. And while Burpee is a big company, its "organics" line is filled with great organic & heirloom seeds. (https://www.burpee.com/organics/).

OTHER PERMIE RESOURCES

There are dozens of *permaculture* and gardening communities online — and maybe near you locally — filled with people who are just like you: eager to learn, grow food, and make the world a better place!

A great forum I've used many times is at https://permies.com/, an online permaculture and homesteading community. People there are always asking and answer questions, sharing tips and resources, etc. If you've got a question, ask away or see if somebody's already asked!

If you *really* want to learn the ins and outs of permaculture, you could take your PDC (Permaculture Design Course). This is a 72-hour course, and you end up an officially certified permie.

Just search for "permaculture design course near me" and ask around. See if there are any instructors in your area, or look into what online courses you can take. Then compare between the options (instructor biographies, course outlines) and see what resonates with you.

Lastly, credit where credit is due! I discovered the awesome online plant database, PFAF, from some fellow permies over at Perennial Publishing (2022). I encourage you to read other permaculture books and continue the learning!

APPENDIX A: COMPANION PLANTING

These are some of the most popular food plants and some of their most agreed-upon companions (and foes!). As we've covered, gardeners have varying results and opinions. I've marked contested plant relationships with a (?), and made lists where there are mixed opinions. An asterisk (*) means that some have reported enhanced flavor from the pairing.

Some plants are swell buddies. They're popular, and companions to most. You'll notice marigolds on everyone's list here. Nasturtium and borage are pretty great universal companions, as well as lovage, thyme, chamomile, and other herbs and flowers. Some are pretty great all-around, with a few exceptions. Like marjoram and basil, as well as spinach and legumes.

Other plants are tricky to work with (e.g. fennel and black walnut). However, there are exceptions with good results. Just research a little.

You'll notice a few family names listed to cover whole groups of plants. Examples include Alliums (onion, garlic, chives, leek, etc), Brassicas (broccoli, cauliflower, cabbage, kale, etc), and Legumes (beans, peas, etc).

Careful with invasive plants like mint. If you don't want it spreading everywhere, best to try pairing up with these in containers.

Lastly, these are *just ideas* to light the spark. Every garden is unique, so find out what works for yours! And remember ... *it's all an experiment.*

ASPARAGUS

Friends: asters, basil, cilantro, comfrey, coriander, dill, eggplant, grapes, horseradish, marigold, nasturtium, parsley, petunias, rhubarb, strawberry, tomato

Foes: Alliums, carrot (give a little distance), potato

BEANS

Friends: (friend to most ... see below)

Foes: Alliums, fennel, gladioli, peppers, wormwood

Mixed opinions: Brassicas

BEANS (BUSH)

Friends: basil, beets, borage, catnip, celery, chamomile, corn, cucumber, dill, eggplant, fruit trees, marigolds, nasturtium, oregano, peas, petunias, potato, pumpkin, radish, rhubarb, rosemary, strawberry, summer savory*

Foes: Alliums, fennel, gladioli, peppers, wormwood

Mixed: Brassicas

BEANS (POLE)

Friends: basil, borage, carrot, catnip, celery, chamomile, corn, cucumber, dill, eggplant, fruit trees, marigolds, nasturtium, oregano, peas, petunias, potato, pumpkin, radish, rhubarb, rosemary, spinach, squash, summer savory*

Foes: Alliums, beets (do fine with bush beans), fennel, gladioli, peppers, wormwood

Mixed: Brassicas

BEETS

Friends: Alliums, aromatic herbs, beans (bush), Brassicas, catnip, corn, garlic*, lettuce, marigolds, oats, radish, sorrel, spinach, tomato

Foes: beans (pole & runner), chard, field mustard

BLUEBERRY

Friends: azalea, basil, borage, columbine, cranberry, dill, dogwood, fern, heather, holly, hydrangea, lavender, lilac, marigolds, marjoram, mountain laurel, nasturtium, parsley, rhododendron, strawberry, thyme

Foes: asparagus, beans, beets, Brassicas, dill, eggplant, melons, peppers, potato, tomato, (plants that don't like acidic pH should not be planted near acidic-loving blueberries)

Mixed: lettuce

BRASSICAS (BROCCOLI, CABBAGE, CAULIFLOWER, KALE)

Friends: agastache, Alliums, basil, beans (?), beets, borage, buckwheat, calendula, carrot, celery, chamomile*, coriander, cucumber, hyssop, lettuce, marigolds, marjoram, mint*, nasturtium, oregano, pennyroyal, rosemary, sage, soybeans, spinach, swiss chard, tansy, thyme, yarrow

Foes: asparagus, cucumber, eggplant, grape, lettuce, mustard plants, peppers, pumpkin, radish (?), rue, squash, strawberry, sweetcorn, tomato, watermelon

Mixed: beans, dill, peas, potato, radish

CARROT

Friends: Alliums, Brassicas, candy tuft, chives*, cilantro, Legumes, lettuce, marigolds, nasturtium, oregano, parsley, peas, pepper, radish, rosemary, sage, tomato (?), wormwood

Foes: celery, dill, fennel, parsnips, potato

Mixed: tomato

CELERY

Friends: Alliums*, basil, beans, bee balm, Brassicas, chamomile, cosmos, cucumber, dill, marigolds, mint, nasturtium, oregano, rosemary, sage, spinach, thyme, tomato

Foes: carrot, corn, parsley, parsnip, potato, rutabaga, turnip

Mixed: cilantro

COLLARDS

Friends: artichoke, beets, celery, chamomile, dill, hyssop, marigolds, onions, peppermint, potatoes, rosemary, sage, southernwood, thyme, wormwood

Foes: basil, beans (pole), grapes, mustard, strawberry

Mixed: tomato

CUCUMBER

Friends: Alliums, alyssum, beets, borage, Brassicas, calendula, carrot, catnip, chamomile*, corn, dill (sparingly), eggplant, Legumes, lettuce, marigolds, nasturtium*, oregano, radish, sunflowers, tomato

Foes: aromatic herbs (most), basil, fennel (?), marjoram, melons, mint, potato, rosemary, sage, summer savory

Mixed: fennel

EGGPLANT

Friends: amaranth, beets, borage, Brassicas, calendula, carrot, catnip, chive, cilantro, cucumber, dill, lavender, Legumes, lettuce, marigolds, marjoram, mint, nasturtium, onion, oregano, peppers, potato, radish, snapdragons, spinach, tarragon, thyme, wormwood

Foes: beans (?), corn, fennel, geraniums, melons, pumpkin, tomato (?)

Mixed: beans, kohlrabi, tomato

LETTUCE

Friends: Alliums, alyssum, basil, beets, calendula, carrot, cauliflower, chamomile, chervil*, cilantro, cucumber, dill (sparingly), kale, marigolds, nasturtium, parsnip, peas, poached egg plant, radish, strawberry, turnip

Foes: Brassicas (except cauliflower and kale), celery, fennel (?), parsley

Mixed: fennel

MELONS

Friends: Alliums (?), Brassicas, carrot, catnip, corn, dill, garlic, Legumes, lettuce, marigolds, mint, nasturtium, okra, radish, spinach, squash (?), sunflowers (?), tansy, tomato

Foes: cucumber, potato, squash (?) / pumpkin, summer squash / zucchini

Mixed: Alliums, squash, sunflowers

OKRA

Friends: basil, beans (?), calendula, cantaloupe, cayenne peppers, coneflowers, cosmos, cucumber, lettuce, marigolds, melons, mesclun, oregano, peas, peppers (?), radish, snap peas, sunflowers, zinnias

Foes: blueberry, carrot, potato, pumpkin, squash, sweet potato, tomato, vining plants

Mixed: beans, peppers

ONION & GARLIC

Friends: *(friend to many, including)* beets, Brassicas, carrot, chamomile*, lettuce, marigolds, strawberry, summer savory*, tomato, many herbs and flowers

Foes: asparagus, Legumes (beans, lentils, peas, etc), parsley, sage, turnip (other Alliums tend to need a little distance)

PEAS

Friends: alyssum, aromatic herbs, arugula, basil, beans, beets, Brassicas (?), calendula, carrot, celery, cilantro, corn, cucumber, eggplant, leafy greens (lettuce, spinach), marigolds, nasturtium, parsley, parsnip, potato, radish, sweet corn, turnip

Foes: Alliums, gladioli

Mixed: asparagus, Brassicas, fennel, mint, peppers, tomato

PEPPERS

Friends: Alliums, basil*, borage, carrot, catnip, chives*, cilantro, Legumes, marigolds, marjoram, nasturtium, okra, oregano, parsley, spinach, tomato

Foes: Brassicas, corn, fennel, potato, strawberry

Mixed: eggplant

POTATO

Friends: Alliums, alyssum, basil, buckwheat, catnip, celery, chamomile, cilantro, coriander, corn, cowpeas, garlic, horseradish, Legumes, lettuce, marigolds, nasturtium, parsley, petunias, radish, tansy, thyme, yarrow

Foes: asparagus, carrot, cucumber, fennel, fruit trees (apple, peach, etc), okra, parsnip, pumpkin, raspberry, squash, sunflowers, tomatillo, turnip

Mixed: Brassicas, eggplant, peppers, spinach, tomato

RADISH

Friends: Alliums, beets, borage, Brassicas (?), calendula, carrot, chervil*, cucumber, dill, eggplant, kohlrabi, Legumes, lettuce, marigolds, mint, mustard, nasturtium*, oregano, parsnip, peas, peppers, petunias, rosemary, spinach, squash, tomato

Foes: corn, hyssop, potato, pumpkin, sunflowers, turnip

Mixed: Brassicas, melons

SPINACH

Friends: (*friend of many, including ...*) Alliums, alyssum, asparagus, basil, borage, Brassicas (?), calendula, carrot, celery, cilantro, clover (crimson), collard, cosmos, cucumber, dill, eggplant, Legumes, lettuce, marigolds, nasturtium, oats, other leafy greens (chard, lettuce, mesclun, mustard greens, watercress), parsley, peppers, petunias, radish, squash, strawberry, sugar snap peas, tansy, tomato, yarrow, zinnias, zucchini

Foes: corn, fennel, potato

Mixed: (a lot of differing opinions on spinach ... including these maybe's) beets (okay with plenty of spacing), Brassicas, dill, melons, mint, Nightshades, pumpkin, sunflowers

SQUASH & PUMPKIN

Friends: borage*, buckwheat, catnip, celeriac, celery, chamomile, corn, dill, Korean licorice mint, lavender, Legumes, lemon balm, lettuce, lovage, marigold, marjoram, melon, mint, nasturtium, oregano, radish, spinach, sunflowers, tansy

Foes: beets, Brassicas, fennel, potato, sweet potato ... avoid crowding with other vining plants

STRAWBERRY

Friends: alfalfa, Alliums, asparagus, borage*, caraway, catnip, clover (white, crimson), dill, Legumes, lettuce, lupins, marigolds, sage, spinach, thyme, yarrow

Foes: brambles (gooseberries, raspberries), Brassicas, chrysanthemums, clover (red), cucumber, eggplants, fennel, melons, mint, okra, peppers, potato, roses, squash, tomato

SWISS CHARD

Friends: Alliums, alyssum, basil, beans (bush), Brassicas, celery, collard greens, lavender, Legumes, lettuce, marigolds, marjoram, mint, nasturtium, radish, rosemary, thyme, tomato

Foes: beans (pole), beets, corn, cucumber, melons, others in goosefoot family (beets, spinach, amaranth, quinoa), potato, pumpkin, squash, strawberry, sunflowers

Mixed: a lot of herbs are debated (mint has the best reputation)

TOMATO

Friends: Alliums, alyssum, asparagus, basil*, bee balm*, black-eyed peas, borage*, buckwheat, calendula, carrot (?), celery, chives*, cilantro, crimson clover, lavender, lettuce, lovage, marigolds, mint*, nasturtium, oregano, parsley, petunias, radish, roses, sage, sunflowers, thyme, zinnias

Foes: Brassicas, corn, dill (?), fennel, other Nightshades (eggplant, peppers, potato), potato, rosemary, sweet corn

Mixed: carrot, cucumber, dill (depends on maturity; *mature* dill can stunt tomato), nasturtium (great companion, just not too close)

TURNIP / RUTABAGA

Friends: artichoke, basil, Brassicas, catnip, celery, chives, dill, garlic, hyssop, lavender, Legumes, marigolds, mint, nasturtium, oregano, radish, rosemary, sage, southernwood, spinach, thyme, vetch, wormwood

Foes: beets (?), fennel, hedge mustard, horseradish, knotweed, mustard, Nightshades (tomato, peppers), onions, parsnip, peas (?), potato

Mixed: beans & peas, beets, carrot

ZUCCHINI / SUMMER SQUASH

Friends: borage, buckwheat, catnip, chamomile, corn, cucumber, dill, Hubbard squash, lavender, Legumes, lemon balm, lettuce, lovage, marigolds, marjoram, melons, nasturtium, oregano, pumpkin, radish, spinach, sunflowers, tansy

Foes: Brassicas, fennel, potato, sweet potato

APPENDIX B: GUILD ROLES

Over the next few pages, you'll see big table of popular plants, along with roles they can play in a plant guild. (This list is by no means exhaustive). Here is a review of the main roles in a permaculture plant guild:

- An **attractor** attracts pollinators or beneficial insects that eat pests.
- A **repeller** is a strong-smelling herb that confuses pests.
- A **suppressor** acts as a barrier and/or ground cover. It prevents weeds and grasses from moving in and absorbing nutrients.
- A **mulcher** is a plant that supplies compost in the form of dried leaves or dead foliage (mulch). It incorporates more carbon into the soil and retains moisture, like mulch.
- A **fixer** (nitrogen-fixer) is a plant that takes nitrogen from the air and deposits or "fixes" it in the soil so other plants can use it.
- A **dynamic accumulator** is a deep-rooted plant that breaks up soil, "mines" nutrients from below, and improves plant nutrient uptake.

Note: many of these plants are also *edible* and/or *medicinal*. Those marked with an asterisk (*) are considered *edible*. However, *always* double-check *instructions* as well the *variety* before consuming anything.

My inspiration for this table originally came from the blog, *Beginner Gardener Tips*, by Jones (2020). Link is in the *References* section.

Plant Name	Att	Rep	Sup	Mul	Fix	Acc
Alfafa *	✓			✓	✓	✓
Artemisia *		✓	✓	✓		
Artichoke *	✓			✓		✓
Barberry *	✓			✓		
Basil *	✓	✓				
Bee Balm *	✓	✓				
Borage *	✓			✓		✓
Buckwheat *	✓		✓	✓	✓	✓
Calendula *	✓	✓		✓		
Carrot *	✓			✓		
Chia *	✓	✓	✓	✓		✓
Chicory	✓		✓	✓		✓
Chives *	✓	✓	✓			✓
Clover, Dutch	✓		✓	✓	✓	✓
Clover, White *	✓		✓	✓	✓	✓
Comfrey	✓	✓	✓	✓		✓
Coriander / Cilantro *	✓	✓				
Curly Dock *	✓			✓		✓
Daffodils	✓	✓	✓			

Plant Name	Att	Rep	Sup	Mul	Fix	Acc
Dandelion *	✓			✓	✓	✓
Dill *	✓	✓				
Fennel *	✓	✓		✓		✓
Garlic *		✓	✓			✓
Hosta *			✓	✓		
Iris	✓		✓			
Lambsquarters *					✓	✓
Lavender *	✓	✓	✓			
Leek *		✓	✓			
Legumes (Various) *	✓		✓	✓	✓	
Lemonbalm *	✓	✓	✓	✓		✓
Licorice *	✓			✓	✓	
Lovage *	✓					
Marigolds *	✓	✓				✓
Mint *	✓	✓	✓	✓		✓
Mulberry *	✓					✓
Nasturtiums *	✓	✓	✓	✓		
Nettle *	✓	✓		✓		✓
Onions *		✓	✓			

Plant Name	Att	Rep	Sup	Mul	Fix	Acc
Oregano *	✓	✓				
Parsley *	✓	✓		✓		✓
Petunias	✓	✓				
Phacelia	✓				✓	
Radish *		✓	✓	✓		✓
Rhubarb *		✓	✓	✓		
Rue	✓	✓				
Rye *			✓	✓		
Sage *	✓	✓	✓	✓		✓
Shallots *		✓	✓			
Squash & Pumpkins *			✓			✓
Strawberry *	✓		✓		✓	✓
Sunflowers *	✓		✓	✓		✓
Tansy	✓	✓				✓
Thyme *	✓	✓	✓			
Turnip *				✓		✓
Vetch *	✓		✓	✓	✓	✓
Watercress *	✓					✓
Yarrow	✓	✓		✓		✓

APPENDIX C: COMPOSTING

TO COMPOST OR NOT TO COMPOST

Here are more thorough lists of items you **do compost** — separated into lists of *green materials* (nitrogen-rich) and *brown materials* (carbon-rich).

Then, a more thorough list of items you **do not compost**. Lastly, there are a few notes on certain items with unique considerations.

✓ Do Compost ✓

Greens (nitrogen-rich)

DO Compost These

Alfalfa, algae, clover, coffee grounds, food scraps (vegetable, etc), feathers, *fresh* plant cuttings & flowers, grains, grass clippings, hair & fur, hedge clippings, jams/jellies/preserves, manure (herbivores only; see note below), nail clippings, old spices, seaweed/lake weed/kelp, soybean meal, sprouts, stale bread, tea leaves, tofu, water from a freshwater aquarium, wine/beer/spirits.

Browns (carbon-rich)

Ashes (wood), bark, bedding from herbivore pins (rabbits, chickens, etc), burlap, cardboard, coffee filters & tea bags (only natural materials), corks, cotton & wool fabrics like towels/sheets/clothes (100% natural fibers), *dead/dried* plants & grass, dead leaves, egg cartons (biodegradable), lint & dust, loofahs (natural), paper material (see note below), nut shells, parchment paper, pasta & rice (*not* if cooked with oil or meat), pencil shavings, pine needles & pinecones (limit these), sawdust, straw, toilet paper rolls, twigs & prunings, used matchsticks, wood ash, wood chips (untreated).

Somewhere in the middle / "it depends"

Some things can be more nitrogen-rich when fresh, and become more carbon-rich when dried out. Sometimes they're kind of in the middle.

Corn cobs & stalks, egg shells, fruit waste, spoiled hay, and a lot of garden waste / plant & weed cuttings.

X Do NOT Compost X

DON'T Compost These

You generally want to avoid putting the following items in your compost:

Ash from *coal/charcoal*, bioplastics, black walnut products, bones, cellophane, chemically treated wood/sawdust, charcoal, cigarettes, coated cardboard & glossy paper (see note below on paper), dairy products, diapers (see note below), diseased or contaminated plants (see below), excrement from carnivores or humans, foil, glass, grasses with roots that spread under the soil, labels from produce, leather goods, meat/seafood products, metal, netting from produce, oils & grease (see below), plastic, styrofoam, synthetic fabrics, synthetic soaps, wax paper, and weeds gone to seed (see note below on weeds).

SPECIAL CONSIDERATIONS

Bread

Some will say don't do baked goods because it attracts pests. But in general: *if you can eat it, you can compost it.* It's best for bread to be stale, torn into smaller pieces, tossed into the center of the pile, and covered.

Citrus peels, onions, and garlic

Many will advise not to put too much of these items in your compost. Yes, they are acidic, and can theoretically make your compost more acidic. However, unless you're running a lemon farm, you're probably okay. (Composting Magazine, 2023a). That said, when it comes to vermicomposting (with worms), you might wanna limit these (see below).

Oils

Again, oils are often on the composting naughty list, since they can make your pile stinky and attract pests. Of course, unavoidable smaller amounts (such as leftover grease on a pizza box) won't really hurt.

On top of that, some research has found that cooking oils may actually help the composting process. (Compost Magazine, 2023b).

Try it with hot composting, dump it in the middle, and cover it up.

Paper

Paper is great for the compost bin. And worms LOVE it. It's generally best to avoid paper that is glossy, waxy or coated, and from magazines.

Manure

Refer back to Chapter 13 for the bigger scoop on poop. The general rule of thumb here is herbivore manure only. Generally, you won't want to use waste from carnivorous animals and pets (dogs, cats), or from humans.

However, if you want to compost any of these, it just takes some research, and probably best done in a separate bin. And while we're on the topic:

Diapers, hygiene, toilet paper, etc.

There *are* compostable diapers, feminine hygiene products, etc, for those who are interested! Again, just do some research. FYI: With diapers, it's easier to compost wet ones than the #2 kind, for the reasons mentioned above.

Weeds & plant matter

As we've discovered, yes! Weeds *can* be composted. There are a few tricks to optimizing their use. Refer to the section on *Weeds* in Chapter 13. If you're *hot* composting, most diseases can be eradicated. If you wanna take the risk, use an "experimental" pile (see below on "bending the rules").

It's best to stay away from *chemically* contaminated plants, though.

Vermicomposting & worm food

You can basically follow all the guidelines above, with a few tweaks:

It's best to avoid onion, garlic, citrus, peppers, animal products, carnivore and "hot" manure, any spices, and cooked, salty or oily foods.

Limit bread and grains, and use coffee grounds in moderation. Let grass clippings dry a bit before putting them in hot and fresh (they can heat up a lot), and keep eggshells dried and crushed. As mentioned above, worms love paper, but not glossy or coated. Just a few tips.

Bending the rules a little ...

Of course, in the wild ... animals just die and become compost, right?

Yep! So here's the thing. These are just guidelines. If you want to make use of that dairy, meat, cooking oil and doggie doo, then go you!

Here's a tip for extra due diligence. Make a *separate compost pile* that you'll use on *non-edible plants* (e.g. landscaping). Put all your "experimental" materials in this pile. Best to make it a *hot composting* pile to kill off disease, weed seeds, etc. Bury experimental materials (meat, dairy, oils, etc) under other *standard* materials (leaves, sawdust) to keep out pests.

Still: some things just don't break down (like plastic) or are best processed in a commercial composting facility (like contaminated plants), but most "natural" things you can technically compost. In general, if you can eat it ... or if it breaks down ... it'll probably compost over time.

COMPOSTING RATIOS

At the end of the day, you're probably okay just estimating your "greens and browns" balance, checking in on the pile periodically, and adjusting as needed. Just like we talked about in Chapter 13.

However, the chart below can help you flex your compost balancing muscle. Some greens are more nitrogen-rich than others. Some browns are more carbon-rich than others. With that in mind, greens and browns have been separated into three easy groups, each with a "score." The goal is simply to try and keep the score balanced.

For example, food scraps are a "low" nitrogen green, and have a -1 score. Sawdust is a high carbon brown, and has a +3. That means 1 handful of sawdust could balance out 3 handfuls of food scraps.

Or, if you throw in 2 handfuls of food scraps, balance it with 1 handful of shredded paper. Or 1 handful of leaves for 1 handful of kitchen scraps.

This won't be at all exact, but it may help you get a basic grasp of things.

My inspiration for this balancing technique first came from a video by "Give it a Grow" (2018). Link is in the *References* section.

Green Materials

C:N Nitrogen Balance	Composting Ingredients
–1 ... Low (> 20:1)	food scraps, coffee grounds, tea leaves, many plant cuttings
–2 ... Med (12:1-20:1)	grass clippings, legumes, leafy green veggies, seaweed
–3 ... High (5:1-12:1)	hair/fur, soybean meal, many fresh manures

Brown Materials

C:N Carbon Balance	Composting Ingredients
+1 ... Low (< 60:1)	dried leaves, nut shells, corn cobs, wood ash
+2 ... Med (75:1-200:1)	straw, corn stalks, pine needles, shredded paper
+3 ... High (300:1+)	sawdust, wood chips, shredded cardboard

REFERENCES

CHAPTER 1

Hemenway, T. (2009). *Gaia's Garden: A Guide to Home-Scale Permaculture*. Chelsea Green Publishing.
Mollison, B., & Slay, R. M. (1991). *Introduction to Permaculture*. Permaculture Resources.

CHAPTER 2

Hall, C. B., & Knuth, M. (2019a). An Update of the Literature Supporting the Well-Being Benefits of Plants: Part 3 - Social Benefits. *Journal of Environmental Horticulture*, 37(4), 136–142. https://doi.org/10.24266/0738-2898-37.4.136
Hall, C. B., & Knuth, M. (2019b). An Update of the Literature Supporting the Well-Being Benefits of Plants: A Review of the Emotional and Mental Health Benefits of Plants. *Journal of Environmental Horticulture*, 37(1), 30–38. https://doi.org/10.24266/0738-2898-37.1.30

CHAPTER 5

Schauder, N. (2020, July 3). Permaculture Techniques for Container Gardening {Guest Post}. *Kitchen Stewardship | Caring for All Our Gifts*. https://www.kitchenstewardship.com/permaculture-container-gardening/

CHAPTER 6

Baker, K.F. Editor. (1957). *The U.C. System for Producing Healthy Container Grown Plants, Manual 23*. University of California, Division of Agricultural Sciences, Agricultural Experiment Station Extension Service. Retrieved June 30, 2023, from https://archive.org/details/ucsystemforprodu23bake/page/240/mode/2up. (Data used in Table 6.1. *The Effects of Heating Soil*)
Bernhardt, E., & Swiecki, T., Phytosphere Research. (2021, March 27). Using heat to eradicate soil-borne plant pathogens from nursery potting media ("soil sterilization"). *Phytophthora in nursery stock and restoration plantings*. Retrieved June 28, 2023, from http://phytosphere.com/soilphytophthora/soilsterilization.htm

CHAPTER 8

Gatiboni, L. (2022). Soils and Plant Nutrients, Chapter 1. In: K.A. Moore, and. L.K. Bradley (eds). *North Carolina Extension Gardener Handbook*, 2nd ed. NC State Extension, Raleigh, NC. https://content.ces.ncsu.edu/extension-gardener-handbook/1-soils-and-plant-nutrients
Hubbard, V. C., Jordan, D., & Stecker, J. A. (1999). Earthworm response to rotation and tillage in a Missouri claypan soil. *Biology and Fertility of Soils*, 29(4), 343–347. https://doi.org/10.1007/s003740050563
Paddock, C., PhD. (2007). Soil Bacteria Work In Similar Way To Antidepressants. *Medical News Today*. https://www.medicalnewstoday.com/articles/66840#1
Torppa, K. A., & Taylor, A. (2022). Alternative combinations of tillage practices and crop rotations can foster earthworm density and bioturbation. *Applied Soil Ecology*, 175, 104460. https://doi.org/10.1016/j.apsoil.2022.104460

CHAPTER 10

Rawat, L. S., Maikhuri, R. K., Bahuguna, Y. M., Jha, N. K., & Phondani, P. C. (2017). Sunflower allelopathy for weed control in agriculture systems. *Journal of Crop Science and Biotechnology*, 20(1), 45–60. https://doi.org/10.1007/s12892-016-0093-0

CHAPTER 12

Spirko, J. (2015, November 6). Don't Try Building Hugel Swales – This is a Very and I Mean Very Bad Idea. *The Permaculture Research Institute*. https://www.permaculturenews.org/2015/11/06/dont-try-building-hugel-swales-this-is-a-very-and-i-mean-very-bad-idea/

CHAPTER 14

Davis, J. N., Pérez, A., Asigbee, F. M., Landry, M. J., Vandyousefi, S., Ghaddar, R., Hoover, A., Jeans, M., Nikah, K., Fischer, B., Pont, S. J., Richards, D., Hoelscher, D. M., & Van Den Berg, A. E. (2021). School-based gardening, cooking and nutrition intervention increased vegetable intake but did not reduce BMI: Texas sprouts - a cluster randomized controlled trial. *International Journal of Behavioral Nutrition and Physical Activity*, 18(1). https://doi.org/10.1186/s12966-021-01087-x

Moore, M., MBA, RDN, LD, & Ellis, E., MS, RDN, LDN. (2022, April 14). Kids in the Garden: A Nutritious and Fun Experience. *Academy of Nutrition and Dietetics*. Retrieved June 28, 2023, from https://www.eatright.org/food/planning/food-security-and-sustainability/kids-in-the-garden-nutritious-and-fun

NOTE: INSPIRATIONAL QUOTES

All of the short, inspirational quotations included throughout this work have been sourced from various online collections of quotes, proverbs, and inspirational sayings. (All other references were noted in the text and cited above). These collection websites include:

- https://www.azquotes.com/
- https://www.brainyquote.com/
- https://www.goodreads.com/
- https://loveexpands.com/
- https://permies.com/
- https://www.southernliving.com/
- https://www.wikipedia.org/

SUPPLEMENTAL RESOURCES

Perennial Publishing. (2022). *Permaculture Gardening Made Easy*.

APPENDIX B: GUILD ROLES

Jones, A. (2020, June 18). *Create A Permaculture Fruit Tree Guild | what to plant next to fruit trees & why*. Beginner Gardener Tips. https://beginnergardenertips.com/permaculture-fruit-tree-guild/

APPENDIX C: COMPOSTING

Compost Magazine. (2023a, April 17). *Composting Myths Debunked: The truth about 'non-compostable' items.* https://www.compostmagazine.com/debunking-non-compostable-myths/

Compost Magazine. (2023b, June 18). *Researchers May Have Just Discovered A New Composting Hack – Cooking Oil!* https://www.compostmagazine.com/compost-hack-cooking-oil/

Give it a Grow. (2018, July 3). *Compost Carbon:Nitrogen Ratios Made Simple ...* [Video]. YouTube. https://www.youtube.com/watch?v=jTHUalsT8sQ

FIGURES

CHAPTER 4

Figure 4.1. *USDA Plant Hardiness Zone Map* ... U.S. Department of Agriculture. (2012). *USDA Plant Hardiness Zone Map.* https://planthardiness.ars.usda.gov/

CHAPTER 8

Figure 8.1. *Soil Composition Across the U.S.* ... NASA Earth Observatory. (1998). *Soil Composition Across the U.S.* https://earthobservatory.nasa.gov/images/87220/soil-composition-across-the-us

Figure 8.2. *Soil Textures and Their Properties.* ... (Adapted from) Kaerii, CC BY-SA 4.0 <https://creativecommons.org/licenses/by-sa/4.0>, via Wikimedia Commons. (2023). Retrieved June 28, 2023, from https://commons.wikimedia.org/wiki/File:Soil_texture.png

Figure 8.3. *USDA Soil Texture Triangle and Textural Classes* ... cmglee, Mikenorton, United States Department of Agriculture, CC BY-SA 4.0 <https://creativecommons.org/licenses/by-sa/4.0>, via Wikimedia Commons. (2020). Retrieved June 28, 2023, from https://commons.wikimedia.org/wiki/File:SoilTexture_USDA.svg

CHAPTER 10

Figure 10.1. *Monoculture vs. Polyculture.* ... (Adapted from) Tobi Kellner, CC BY-SA 4.0 <https://creativecommons.org/licenses/by-sa/4.0>, via Wikimedia Commons. (2019). Retrieved June 28, 2023, from https://commons.wikimedia.org/wiki/File:Land_Equivalent_Ratio_of_polyculture_vs_monoculture.png

Printed in Great Britain
by Amazon

47877527R00185